AutoSketch
for Drafting and Design

by

Brian L. Duelm

South Holland, Illinois

THE GOODHEART-WILLCOX COMPANY, INC.

Publishers

Library of Congress Catalog Card Number 89-23715
International Standard Book Number 0-87006-791-5

3456789-91-98765

Library of Congress Cataloging-in-Publication Data

Duelm, Brian L.
    AUTOSKETCH for drafting and design / by Brian L. Duelm.

    p.   cm.
    ISBN 0-87006-791-5
    1. AutoSketch (Computer program)   I. Title.
T385.D83   1991
604.2'0285'5369--dc20
89-23715

Hardware for the cover photograph courtesy of Kinsey & Kinsey, Inc. Cover drawings plotted with a DMP-61DL plotter; courtesy of Houston Instrument, Division of AMETEK, Inc.

INTRODUCTION

AUTOSKETCH FOR DRAFTING AND DESIGN is an innovative text written to help you learn the application of AutoSketch for drafting and design tasks. In addition to completely covering AutoSketch, the text also covers the hardware, practices, and technical language of computer-aided drafting and design. It will make your transition from pencil and drafting board to computer much smoother, and more enjoyable.

This text is a valuable resource for anyone interested in using AutoSketch for drawing, design, and technical illustration. Readers who are preparing for a career as a CAD drafter or designer will find this text to be a valuable part of their studies.

The topics in AUTOSKETCH FOR DRAFTING AND DESIGN are covered in an easy-to-learn sequence, and progress in a manner that allows you to become comfortable with the commands as your knowledge builds from one chapter to the next. In addition, this text offers the following features:
- Step-by-step use of AutoSketch's commands.
- Detailed explanations of how and why the commands function.
- Tips on how to use AutoSketch effectively and efficiently.
- Review questions at the ends of the chapters to review the commands and concepts.
- End-of-the-chapter activities allow you to apply the commands discussed in the chapter.

AUTOSKETCH FOR DRAFTING AND DESIGN not only allows you to learn AutoSketch commands, but also makes you familiar with:
- Hardware used with AutoSketch.
- Benefits of computer-aided drafting and design.
- Care of removable disks.
- Coordinate systems used by AutoSketch.
- Line types and their uses.
- Editing operations that increase productivity.
- Accepted dimensioning techniques and practices.
- Plotting and printing drawings.
- Using MS-DOS commands.

Brian L. Duelm

ACKNOWLEDGEMENTS

The Author would like to especially thank the following people and companies whose support, in the form of software and hardware, made this book possible.

Carl Hansen for his engineering sketches.

Apple Computer, Inc. for the use of a *LaserWriter Plus* printer to output the screen images and many of the drawing exercises.

Application Techniques, Inc. for the use of *Pizazz Plus* to capture screen images and print them with such high resolution.

Autodesk, Inc. for the latest versions of *AutoSketch*® and *AutoCAD*®.

Houston Instrument, A Division of Ametek, for the use of a DMP-61 pen plotter and HIPAD Plus digitizer.

The following companies have supplied a variety of materials for this project, including user manuals, software, hardware, computer-generated drawings, photos, technical specifications, research data, curricula, and training materials.

Apple Computer, Inc.
Application Techniques, Inc.
Autodesk, Inc.
BNN Software Products
CADAM
Cincinnati Milacron
Daratech
Datagraphic Systems
Fairchild Space Company
G. Bart Stryker

GMD, Inc.
Hearlihy & Co.
Houston Instrument, A Division of Ametek
Intergraph
International Business Machines Corporation
Logitech
Seagate
Spectragraphics
Tallgrass Technologies
Twin Disc

AutoCAD is registered in the U.S. Patent and Trademark Office by Autodesk, Inc.
AutoSketch is registered in the U.S. Patent and Trademark Office by Autodesk, Inc.

CONTENTS

USING THIS TEXT

What makes this text important? How is it different from the *AutoSketch Reference Manual?* These are typical questions you might have upon opening this book. Probably the most important response is that this textbook teaches you how to apply AutoSketch to typical drawing tasks. It leaves information on installing hardware and connecting cables to the AutoSketch documentation where it is described in detail. This allows room for topics on drafting, expressing your design ideas, and getting the most out of AutoSketch. There are plenty of drawing exercises to help you develop your skills.

AUTOSKETCH FOR DRAFTING AND DESIGN introduces AutoSketch commands in the order you might need them. It is not arranged in alphabetical order or in the order of menus. The book assumes that you have very little knowledge of computers or the AutoSketch software. The topics follow a step-by-step approach, and each chapter builds on the previous one. Thus, it is best to proceed through the chapters in order. The text also presents topics on drafting in the same way you would learn traditional drafting instruction. Each chapter shows how to apply AutoSketch to typical drawing tasks.

Each chapter begins with learning objectives and an overview. Review the objectives so that you know what important topics to look for in the chapter. Refer to the illustrations as you read the text. Each one points out an important feature of AutoSketch or a drafting practice. As you learn AutoSketch, you will also learn skills required by industry. If you have access to an AutoSketch system, work through the commands as you read.

Different type styles are used to define terms. **Bold words** usually indicate an on-screen menu, command, or dialogue box of AutoSketch. Examples are the **Draw** menu and **Line** command. AutoSketch terms in *italics* point out information you must enter in dialogue boxes. Terms in brackets [ ] refer to a key on your keyboard, such as the [Alt] key. Single lines in special type, such as:

Line Enter point:

Refer to messages AutoSketch gives on screen. Look for these as you work through the chapters. New technical terms are always printed in *italics* and immediately defined. These terms are then listed at the end of the chapter for your review. The index shows the page number of important terms in italic type, and the commands.

Each chapter concludes with review questions and carefully selected activities. Review questions test your comprehension of the chapter topics. Activities include drawing exercises in which you apply learned skills on an available AutoSketch system. If a computer and AutoSketch are not available, sketch the exercises in pencil and write down the commands you might choose. Then, when you are able to use a system, work through the activities on screen. No part of AutoSketch is impossible to learn, but you will need time at the computer to practice.

Chapter 1

INTRODUCTION TO DRAFTING AND CAD

After studying this chapter, you will be able to:
- Explain how drawings help document an idea.
- Describe how computer-aided drafting is different from manual drafting.
- Identify the different fields of drafting and graphic design.
- Specify the hardware that makes up a CAD system.
- Recognize the different drafting positions.
- List the qualifications you should have to be a CAD drafter.

INTRODUCTION TO DRAFTING

Drafting is a language, a method to communicate ideas with drawings. Most products you see around you began as a sketch on paper or a computer screen. Completed *working drawings* convey the information other people need to build, machine, assemble, install, or service a product, Fig. 1-1. Drafting applies to the hobbyist and homeowner as much as it does to industry. If you want to design a new basketball backboard, a good way to show your ideas is with a drawing.

Why draw rather than give written or spoken directions? One reason is because words cannot describe everything. Have you ever tried to give someone directions to a place, only to have the person get lost? Your directions may have been accurate, but words mean different things to different people. A simple sketch on scratch paper may have solved the problem. A well prepared drawing does the same thing; it conveys a single product idea that should not be misunderstood.

In this text, you will learn that drafting is a universal language. Lines, measurements, notes, and symbols describe the size, shape, material, finish, and assembly of a product. Using standard symbols and measurements means that drafters in California can interpret the drawing the same way as drafters in New York. *Standards organizations* set the

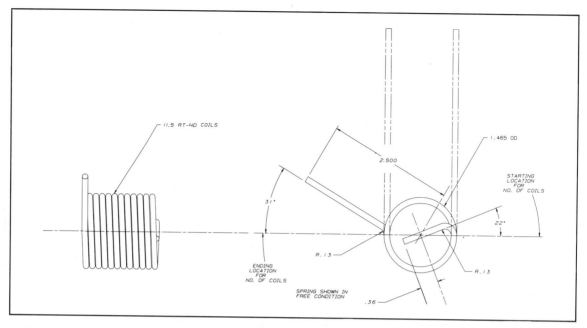

Fig. 1-1. This working drawing provides the information needed to manufacture a spring. The part will be installed in a satellite. (Fairchild Space Company)

guidelines that companies should follow to prepare their drawings. Two such organizations are the American National Standards Institute (ANSI) and International Standards Organization (ISO).

WHAT IS CAD?

To understand computer-aided drafting, you should first know a little bit about manual drafting. *Manual drafting* is the process of creating a drawing on paper using drafting instruments. These tools include: a pencil, T-square or drafting machine, scale, dividers, compass, eraser, erasing shield, French curve, and triangles. Some of these are shown in Fig. 1-2. By handling these tools, you can draw accurate straight lines, circles, arcs, and curved lines.

Computer-aided drafting (CAD) is the process of creating a drawing on screen using a computer and drawing software, Fig. 1-3. AutoSketch is a product of this new technology–the use of personal computers for drawing and design. Companies are replacing their pencils, drawing boards, and scales with personal computers and CAD software. These new tools help drafters prepare drawings quicker and more accurately. The key word is *help*. No CAD program, including AutoSketch, can create a drawing by itself. The process of drafting still requires the knowledge and experience of the drafter.

Benefits of CAD

You might ask "What makes CAD so much better than manual drafting?" Here are several answers:

1. It is simply easier to draw objects using the computer. A manual drafter must create all images by moving a pencil. With CAD, you enter a command and one or two points. For

Fig. 1-2. Typical manual drafting tools—board, scale, triangle, pencil, and eraser.
(Hearlihy & Co.)

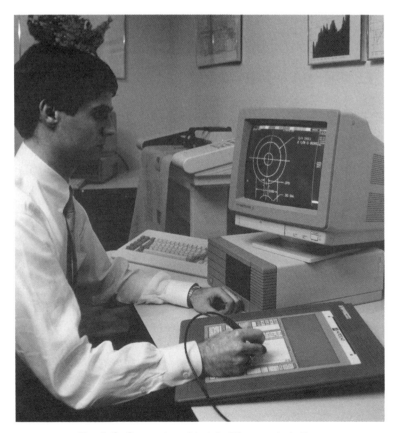

Fig. 1-3. Computer-aided drafting workstation.
(Houston Instrument)

example, to draw a circle just choose the **Circle** command, pick the circle's center, and pick one other point. Drawing circles, lines, and other objects is discussed in Chapter 4.

2. You never draw the same shape twice using the computer. With manual drafting, you must draw identical shapes one at a time. However, with AutoSketch you simply choose the **Copy** command, pick the objects to copy, and place as many copies as needed. Copying objects is discussed in Chapter 6.

3. A CAD drawing is more accurate and readable. It is more accurate because the computer stores the drawing in very precise computer code. The drawing is more readable because you cannot smear or tear a drawing stored in computer memory. This can happen to a paper drawing. Also, the CAD system outputs perfect line widths on paper. Outputting drawings from memory to paper (called *plotting*) is discussed in Chapter 14.

4. Revisions are often made to a drawing. Editing a drawing on paper is time consuming. You have to tape the drawing to the drafting board, erase the mistakes, and draw the changes. With CAD, the drawing can be changed on screen easily. Editing drawings is discussed in Chapter 6.

5. A CAD system improves communication. The drawing can be stored in a main computer, called a *server,* where different departments can access it through a network. A *network* is simply a connection of individual computers. Communications also improve when a company standardizes drawing practices. The drafting department supervisor may set up a model drawing, called a *prototype drawing*. This prototype drawing has a border and a title block. It is set up with the proper text size, linetypes, and standard symbols. All drafters within the drafting department begin their own drawings on this prototype drawing.

DRAFTING, DESIGN, AND THE APPLICATION OF COMPUTERS

Every person who has reason to draw is a candidate for CAD. Each year, people find a wider spectrum of applications for computers. Any drawing done manually can be drawn faster and more precisely using a computer and CAD software. Applications described in this section cover only a few of the many areas where you might use AutoSketch or other CAD software.

Technical Drafting

Technical drafting includes preparing drawings for manufacturing, construction, electronics, and land development, just to name a few.

Mechanical drafting. *Mechanical drafting* involves making drawings that describe the shape and size of manufactured products, Fig. 1-4. The product could be simple (a hinge) or complex (a lawn mower). Mechanical applications were the first use of CAD and remain the most prominent. Most companies have found that replacing manual drafting tools with computers makes drafters two to three times as productive.

In many industries, the CAD system is connected to a *computer-integrated manufacturing* (CIM) system. A CIM system controls manufacturing machinery and the production of products with computers. The CIM system uses the data stored in the CAD drawing as the basis for the manufacturing process. This data is stored in the engineering database and is used by many departments, Fig. 1-5. A CIM system speeds the manufacturing process, reduces costs, and improves quality.

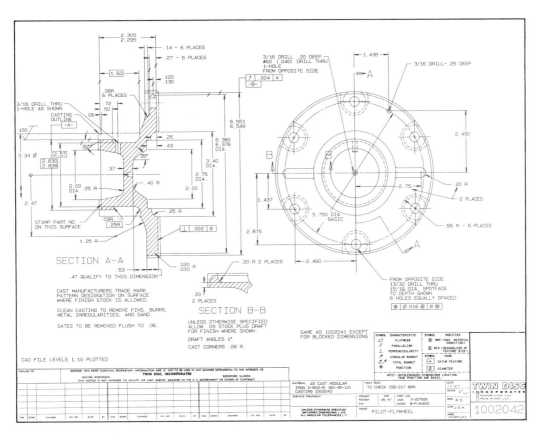

SECTION A-A

CAST MANUFACTURERS TRADE MARK
PATTERN DESIGNATION ON SURFACE
WHERE FINISH STOCK IS ALLOWED.

CLEAN CASTING TO REMOVE FINS, BURRS,
METAL IRREGULARITIES, AND SAND.

GATES TO BE REMOVED FLUSH TO .06.

CAD FILE LEVELS 1, 10 PLOTTED

SECTION B-B

UNLESS OTHERWISE SPECIFIED:
ALLOW .09 STOCK PLUS DRAFT
FOR FINISH WHERE SHOWN.

DRAFT ANGLES 1°

CAST CORNERS .06 R.

SAME AS 1002041 EXCEPT
FOR BLOCKED DIMENSIONS

SYMBOL	CHARACTERISTIC	SYMBOL	MODIFIER
⌀	FLATNESS	Ⓜ	MMC (MAX. MATERIAL CONDITION)
//	PARALLELISM	Ⓢ	RFS (REGARDLESS OF FEATURE SIZE)
⊥	PERPENDICULARITY	SYMBOL	NAME
↗	CIRCULAR RUNOUT	-A-	DATUM FEATURE
↗↗	TOTAL RUNOUT	⌀	DIAMETER
⊕	POSITION		

NOTE: UNTOLERANCED DIMENSIONS LOCATING
TRUE POSITION ARE BASIC.

MATERIAL AS CAST NODULAR
IRON S-602-B (60-45-12)
CASTING 1002043

HEAT TREAT
TO CHECK 156-217 BHN

NAME PILOT-FLYWHEEL

TWIN DISC
INCORPORATED

1002042

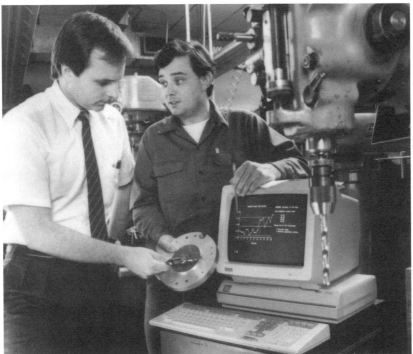

Fig. 1-4. Mechanical drafting involves making drawings that describe the
shape and size of manufactured products. Here, a flywheel was machined.
(Twin Disc, BNN Software Products)

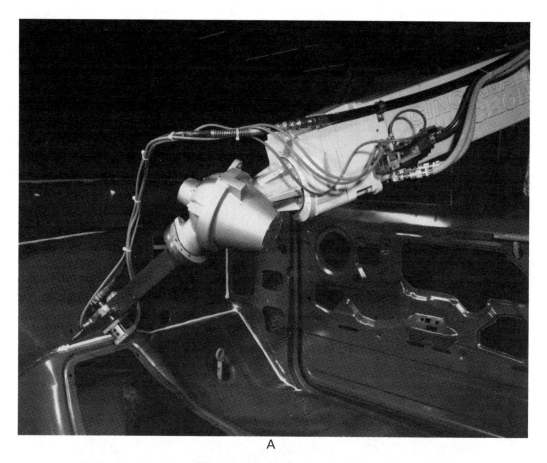

A

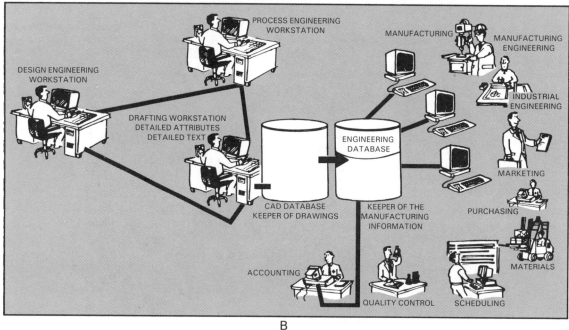

B

Fig. 1-5. A — This robot which welds door panels is part of a computer-integrated manufacturing system. (Cincinnati Milacron) B — A CIM system improves quality and productivity because the same data can be used by many departments. (GMD, Inc.)

Architectural drafting. *Architectural drafting* involves preparing drawings that describe the structure and materials for residential and commercial buildings, Fig. 1-6. There are a number of drawings, or plans, that make up working architectural drawings.

- Plot plans describe the parcel of land, its perimeter, elevations, and the building location.
- Foundation plans describe the concrete, block, or other materials and members needed to support the structure.
- Floor plans show the division of space and location of walls, doors, and windows.
- Electrical plans explain the fixtures and wiring necessary to distribute electricity.
- Heating, ventilation, and air conditioning (HVAC) plans show how the building environment will be controlled.
- Plumbing plans trace the flow of water and waste.
- Elevation plans present the appearance of the building.
- Landscape plans show the layout of trees, shrubs, and other ground cover surrounding a building.

Architectural drawings contain many symbols that represent doors, windows, lights, sinks, and appliances. AutoSketch, and most CAD programs, allow you to store important shapes and symbols on disk. Then, rather than drawing each symbol, you simply insert them on the drawing from disk storage. Drawing, storing, and inserting parts (symbols) are covered in Chapter 15.

Another CAD feature useful in architectural and mechanical drafting is automatic dimensioning. The drafter simply points to the distance to dimension. The CAD program responds by drawing the dimension lines and adding the measurements. Dimensioning is discussed in Chapter 13.

Electronics drafting. *Electronics drafting* involves the design and layout of circuits, parts, and wiring for electrical and electronic products, Fig. 1-7. The initial layout is often done by inserting predrawn symbols that represent standard electronic parts. A drafter can manually add the lines that connect parts or have it done automatically by routing software.

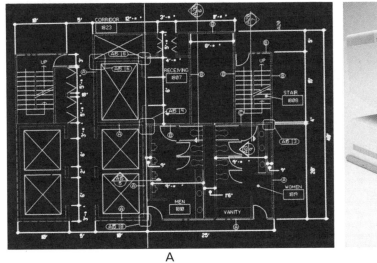

A   B

Fig. 1-6. A – This floor plan shows the division of space and location of utilities. (Intergraph)
B – An elevation view being drawn on a microcomputer CAD system. (IBM)

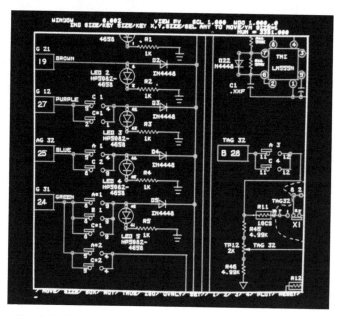

Fig. 1-7. Electronics drafting involves designing circuits for electrical and electronic products. (CADAM)

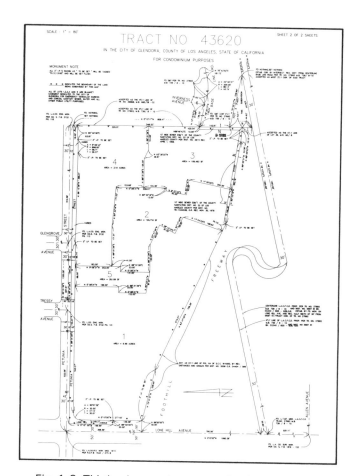

Fig. 1-8. This land survey is an example of civil drafting. (G. Bart Stryker)

Fig. 1-9. This technical illustrator is labeling the mounting parts for a starter of a car motor. (Datagraphic Systems)

Civil drafting. *Civil drafting* is the process of making drawings that describe land terrain, road systems, and utility systems, Fig. 1-8. With CAD, diagrams can be drawn and modified easily.

Technical Illustration

Technical illustration involves making two- or three-dimensional (pictorial) drawings for assembly or presentation, Fig. 1-9. A technical illustrator draws the part and may use shading or color to make it look realistic. The drawing could be an exploded view to show how parts fit together. Each part may be identified by name and number. An illustration for presentation usually shows the product assembled, and in full color.

Graphic Design

Many advertising firms, publishing companies, and corporate printing departments have replaced pencils with computers for graphic design. The special effects computers create have become a trademark of modern graphic design, Fig. 1-10.

Publishing firms apply a CAD system in creating artwork for books and magazines. Much of the art in this book was drawn using a CAD system. In the past, artwork was slowly done by hand using technical pens. When corrections were needed, the artist carefully whited out and redrew them. Such modifications are quite time consuming. With a computer, changes are made quickly using editing commands. Artwork is then produced using a hardcopy device to insure smooth, consistent linework.

A benefit of graphics created on computer is that they can be brought directly into desktop publishing (DTP) programs. DTP programs combine existing text and graphics to create

Fig. 1-10. Graphic designers have turned to computers. (Spectragraphics)

pages for brochures, advertisements, and books. The text can come from any word processor, spreadsheet, or database software. The graphics can come from paint programs, scanned photographs, or CAD programs such as AutoSketch.

Business Graphics

Companies use CAD to create charts and graphs, Fig. 1-11, in addition to product drawings and illustrations. These might include diagrams of production flows and process sequences. Charts also present sales and marketing data clearly. Coloring different parts of the graph further explains the information.

TOOLS OF CAD—HARDWARE AND SOFTWARE

Earlier in the chapter, you were introduced to some manual drafting tools. Most drafters find that a computer is simply a more efficient drawing tool. Your computer-aided drafting system is a combination of software and hardware. The software for the purpose of this text is AutoSketch. The hardware includes:

- *Computer.* The computer is the brains of your CAD system. It runs the AutoSketch software.
- *Data storage device.* A data storage device stores the CAD program and your drawings. AutoSketch works with a hard disk or removable disks, such as floppy disks and microdisks.
- *Display screen.* The display screen, or monitor, is your window to the drawing. It shows the drawing held in computer memory and also AutoSketch menus and commands.
- *Input devices.* Input devices allow you to enter commands and draw on screen. With AutoSketch, you will use a keyboard and a mouse or digitizer.

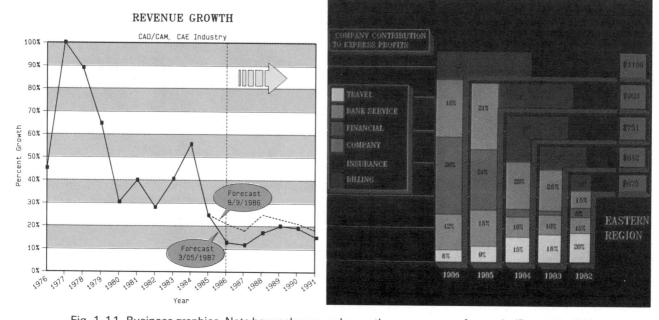

Fig. 1-11. Business graphics. Note how color can enhance the appearance of a graph. (Daratech, IBM)

- *Hardcopy device.* A hardcopy device makes a paper copy of the drawing held in memory or stored on disk. This paper copy is called a *plot* or *hardcopy.* There are many types of hardcopy devices, but the most popular is the pen plotter.
- *Peripheral device.* A peripheral device is simply another piece of equipment, separate from the computer, which performs a certain input or output function.

Computers

The *computer* is the center of activity in your CAD system. Any computer is an electronic machine which performs operations on information. The information may be a research paper or your CAD drawing. AutoSketch runs on a microcomputer, also known as a personal computer (PC), Fig. 1-12. A *microcomputer* is a computer that uses a single computer chip to process data. Microcomputers have only become available in the last 10 years. Until recently, it would take a much larger, more powerful computer to do the same tasks you will do with AutoSketch.

Although there are many brands of microcomputers, AutoSketch works only on IBM (International Business Machines) personal computers and compatibles. The most important parts of the computer you should learn are the microprocessor, math coprocessor, memory, ports, and expansion slots.
- The *microprocessor* is a single integrated circuit, or "chip," that executes the software program. Currently, there are three microprocessors used in IBM and compatible personal computers, Fig. 1-13. Each new microprocessor is faster and more powerful than its predecessor.

Fig. 1-12. Typical microcomputer, also known as a personal computer. (Wyse)

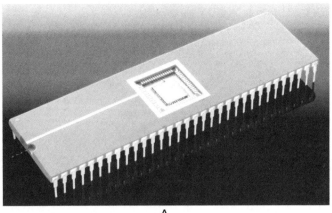

A

Computer	Chip	Clock Speed	Size
IBM PC	8088 (Intel)	4.77 MHz	16 bit
IBM XT	8088 (Intel)	4.77 MHz	16 bit
PC AT	80286 (Intel)	6 MHz	16 bit
Most PC Clones	8088 (Intel)	5-6 MHz	16 bit
Turbo PC Clones	8088 (Intel)	6-8 MHz	16 bit
AT Clones	80286 (Intel)	8 MHz	16 bit
Compaq 386	80386 (Intel)	16-33 MHz	32 bit
Apple MacII	68020 (Motorola)	16 MHz	32 bit
Compaq 486	80486 (Intel)	25-33 MHz	32 bit

B

Fig. 1-13. Microprocessors. A–An example of a microprocessor. (Motorola) B–The power of a microprocessor is expressed as clock rate and bits. The clock rate is the speed, given in megahertz (MHz) or million cycles per second, that the chip executes the software. The number of bits is the size of each instruction that the microprocessor can perform. Larger instruction sizes and faster clock rates make a microcomputer faster and more powerful.

- The *math coprocessor* is an optional chip that speeds up the computer. It is a "number cruncher" that relieves the microprocessor to do more important things. The Speed Enhanced version of AutoSketch requires a math coprocessor.
- As you create a drawing, it is stored in the computer's memory. Microcomputer *memory,* called *RAM* (random access memory), is a collection of computer chips that is able to hold information *while the computer is on.* The amount of memory is expressed in bytes. A byte is equal to about one character, like the letter "A." Typical personal computers have from 640,000 (640K) to 2,000,000 (2MB) bytes of memory. Do not confuse RAM with permanent data storage on disk.
- *Ports* are connections on the back of the computer where you hook up other input and output devices, Fig. 1-14. Most microcomputers have a parallel port and serial port. The terms "parallel" and "serial" refer to how data is sent through the port. Each input and output device requires its own port.
- Sometimes you need to add more ports or memory to the computer. To do this, you must insert special circuit boards into vacant slots inside the computer, Fig. 1-15. These slots

are called *expansion slots*. The circuit board you insert is often called a *card*. You attach new devices to a connector on the card that shows through the back of the computer.

Data Storage Devices

Data storage devices save information for use at a later time. They include disk drives and tape drives. When you work with AutoSketch, the computer stores the drawing in memory. When you are ready to save your drawing, choosing the **Save** command tells AutoSketch to save the information from memory to disk.

Floppy disks. *Floppy disks* are 5 1/4 inch plastic disks, coated with magnetic particles, and enclosed in a vinyl jacket for protection, Fig. 1-16. The floppy disk drive has a read/write head that saves, or "writes," data by charging magnetic particles on the disk's surface. It loads data into computer memory by "reading" the charges of the particles. To use the disk, simply insert it into the drive. Turn the drive lever, if necessary, to lock the disk in place.

Fig. 1-14. Ports are connections on the back of the computer where you hook up other input and output devices. There are several shapes, each having a different number and/or pattern of pins. (Apple Computer)

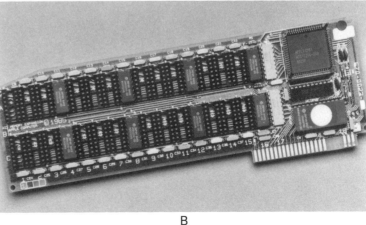

A   B

Fig. 1-15. A—This look inside a microcomputer shows the expansion slots. (IBM) B—Placed in an expansion slot, this card increases the computer's memory by one megabyte. (Apple Computer)

The features of a floppy disk are shown in Fig. 1-16B. The write-protect notch determines whether data can be written onto the disk. If you cover the notch with a write-protect tab, the disk drive cannot store data on the disk.

Not all floppy disks are the same. There are double-density and high-density disks. The density is the compactness of the magnetic particles on the disk's surface. High-density disks store more data. Make sure that you select the right disk for your computer. Chapter 3 gives some guidelines for buying disks.

Microdisks. *Microdisks* are 3 1/2 inch disks that are sealed in a rigid plastic case, Fig. 1-17. They store more information than floppy disks because the disk is more rigid and the magnetic particles are much denser. Like floppy disks, there are both double-density and high-density microdisks. Make sure that you select the right disk for your computer.

To use the disk, insert it into the drive. It will click into place. Microdisks have a write-protect switch rather than a notch. Make sure it is set to WRITE DATA if you plan to store drawings on the disk. Push the switch to the READ ONLY setting to prevent you or someone else from accidentally erasing files or storing more data.

Hard disk drives. *Hard disk drives* are nonremovable mass storage devices that have become standard on most personal computers, Fig. 1-18. Also called fixed disk drives, they

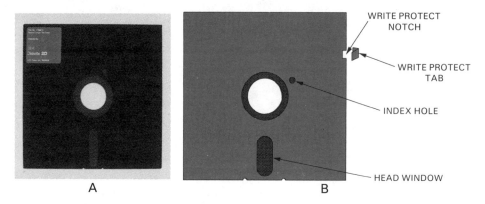

Fig. 1-16. A—This 5 1/4 inch floppy disk stores 360,000 bytes of data. (IBM)
B—Features of a floppy disk.

Fig. 1-17. Although they look similar, microdisks can be either double density (720K capacity) or high density (1.44 MB capacity). (IBM)

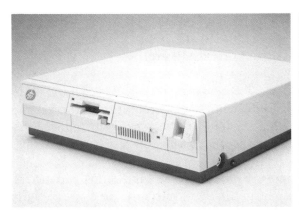

Fig. 1-18. From the outside of the computer, all you see is the light that indicates the hard disk drive is storing or reading data. Inside a hard disk drive are platters on which read/write heads store information. (IBM,Seagate)

can store more information and retrieve it faster than floppy or microdisk drives can. This is important because CAD programs are becoming bigger. In fact, some programs for personal computers require a hard disk since the software is too large to fit on a single floppy disk or microdisk.

A hard disk consists of several stacked aluminum disks, called platters, coated with magnetic particles. Several read/write heads store and load information between memory and the platters. The hard disk is sealed in an airtight enclosure and is not removable. All you see on the front of the computer is a small light. When lit, it tells you that the hard disk is saving or looking for information.

Hard disks can store from 20 to 150 megabytes (million bytes) of information. Compare this to floppy disks and microdisks, which typically store less than one megabyte.

Tape cartridge drives. *Tape cartridge drives* store information on a length of plastic tape coated with magnetic particles. The tape is wound around two reels enclosed in a plastic cartridge just bigger than a cassette tape, Fig. 1-19. The tape passes against a read/write head which sends data back and forth between computer memory and the tape. Tape cartridge devices are also known as streaming tape drives.

Fig. 1-19. Tape cartridge drives are used primarily for backing up the data on your hard disk.
(Tallgrass Technologies)

Tape cartridge systems are popular for backing up hard disks. Because of their small size and large storage capacity, they can hold the entire contents of a hard disk drive. This is important since you cannot remove the hard disk to store it elsewhere.

Display Screens

With manual drafting, you create and view your drawing on paper. With a CAD system, you view the drawing on a *display screen,* also called a monitor. It becomes your "paper." As you draw and edit objects, they appear and change on screen. You never touch the drawing. Instead, the display shows the drawing held in computer memory.

There are many types of display screens. Some are monochrome (one color) and others show many colors. Color displays help you separate different parts of the drawing with different colors, Fig. 1-20.

Display screens may be large and bulky, or small and flat. Their size is given in inches measured diagonally between opposite corners. Common sizes are 13, 15, and 19 inch.

The most noticeable difference between display screens is resolution. *Resolution* refers to the clearness of the image. It is measured by the number of pixels horizontally and vertically. Pixels (an abbreviation for picture elements) are small dots or rectangles used to create an image. If you look closely at the screen, you can see the pixels. High resolution displays make the drawing easier to see.

Display screens require a compatible graphics adaptor installed in the computer. The *graphics adaptor* is a circuit board, or card, that controls the display screen and determines its resolution. The three current types are CGA (color graphics adaptor), EGA (enhanced graphics adaptor), and VGA (video graphics array).

Input Devices

Input devices allow you to draw on screen as well as enter text and commands. An arrow, hand, or crosshairs appears on screen to show you where the input device will interact. To select a point or command, you press a *pick button* on the input device.

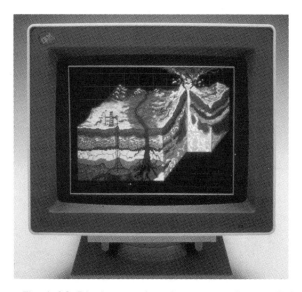

Fig. 1-20. Displays can be color or monochrome. Color displays let you organize information with different colors. (IBM)

There are three basic types of input devices that AutoSketch supports: keyboards, mice, and digitizers. The latter two are often called pointing devices.

Keyboard. A *keyboard* is found with every computer system. You use the keyboard to enter commands and type in text. A typical microcomputer keyboard, Fig. 1-21, has character keys, function keys, command keys, and cursor keys.

Character keys are letters of the alphabet, numbers, and symbols like $, %, and &. These keys let you add lettering to the drawing. After typing in text, you must press the [Enter] or [Return] key.

Function keys, labeled F1 to F10, provide instant access to important commands. Pressing a function key might display a grid or erase an object. Also, pressing a function key while holding down a command key might change its meaning.

Command keys are labeled Alt (alternate), Ctrl (control), and Shift. You change the meaning of character keys and function keys by holding down a command key. AutoSketch uses the [Alt] key. For example, pressing function key [F1] will **Undo** a command. However, if you hold [Alt] down while pressing [F1], AutoSketch will perform the **Line** command.

Cursor keys are labeled with arrows and the words Home, End, PgUp, and PgDn. They move the cursor around on screen if you do not have a mouse or digitizer.

Fig. 1-21. Microcomputer keyboard with important groups of keys labeled.

Mouse. A *mouse* is a hand-held device that is rolled around a flat surface to move the screen pointer, Fig. 1-22. A mouse allows you to move the pointer around on screen, pick points, and select commands.

Mechanical mice have a ball underneath that, when moved, senses motion. Optical mice are placed on a special reflective pad. A light and sensor under the mouse detect movement when the mouse passes over lines etched in the reflective pad.

A mouse shows movement, not absolute position. Thus, you can pick it up and set it down again without moving the screen pointer.

A mouse has one or more buttons. One button is the *pick button.* Push it to select a command or place a point. Other buttons are used by more powerful CAD programs to perform commands instantly. These buttons work just like function keys.

Fig. 1-22. Moving a mouse across a flat surface or special pad moves the pointer shown on the display. (Logitech)

Another pointing device similar to the mouse is the *joystick*. It is a small box with a movable shaft. Pushing the shaft in one direction moves the screen pointer in that direction. Pressing the pick button selects commands and points. The pick button is found on the box or shaft. Although once very popular, joysticks mostly have been replaced by mice.

Digitizer. A *digitizer* consists of a rectangular plastic tablet and stylus or puck. Moving the stylus/puck over the tablet moves the screen pointer and can be used to trace existing drawings, Fig. 1-23. The most popular sizes are 9 x 9, 12 x 12, and 12 x 18 inch.

Inside a digitizer tablet is a grid of closely spaced wires. The puck or stylus senses the intersection of wires. It shows the screen pointer in the absolute position of the puck or stylus. A *puck* looks like a small box with a plastic extension. Inside the plastic extension are

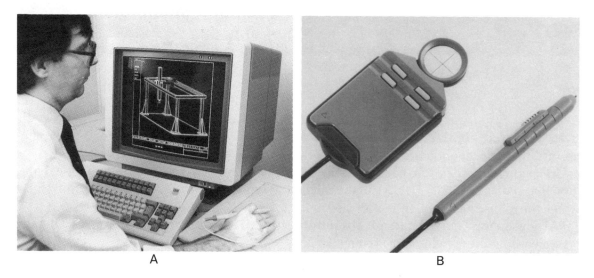

A   B

Fig. 1-23. A—A digitizer is a common input device for CAD systems. (IBM) B—A stylus or puck attached to the digitizer is used to enter commands and draw. (Houston Instrument)

metal crosshairs that sense position on the digitizer. One button on the puck is the pick button. The other buttons may perform other commands. The *stylus* looks like a ballpoint pen. Moving it close to the tablet moves the screen pointer. If you press down on the stylus, you activate the pick function.

The advantage of a digitizer compared to mice and joysticks is that you can trace existing drawings. To do so, tape the drawing to the surface. Then, select the proper commands to trace the lines, circles, arcs, and curves.

Hardcopy Devices

A *hardcopy device* takes your drawing from memory and puts it on paper. Popular hardcopy devices include pen plotters, electrostatic plotters, ink jet printers, laser printers, thermal printers, and dot matrix printers.

Pen plotters. *Pen plotters* move a pen across a drafting medium–paper, vellum, or film–to create your drawing, Fig. 1-24. With a flatbed pen plotter, you tape the paper to the flat surface. The paper remains fixed while the pen moves. A microgrip pen plotter is somewhat different. Pinch rollers hold the paper on the plotter surface. Both the pen and paper move to draw the image. The pen moves in one direction along a rail. The pinch rollers move the paper to produce the other direction.

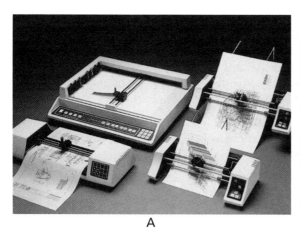

A   B

Fig. 1-24. Various pen plotters. A–One flatbed plotter and three microgrip plotters for A and B size drawings. B–A large format multipen microgrip plotter for drawings up to D size. (Houston Instrument)

Pen plotters are either single-pen or multiple-pen. Both can plot drawings using more than one pen. Although single-pen plotters hold only one pen, the plotter will stop after a certain linetype or color is finished. Then, you insert a different pen. Multipen plotters hold more than one pen in a rack or carriage. The plotter selects and exchanges pens automatically.

There are several types of pens. Wet ink, or liquid ink, pens feed ink through a narrow metal tip. Felt-tip and plastic-tip pens are just like markers. Pressurized roller ball and ballpoint pens are very similar to ballpoint writing pens. Pens are discussed in more detail in Chapter 14.

Electrostatic plotter. An *electrostatic plotter* is one of the more versatile hardcopy devices. It can plot drawings or print other graphics and text. It does not draw one line at a time like the pen plotter does. Instead, it forms images with a pattern of small dots.

Inside the plotter is a writing head that moves across the paper to apply tiny electrostatic charges. The writing head places the charges on paper in the dot pattern. The paper then passes through toner which sticks to the paper where the charges were placed. Most plots are made with black toner on white paper. However, some plotters make colored drawings by using red, blue, and yellow toner. By combining the colors, the plotter can create multicolor drawings.

The number of dots placed per inch determines the *resolution*. The more dots placed per inch, the sharper the image will be. Most electrostatic plotters have resolutions of at least 600 dots per inch. You will find that many other hardcopy devices make images using a dot pattern. The resolution of these devices is given in *dots per inch*.

The advantage of electrostatic plotters over pen plotters is speed. A pen plotter takes a long time to draw each individual line of a complex drawing. An electrostatic plotter can place its dot pattern much quicker, usually 20 times as fast. The disadvantage of electrostatic plotters is cost. Most are 10 times as expensive as pen plotters.

Ink jet printers. *Ink jet printers* form images by shooting ink droplets onto paper. The printer guides the drops in flight to hit the paper at precise locations. Like electrostatic plotters, ink jet printers use a dot pattern to form images. Most have a resolution of 200 to 300 dots per inch.

An ink jet printer prints one line at a time. After completing one line, the printer moves the paper up and prints the next line.

Laser printers. *Laser printers* form an image by exposing a photosensitive belt with laser light. The belt, mounted on a drum, becomes electrically charged by the light. The drum then rolls the belt through toner. Toner is attracted to the belt and then transferred to a sheet of paper. The belt is erased after each drawing and re-exposed to make a new drawing. Laser printer resolution can range from 300 to 600 dots per inch.

Thermal printers. *Thermal printers* are becoming very popular because they can make high-quality multicolor prints. The plotter works by melting ink on a ribbon or transfer sheet and applying the hot ink to paper. It is possible to have ribbons or sheets that carry several colors. The colored ink is deposited in several layers to produce a multicolor image. Like most devices, thermal printers use a dot pattern to form images. Most have a resolution of 300 dots per inch.

Dot matrix printer. The *dot matrix printer* is found with almost every computer to print documents, Fig. 1-25. It can also print a low- to medium-quality plot. The image is formed by the impact of 9 or 24 steel wires mounted in a print head. The wires push out and impact the paper through an inked ribbon.

The printer makes one line at a time. The print head moves across the paper. The paper then moves up one line and the print head prints another line. The resolution can be as high as 150 dots per inch.

DRAFTING POSITIONS AND QUALIFICATIONS

Drafters spend hours preparing detailed drawings. Most have specialized training in a single field, such as electronics, automotive, mechanical, architectural, civil, and aerospace. You should know the materials and processes of that field as well as how to make drawings.

The introduction of computer-aided design has affected many drafting-related occupations. Tedious tasks have been greatly reduced. In the future, basic drafting skills may

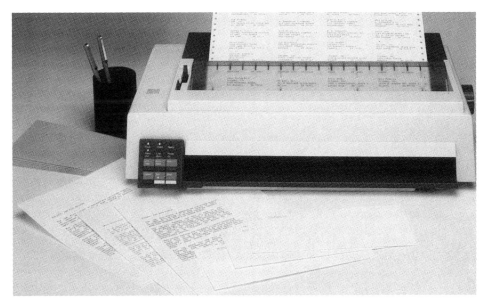

Fig. 1-25. Although dot matrix printers are mostly used to print text, they can be used to plot low-resolution drawings. (IBM)

become skills of problem solving. As systems become more advanced, the actual task of drawing could decline. Drafters may then work more with specifying and analyzing designs.

Traditional Drafting Occupations

The following titles appear most in fields of technical drafting:

- An *apprentice drafter* redraws, revises, and repairs existing drawings. He or she also may develop simple drawings under the close supervision of a drafter.
- A *drafter,* or *detailer,* develops detail and assembly drawings from specifications received by word, with sketches, and from notes made by an engineer or designer, Fig. 1-26.
- A *checker* reviews prepared drawings and looks for errors that were not caught by the original drafter. The checker usually has worked as a drafter for some time.
- A *chief drafter,* or *senior drafter,* supervises the work of the drafting department. This person also may develop complex working drawings. He or she usually has production experience as well as drafting skills.
- A *technical illustrator* prepares two- and three-dimensional (pictorial) drawings for assembly or presentation. This may involve adding shade and colors to the drawings. A technical illustrator has both technical and artistic skills.
- A *designer* prepares sketches and writes specifications to develop new products. These materials are turned over to a drafter for detailing. Designers should know processes and materials, standards, and codes of their field. An *industrial designer* tries to improve the function and appearance of industrial products. A *tool and die designer* develops tools and devices needed to manufacture industrial products. This could include cutting tools, fixtures, jigs, and dies.
- An *engineer* develops ideas into practical designs. This position requires college training, practical experience, and usually a professional license. A *product engineer* designs products used directly by a consumer. A *manufacturing engineer* develops parts and machines used to make products.

- *Architects* design plans for residential, commercial, and industrial structures. A professional architect typically has a four-year degree, possibly a masters degree, and a license.

Positions Related to CAD

Job titles have been added to most drafting departments that use computers. The duties of apprentice and detail drafters have remained much the same. Some of the job titles have changed to that of *CAD operator*. Also, some designers are now called *graphics designers*. Two new titles often found in the drafting department are systems manager and CAD programmer.

A *systems manager* supervises the entire CAD system. The tasks include loading software, scheduling system use, and reporting hardware problems and software errors.

A *CAD programmer* develops and maintains the functions of the CAD software. As new releases of software become available, the programmer updates the system. A CAD programmer also looks for ways to improve the system.

Training

Training to become a drafter using CAD involves skills in drafting techniques, software, hardware, and attitude.

Drafting skills. The most important skills you can have are those related to drafting techniques. You will need to show competence in developing drawings, dimensioning, and writing specifications. You should also know the materials and processes of your area. Your knowledge of drafting standards is more important than the tools you use to draw. Your education may include training beyond high school at a technical school or college.

Software skills. Many of the skills you learn using AutoSketch apply to other CAD systems. Once you take a job, you should master the functions of the software you will be

Fig. 1-26. Drafters often have to work with both manual drafting equipment and CAD systems. (IBM)

expected to use. These skills are learned over time. Your drafting speed will increase as you become familiar with the system.

Hardware skills. As a CAD drafter, you will be expected to understand different hardware equipment. Learn the basic functions of computers, input devices, display screens, and output devices. Also know the proper care of this equipment.

Attitude. New CAD drafters often fear the unknown. They are afraid that pressing the wrong key might erase their entire drawing. These fears are overcome in time. A positive attitude is the key to becoming a successful drafter. Look for ways to make the computer a more efficient partner.

The Drafting Environment

Computers require special care to maintain their smooth operation. The temperature and humidity level should be controlled, and static must be eliminated. The power source should be free of electrical spikes and surges that can damage delicate computer circuits.

Drafters sit for long periods of time. The seating position in front of a computer is more flexible than a manual drafter's. You are not required to sit above the drafting table on a stool. Choose an adjustable cushioned chair and position your eye level at a convenient angle to the display screen.

Another comfort factor is the display itself. Change the brightness and contrast, so you do not have to squint. Make sure the image is clear. This reduces eye strain.

Job Outlook

Although the use of computers has increased productivity, it has not reduced the number of available jobs. The drafting department historically has been the bottleneck of work flow. Computer-aided drafting makes the flow of drawings through the drafting department much smoother.

The U.S. Department of Labor has indicated a need for future CAD drafters. Computers will not replace drafters. Human talents will continue to be vital. The computer will become more of a coworker than a tool. Using it will require a higher level of education and skill. You can find out information on jobs in the *Occupational Outlook Handbook* or *Dictionary of Occupational Titles*. These books and others are found at your local library.

Manual drafting skills will not be soon forgotten. The majority of drawings are still revised on paper. As a drafter, you may need to make modifications using a pencil and drawing board. Your experience and talents should include both manual and CAD drafting skills.

SUMMARY

Drafting is a language used to communicate product ideas with drawings. Traditionally, drawings have been created on paper using drafting instruments, such as pencils and scales. Now, computers and special drafting software like AutoSketch are used together to create drawings. Many factors make a drafter using CAD more productive than a drafter using manual tools.

A computer-aided drafting system consists of a computer, data storage, input device, display screen, and hardcopy device. AutoSketch runs on a microcomputer. A hard disk, floppy disks, and/or microdisk are used for permanent data storage. The display screen, which shows the drawing in computer memory, can be in color or monochrome. AutoSketch can support a keyboard, mouse, joystick, or digitizer as the input device to enter commands and draw. Hardcopy devices output the drawing from memory to paper. They include pen plotters, electrostatic plotters, ink jet printers, laser printers, thermal printers, and dot matrix printers.

There are many fields of drafting. Mechanical drafting involves making drawings that describe the shape and size of manufactured products. Architectural drafting involves preparing drawings that describe the structure and materials for residential and commercial buildings. Electronics drafting involves the design and layout of circuits, parts, and wiring for electrical and electronic products. Civil drafting is the process of making drawings that describe land terrain, road systems, and utilities. In addition, CAD is used for technical illustration, graphic design, and business graphics.

There are many drafting positions in the fields just discussed. You may begin as an apprentice drafter and move up to a detailer, or drafter. As a chief drafter, you might supervise the work of other drafters. With further education and experience, you might design products or the machines used to create those products. With a college degree and license, you could work as an engineer or architect. Positions related specifically to CAD include a systems manager and CAD programmer. These require computer knowledge and experience.

NEW TERMS

Apprentice drafter, architect, architectural drafting, CAD, CAD programmer, card, character keys, checker, chief drafter, civil drafting, command keys, computer, computer-aided drafting, computer-aided manufacturing, cursor keys, data storage device, designer, detailer, digitizer, display screen, dot matrix printer, dots per inch, drafter, drafting, electronics drafting, electrostatic plotter, engineer, expansion slot, floppy disk, function keys, graphics adaptor, hard disk drive, hardcopy device, ink jet printer, input device, joystick, keyboard, laser printer, manual drafting, math coprocessor, mechanical drafting, memory, microcomputer, microdisk, microprocessor, monitor, mouse, network, pen plotter, pick button, port, prototype drawing, puck, RAM, resolution, senior drafter, server, standards organizations, stylus, systems manager, tape cartridge drive, technical drafting, technical illustration, technical illustrator, thermal printer, working drawings.

REVIEW QUESTIONS

Write your answers on a separate sheet of paper. Do not write in this book
1. The process of creating a drawing on paper using drafting instruments is _____.
2. The process of creating a drawing on screen using a computer and drawing software is _____.
3. List five benefits of CAD over manual drafting.
4. Preparing drawings that describe the shape, size, and features of manufactured products is called _____.
5. List eight plans that typically make up a set of working architectural drawings.
6. The occupation that involves making two- or three-dimensional (pictorial) drawings for assembly or presentation is _____.

7. List the five hardware components that make up a computer-aided drafting system.
8. AutoSketch runs on what type of computer?
9. The single integrated circuit, or "chip," that processes data in a microcomputer is called a _____.
10. Microcomputer memory is known as _____.
11. The connections on the back of the computer where you connect input and output devices are called _____.
12. Removable disks often used with microcomputers include _____ and _____.
13. The nonremovable mass storage device often used with microcomputers is the _____.
14. What type of data storage device is often used for backing up the information on hard disks?
15. With a CAD system, you view your drawing on a _____.
16. The clearness of a displayed image depends on the _____ of the display screen.
17. List the three main input devices used with AutoSketch.
18. What type of hardcopy device can plot a drawing using a pattern of dots?
19. The person who develops detail and assembly drawings from specifications received from an engineer or designer is a _____.
20. Training to become a CAD drafter typically involves skills in what four areas?

ACTIVITIES

1. Contact a firm using computer-aided drafting. Interview the supervisor of the drafting department. Identify four positions in the drafting department and list the qualifications of each.
2. Identify five magazines which provide CAD-related topics. Give the titles of two articles found in each magazine.
3. Identify the manufacturer and model of the computer you, your school or company uses for computer-aided drafting.
4. Identify the microprocessor your computer uses.
5. Identify how much memory (RAM) your computer has.
6. Identify the clock speed rating of your computer.
7. Is your computer connected to a network?
8. What types of disk storage are used by your system?
9. What is the storage capacity of the floppy disk or microdisk used by your system?
10. What is the capacity of the hard disk, if one is used by your system?
11. Determine whether your display screen is a color or monochrome monitor.
12. Where are the contrast and brightness controls on your display?
13. Determine the display standard (graphics adaptor) and resolution of your display screen.
14. Identify the types of input devices used with your CAD workstation.
15. If you use a mouse, note whether it is a mechanical or optical mouse.
16. If you use a digitizing tablet, does it have a puck or stylus?
17. Determine the type of hardcopy device(s) found in your school or company.
18. If you have an electrostatic plotter or laser, thermal, or ink jet printer, identify the resolution (dots per inch).

19. If you have a pen plotter, is it a single- or multipen plotter?
20. Contact the drafting department supervisor of a local industry using CAD. Find out these items:
   A. Identify the computer(s) the company is using.
   B. Identify the data storage devices the company is using.
   C. Identify the display screen technology, or technologies, the company is using.
   D. Identify the input devices used with the CAD workstation.
   E. Identify the hardcopy technology, or technologies, the company is using.

Chapter 2

INTRODUCTION TO AUTOSKETCH

After studing this chapter, you will be able to:
- Explain the difference between AutoSketch and other CAD programs.
- Identify the difference between AutoSketch and paint software.
- List the steps taken to start AutoSketch on your computer.
- Label items that appear in AutoSketch's drawing screen.
- Describe the two types of pointers.
- Move the pointer around the screen using your input device.
- Select menus and commands to perform AutoSketch functions.
- Explain how AutoSketch communicates with the user using the prompt line and dialogue boxes.

WHY USE AUTOSKETCH?

AutoSketch is a unique computer program. It is both an easy-to-use drawing tool and an excellent drafting program. It replaces pencils and paper for making charts, diagrams, illustrations, and working drawings. AutoSketch is used by students, drafters, engineers, and home users. Because your drawings are done with a computer, it is easy to revise them without having to start from scratch. Plus, your AutoSketch drawings will be cleaner and more precise than pencil sketches. All the benefits of CAD discussed in Chapter 1 are offered by AutoSketch.

AutoSketch Versus High-Level CAD

AutoSketch is not the most powerful computer-aided drafting program. It is not meant to be. The makers of AutoSketch purposely designed the program with fewer functions than its big brother, AutoCAD. This has many advantages for new users:
- AutoSketch is simple to learn. Because it has fewer commands than other programs, you will learn fast.

- AutoSketch still contains the main functions often found in more powerful computer-aided drafting software. This makes it easy for you to learn a higher-level program such as AutoCAD.
- AutoSketch is inexpensive. The price makes it affordable for schools and the home user, as well as industry.
- AutoSketch is well suited to sketches, schematics, charts, and simple drawings. It helps you jot down ideas quickly and accurately.
- AutoSketch does not require that you remember command names to type in. All commands are listed in on-screen menus. You simply open a menu and point to the command to perform.

AutoSketch Versus Paint Software

You may have worked with other graphics programs before AutoSketch. Many of these programs found today are paint programs. *Paint programs* create and store images as a dot pattern. The dots, whether black and white or colored, align with the pixels of your display screen. You can recognize paint programs because they allow you to "spray paint" color on screen and use a "brush."

The main drawback to paint graphics is that the resolution is limited. This is because your drawing is created with dots. For example, paint programs do not recognize that a group of dots represents a circle or line. If you enlarge the image, the dots become bigger, more noticeable, and jagged, Fig. 2-1.

AutoSketch is not a paint program; it is a draw program. *Draw programs* are object oriented, meaning that they store each object (line, circle, arc) mathematically as a single item. For example, a circle is a single *object* remembered by its center point and radius. It is not remembered by the individual dots that form the circle on screen. Because of this, draw programs allow you to enlarge, stretch, or reduce the graphic without losing detail.

YOUR AUTOSKETCH SYSTEM

Chapter 1 discussed the pieces of hardware that make up a typical CAD system. Auto-Sketch does not support every computer, input device, display, and hardcopy device currently manufactured. The *Instructor's Guide* that accompanies this textbook lists hardware that AutoSketch supports. It also tells how to install and configure AutoSketch to work with your equipment. Make sure you, your instructor, or supervisor has installed AutoSketch properly before proceeding with this textbook.

AS DRAWN

ENLARGED A LITTLE

ENLARGED MORE

Fig. 2-1. Paint software stores your images as dots. If you enlarge a "painted" shape, the dots become more visible. AutoSketch is a draw program in which you can enlarge objects and maintain fine detail.

STARTING AUTOSKETCH

Before you can use AutoSketch, you must boot the computer. *Booting* is the process of turning on the computer and loading the operating system. The *operating system* is a special program that tells the computer how to think. The version used with IBM and compatible computers is called MS-DOS (Microsoft® Disk Operating System). Once the operating system is loaded, you can run AutoSketch. There are two different procedures to load the operating system and start AutoSketch — one for hard disk systems and another for dual floppy disk systems.

Hard Disk System

Computers with a hard disk drive load the operating system automatically. Simply turn on peripheral devices first, and then the computer. The hard disk drive will buzz and whir while the operating system loads. When the computer is ready, a system prompt, shown as C⟩, appears. The *system prompt* tells you that the computer is ready for your instructions. At the system prompt, enter in the following command. Remember that "enter" means to type in the command, and then press the [Enter] or [Return] key.

C⟩ **SKETCH3**

The hard disk will buzz and whir as it loads the AutoSketch program into computer memory. Then, AutoSketch's drawing screen will appear.

NOTE: The preceding two commands assume that you or your instructor already loaded the AutoSketch software following the instructions given in the *AutoSketch Installation and Performance Guide* or *AutoSketch User Guide* (Version 2.0).

Dual Floppy Disk System

To run AutoSketch (Version 2.0 only) on a dual floppy disk system, first insert the MS-DOS disk in drive A: and turn on the computer. Answer the date and time prompts if they appear. Once the system prompt (A⟩) appears, replace the MS-DOS disk with the AutoSketch Executable disk in drive A:. If you are using 5 1/4-inch, 360K format disks, also insert the AutoSketch Overlay disk in drive B:. Then, enter the following two commands:

A⟩ **FLOPPY**

A⟩ **SKETCH**

If you are using 3 1/2-inch, 720K format disks, insert your drawing files disk in drive B: when the drawing screen appears. Remember to save your work to the drawing files disk in drive B:. If you are using 5 1/4-inch, 360K format disks, replace the Executable disk in drive A: with your drawing files disk and leave the Overlay disk in drive B:.

AUTOSKETCH DRAWING SCREEN LAYOUT

When you start AutoSketch, the drawing screen appears as shown in Fig. 2-2. The different parts of the drawing screen are:
- *Menu bar*. The menu bar displays the seven menu names. Each menu contains a list of AutoSketch commands you might choose.

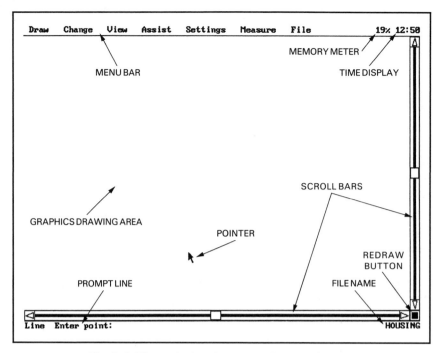

Fig. 2-2. The main drawing screen for AutoSketch.

- *Graphics drawing area.* The graphics drawing area is the space where you will create your drawing. The menu bar is along the top of the graphics drawing area and the prompt line is along the bottom of the area.
- *Pointer.* The pointer shows your current position on screen.
- *Scroll bars.* With Version 3.0, you can move around the drawing by picking the position on the scroll bars. You can redraw the screen by picking the Redraw button.
- *Memory meter.* The memory meter shows the percentage of computer memory consumed by the current drawing.
- *Time display.* The time is given in digital, 24-hour format. (HINT: In the afternoon, simply subtract 12 from the hours to find the time.)
- *Prompt line.* When AutoSketch needs you to supply information or perform an action, it will ask on the prompt line.
- *Filename.* The name of the current drawing is given in the lower-right corner at one end of the prompt line. It says "(Untitled)" until you save the drawing on screen under a specific name.

USING THE POINTER

The *pointer* shows your position on screen. You will use the pointer to choose commands, draw, and select items to edit. In many ways, it is your "pencil" and "eraser." When you first start AutoSketch, the pointer appears as an arrow in the center of the screen. You can move it anywhere on screen by moving your digitizer, mouse, or by pressing arrow keys. How you move the pointer depends on which input device is attached to your computer.

In this text, you will come across the term *pick* quite often. "Pick" means to locate the pointer on screen and press the pick button on your input device. You might "pick" a command to perform, a point to place, or an object to edit.

Arrow and Hand Pointers

There are two types of pointers — arrow and hand, Fig. 2-3. An arrow is the default form of the pointer. With the *arrow pointer* you can pick commands, draw, select point positions, and measure distance. You will use it most often. The *hand pointer* appears only after you choose an editing command from the **Change** menu. AutoSketch expects you to pick, or "grab," objects to change with the hand. Selecting objects to edit is discussed in Chapters 4 and 6.

ARROW
POINTER

HAND
POINTER

Fig. 2-3. Two types of pointers–arrow and hand. Use the arrow to draw. Use the hand to ''grab'' objects to edit.

Moving the Pointer

The easiest way to move the pointer around the screen is with a mouse or digitizer. Simply roll the mouse or move the stylus/puck over the digitizer tablet. Try doing that now. The screen pointer will move the same direction, and about the same distance. Notice that when you move the pointer into the menu bar, the menu name under the pointer highlights.

If no mouse or digitizer is connected to your computer, you can move the pointer with cursor keys. These keys are labeled with arrows and the words PgUp, PgDn, Home, End, and Ins. The function of each key is given in Fig. 2-4.

Key	Meaning
[Arrow key]	Press the appropriate arrow key to move up, down, left, and right. At first, the pointer moves only a small distance when you press an arrow key.
[PgUp]	Each time you press [PgUp], the pointer will move a bit further when you press an arrow key.
[PgDn]	Each time you press [PgDn], the pointer will move less when you press an arrow key.
[Home]	Press [Home] to move the pointer from its location on the drawing to the left end of the menu bar.
[Ins]	Press the [Ins] to open a menu or choose a command under the pointer, pick objects, and place points.
[End]	Press [End] to return the pointer from the menu bar to its former position on the drawing.

Fig. 2-4. If you do not have a mouse or digitizer, you can use cursor keys to move the pointer, select menus, choose commands, and pick points.

SELECTING MENUS AND COMMANDS

To perform an AutoSketch function, you must choose a *command*. Typical AutoSketch commands are **Line, Circle, Move,** and **Copy.** To access them, you must select a menu from the menu bar. A *menu* is a list of commands, just like a restaurant menu is a list of food. Menus help you identify commands to select.

Menu Bar
The menu bar is found at the very top of the display. It lists the seven menus that contain AutoSketch commands. Here are brief definitions of the menus:
- **Draw.** The *Draw menu* contains a list of objects you can add to the drawing. Objects are lines, circles, arcs, boxes, polygons, ellipses, pattern fills, and text.
- **Change.** The *Change menu* contains a list of commands that let you change the objects you draw.
- **View.** The *View menu* offers commands that determine how much and what part of the drawing is shown on screen.
- **Assist.** The *Assist menu* contains drawing aids that help you draw precisely.
- **Settings.** In the *Settings menu* are commands to set the color, text size, and other values that affect the appearance of your drawing.
- **Measure.** The *Measure menu* contains commands to let you measure objects and add dimensions to your drawing.
- **File.** Commands in the *File menu* let you start, save, open, and plot drawings.

Opening Pulldown Menus
The menu bar lists menu names, not AutoSketch commands. To see commands in a menu, move your pointer over a menu name and pick it. Notice that the menu name highlights when the pointer is on it, Fig. 2-5A. When you press the pick button on your pointing device, a *pulldown menu* falls from under the menu name, Fig. 2-5B. In the pulldown menu are the commands you need. Remember, keyboard users must press [Ins] to pick the menu name.

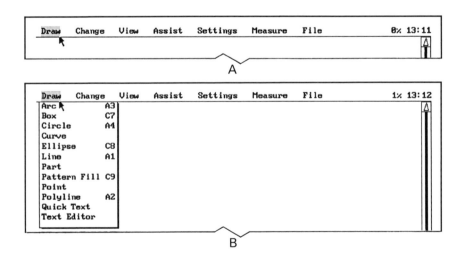

Fig. 2-5. A–When you place the pointer on a menu name, the name highlights. B–After you pick the menu name, a pulldown menu shows the available commands.

Only one menu can be open at any time. Picking a new menu closes the previous one. To close a menu without selecting a command or another menu, press [Esc], the escape key. Try picking several menus now.

Selecting Commands

There are two ways to select commands. You can pick any command from a menu. Also, you can select some commands by pressing a function key. When you are first learning AutoSketch, it is best to pick commands from a pulldown menu. Move your pointer over the command and press the pick button to execute it. Keyboard users should press [Ins]. Notice that the command name highlights when the pointer is on it, Fig. 2-6.

At times, a command may be *grayed out*. This means that the command is not available or useful at the moment. Notice in Fig. 2-7 that the **Undo** and **Redo** commands are grayed out. This is because no command has yet been chosen to undo or redo.

Another way to execute commands is with function keys. You may have noticed that some commands in the pulldown menus have letters and numbers next to them. These show that you can also select the command by pressing a function key. Commands with an F and a number mean to press the numbered function key. Commands with an A and number mean to hold down the [Alt] key while pressing the numbered function key. Commands with a C and number mean to hold down the [Ctrl] key while pressing the numbered function key. The meanings of the function keys are given in Appendix A.

All commands automatically repeat. For example, after drawing a line, AutoSketch will ask you for the first endpoint of another line. This feature reduces the number of times you have to pick menus and commands. To exit the command you're using, simply select another menu and command.

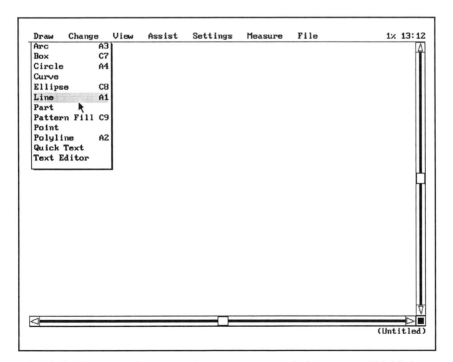

Fig. 2-6. When you place the pointer on a command, the command highlights.

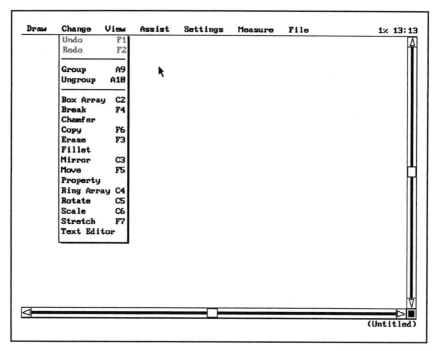

Fig. 2-7. At times, commands may be grayed out. Here, the Undo and Redo commands are grayed because they are not available at the moment.

Prompt Line and Messages

Most commands require that you enter some type of information. AutoSketch might need for you to type a number, pick a point, or select an item to edit. Only a few commands act immediately without your input. When AutoSketch needs information, it asks for it with a *prompt,* or message. Prompts appear at the left end of the prompt line. For example, suppose you are drawing a circle. When you select the **Circle** command, the message "Circle Center point:" appears. After you pick the circle's center, the prompt message "Circle Point on circle:" appears. See Fig. 2-8. Always refer to the prompt line when you're not quite sure how to proceed.

Dialogue Boxes

AutoSketch communicates to the user in another way too — with dialogue boxes. *Dialogue boxes* are windows that pop up on screen with messages, warnings, and settings:

- Message dialogue boxes inform you that you did not act properly, Fig. 2-9. There are dozens of messages AutoSketch might show — too many to discuss here.
- Warning dialogue boxes stop you to confirm your actions. In many instances, they suggest alternatives to the command you selected. For example, Fig. 2-10 shows the dialogue box that appears when you select **Quit** without saving the drawing first.
- Settings dialogue boxes show current values and allow you to set new values. For example, Fig. 2-11 shows the dialogue box for choosing the color to draw with.

Most dialogue boxes have *OK* and *Cancel* buttons at the bottom. Pick *OK* or press the [Enter] key to accept the values and/or clear the dialogue box. Sometimes, you might choose *Cancel* to clear the box and cancel the command without changing a setting. You can also press the [Esc] key to cancel.

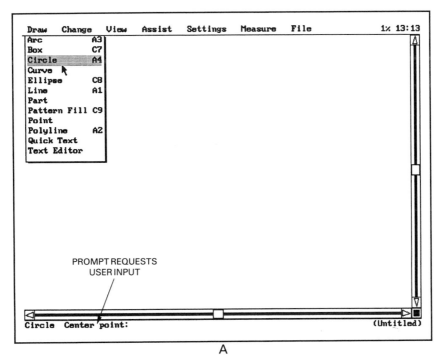

A

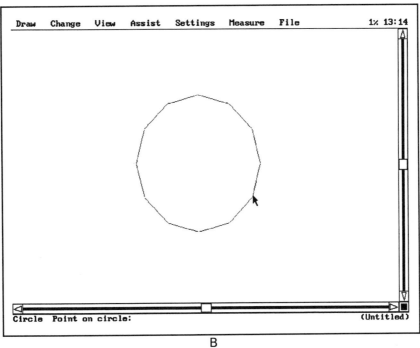

B

Fig. 2-8. Prompts appear when AutoSketch needs information. A–Here, the "Circle Center point:" prompt appears. B–Once you pick the circle's center, the prompt message "Circle Point on circle:" appears.

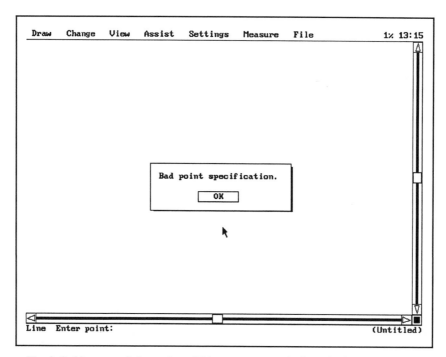

Fig. 2-9. Message dialogue box. This one appeared when the [Enter] key was pressed instead of the [Ins] key to place a point.

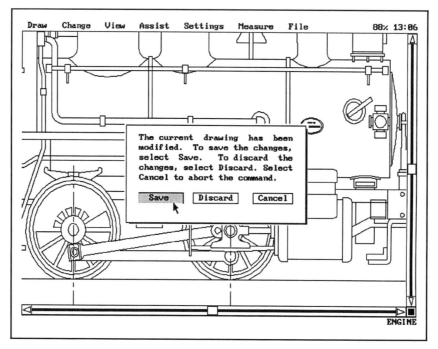

Fig. 2-10. Warning dialogue box. Here, AutoSketch lets you know when you are about to throw away changes made to a drawing.

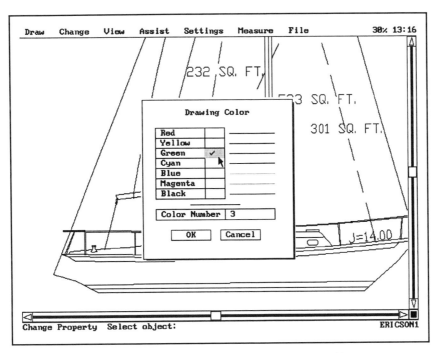

Fig. 2-11. Settings dialogue boxes show current values and let you set new values. This one appears when you are choosing the drawing color.

BASIC DRAWING WITH AUTOSKETCH

The chapters to come will show you how to draw with AutoSketch. To let you experiment, this section will show how to use the **Line** command. Refer to Fig. 2-12 as you follow these instructions:

Pick the **Draw** menu and then the **Line** command. The following prompt will appear:

Line   Enter point:

Move your pointer somewhere on screen and press the pick button on your input device. This action "picks" the first endpoint of the line. The next prompt that appears is:

Line   To point:

Move your pointer and pick a second endpoint. As you do this, a temporary line appears. It helps you locate the second endpoint to place the line.

After you place a line, the **Line** command repeats, prompting for another first endpoint. Continue to draw as many single lines as you want. When finished, exit AutoSketch by picking the **File** menu and **Quit** command. A dialogue box appears like that shown in Fig. 2-10. Pick *Discard* to leave AutoSketch.

SUMMARY

AutoSketch is a unique, easy-to-use drawing tool that replaces pencils and paper for making charts, diagrams, illustrations, and working drawings. Unlike paint programs,

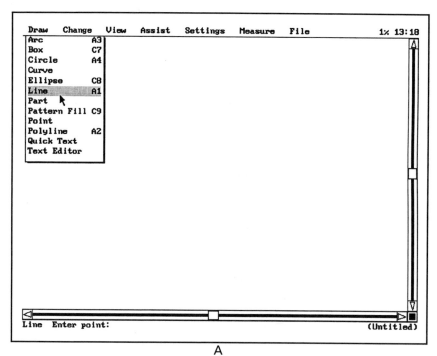

A

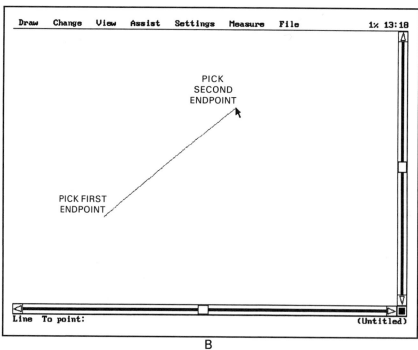

B

Fig. 2-12. Drawing a line with AutoSketch. A–Pick the Line command from the Draw menu. B–Pick the first and second endpoints of the line.

AutoSketch stores each object–line, circle, etc.–mathematically as a single item. Thus, you can enlarge the object without distorting the image.

The steps taken to start AutoSketch depend on your computer system. Hard disk users simply type in two commands. Floppy disk users must insert the MS-DOS disk, and then the AutoSketch program disk. Once AutoSketch is loaded into computer memory, the main drawing screen appears. It contains the menu bar, pointer, memory meter, time, prompt line, filename, and graphics drawing area. Using the pointer, you can pick a menu to see a list of commands available in that menu. Then, to perform a command, simply pick its name from the menu. To draw, you use your pointer to position and pick point locations on screen.

AutoSketch communicates with the user with prompts and dialogue boxes. Prompts are messages that appear on the prompt line. Dialogue boxes are windows that pop up on screen with messages, warnings, and settings. Always look to the prompt line and read any dialogue box when one is given.

NEW TERMS

AutoSketch, paint program, draw program, object, booting, operating system, system prompt, menu bar, graphics drawing area, memory meter, time display, pointer, prompt line, filename, pick, arrow pointer, hand pointer, command, menu, pulldown menu, **Draw** menu, **Change** menu, **View** menu, **Assist** menu, **Settings** menu, **Measure** menu, **File** menu, grayed out command, prompt, dialogue box.

REVIEW QUESTIONS

Write your answers on a separate sheet of paper. Do not write in this book.
1. Paint programs store your drawing as a collection of individual objects. True or false?
2. The process of turning on your computer and loading the operating system is known as _____.
3. A _____ appears on screen to tell you when the computer is ready for you to load AutoSketch.
4. List the eight parts found on the drawing screen for AutoSketch.
5. In what ways will you use the pointer?
6. After selecting an editing command from the **Change** menu, the pointer turns into a _____.
7. Explain why it is easier to move the pointer with a mouse or digitizer than with keyboard keys.
8. If you are using a keyboard only, what key will open the menu or choose the command that the pointer is on?
9. List the seven menus.
10. A command that is not available or useful at the moment is _____ in the pulldown menu.
11. You can select any command with function keys. True or false?
12. Since AutoSketch commands automatically repeat, how do you exit the command you are using?
13. When AutoSketch needs information, it will ask for it with a(n) _____ or _____.

14. List the three general types of dialogue boxes.
15. List the steps taken to draw a line.

ACTIVITIES

1. Identify whether you use a hard disk system or a floppy disk system to run AutoSketch.
2. List the steps needed to start AutoSketch on your computer. Consult your instructor or supervisor when necessary. Identify any special instructions you must enter that are not discussed in this Chapter.
3. Start your AutoSketch system. Pick the **Draw** menu and the **Line** command. Draw several lines. When finished, select the **File** menu and **Quit** command. Select *Cancel* when asked if you want to save the drawing.
4. Identify the names and locations of reference manuals that accompany AutoSketch.
5. Sketch the layout of AutoSketch's main drawing screen. Label each part and area.
6. With your instructor or supervisor's approval, identify a phone number (preferably toll-free) that you could call to receive technical support for your CAD software.
7. With your instructor or supervisor's approval, list the steps taken to install AutoSketch on the computer.
8. Suppose you decide to attach a different brand of input or output device to your computer. With your instructor or supervisor's approval, learn how you would reconfigure AutoSketch to recognize the new input device.
9. In an appendix in the back of this textbook, find the diagram showing AutoSketch's menus and commands. Study it carefully, so that you are familiar with the command structure. Try to guess the function of each command.

Chapter 3

STARTING AND SAVING DRAWINGS

After studying this chapter, you will be able to:
- Select and format new disks to store drawings.
- Properly care for removable disks.
- Start a new drawing.
- Save a new drawing.
- Open a drawing that has been stored on disk.
- Save a drawing previously stored on disk.
- Save a drawing under a new name.
- Quit your drawing session.

FILING DRAWINGS

The drawings you create using AutoSketch are stored as computer files, called *drawing files*. During a drawing session, AutoSketch holds the drawing file in computer memory for you to work on. When finished with the drawing, you must save it from memory to disk storage. Then you can start another drawing or exit AutoSketch. The process of loading and saving drawings is called filing. The commands to open, save, and start new drawings are found in the **File** menu, Fig. 3-1.

SELECTING AND FORMATTING DISKS

As discussed in Chapters 1 and 2, your computer may or may not have a hard disk. AutoSketch users without a hard disk will load AutoSketch from, and save drawings to, floppy disks or microdisks. Hard disk users load AutoSketch from the hard disk, but can save drawings on either the hard disk or removable disks. Before you can store drawings on removable disks, you must carefully select the disk type and prepare it by formatting. Do this before you start AutoSketch.

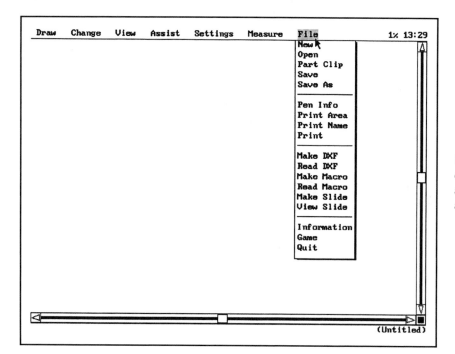

Fig. 3-1. The top five entries in the File menu are commands to open and save drawings.

Selecting Disks

Your computer will use one of several removable disk types. They can be either 5 1/4 inch floppy disks or 3 1/2 inch microdisks. They can also be either double density or high density. If you have an IBM PC, XT or PC compatible computer, select double-density disks. If you have an IBM AT, or an 80286 or 80386 type computer, select high-density disks. Make sure you select the right disk for your computer. If you have doubts, consult your instructor, supervisor, or a computer store salesperson. A lower- or higher-quality disk may not function properly.

Formatting Disks

Floppy disks and microdisks must be formatted before you can store drawings on them. *Formatting* prepares the surface of new disks into a format readable by the computer. This is done from the MS-DOS system prompt, before you start AutoSketch. If you have a hard disk, insert a new disk in the A: drive. Type this command at the prompt line and press the [Enter] or [Return] key. Follow the computer's instructions.

C〉**FORMAT A:**

Insert new diskette for drive A:

and strike ENTER when ready

Format complete

362496 bytes total disk space

362496 bytes available on disk

Format another (y/n)?**N**

C〉

It takes only a few minutes to prepare the disk. Make sure that the values for "total disk space" and "bytes available on disk" are the same. Otherwise, you may have a defective disk. The actual number of bytes given depends on the disk type. With a disk to store drawings prepared, you can start AutoSketch using the procedure given in Chapter 2.

If you have a dual floppy disk system, insert the MS-DOS disk in drive A: and start the computer. When the system prompt appears, insert a new disk in drive B:. Leave the MS-DOS disk in drive A:. Type this command at the prompt line and press the [Enter] key. Follow the computer's instructions:

A)**FORMAT B:**

Insert new diskette for drive B:

and strike ENTER when ready

Format complete

    362496 bytes total disk space

    362496 bytes available on disk

Format another (y/n)?**N**

A⟩

At this point, you can remove the MS-DOS disk from drive A: and insert the AutoSketch program disk. Proceed to load AutoSketch as instructed in Chapter 2.

Care of Removable Disks

Floppy disks and microdisks must be handled carefully. Follow each of these precautions:

- **Do not bend.** Although floppy disks are flexible, bending the disk damages the coating that stores data. Be careful when inserting the disk in the drive.
- **Do not touch.** A portion of the disk is visible through the head window. The surface of the disk is very sensitive. Any dirt or oils from your hand may prevent data from being read or saved.
- **Protect from magnetism.** Since data is stored on disk using magnetism, placing the disk on a speaker, TV, or other magnetic appliance may erase the disk.
- **Protect from extreme temperature or moisture.** Disks are sensitive to temperature and moisture. Do not leave them in cold areas, sunlight, or near moisture.
- **Write on the label with a felt-tip pen.** Place labels on disks to keep track of the drawings. Write on them with a felt-tip pen.
- **Make frequent backups.** The MS-DOS program DISKCOPY allows you to make a copy of an entire disk. Make frequent backups in case your original disk is damaged. Making backups is discussed in Chapter 16. You may wish to review that chapter now.

STARTING A NEW DRAWING

When you first load AutoSketch, the message "(Untitled)" appears at the right end of the prompt line. This means that you are working with a new drawing. Your new drawing will remain unnamed until you use the **Save** command to give it a name. However, the **Save** command does not clear the current drawing from the screen. Suppose you want to start a new drawing, and begin with a clear screen. To clear the drawing from screen and memory to begin a fresh drawing, select the **New** command. If you have saved the drawing just prior to choosing **New**, the drawing immediately clears from screen and the filename "(Untitled)" reappears.

If you have not saved the drawing since making changes, AutoSketch will warn you with a dialogue box, Fig. 3-2. Select *Save* to save the drawing before clearing it. Select *Discard* to not save the drawing before clearing it. Either of these will clear the drawing and replace the message "(Untitled)." Select *Cancel* to disregard the **New** command altogether. NOTE: The **New** command does not erase the file from disk.

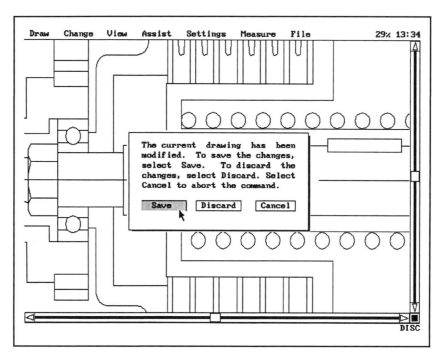

Fig. 3-2. A warning dialogue box appears if you select the New command
without saving changes to the drawing first.

SAVING A NEW DRAWING

Once you have added objects to a new drawing, save it to disk under a name. The drawing may not be complete; most take hours, days, or even weeks to finish. Yet, it is best to save your work before going too far into a drawing session, just in case a power outage erases the drawing from memory.

To save a new drawing, select either the **Save** or **Save As** command. Either will bring up the **Save As File** dialogue box, Fig. 3-3A. Move the pointer to highlight the box opposite *Filename*. Type in the drawing name and pick the extended *OK* box or press the [Enter] key. Then pick the *OK* button of the dialogue box. Once you save the drawing, its name appears at the right end of the prompt line, Fig. 3-3B.

You can use up to eight characters (letters and numbers) to name a drawing. The name should reflect the topic of the drawing. You would soon forget what names such as

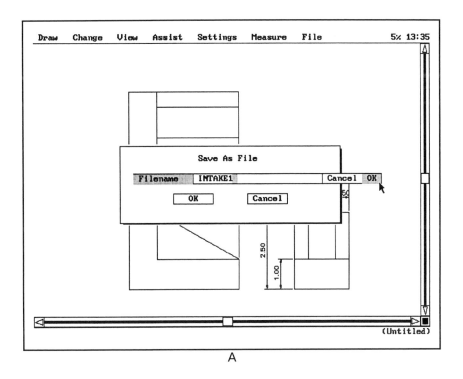

A

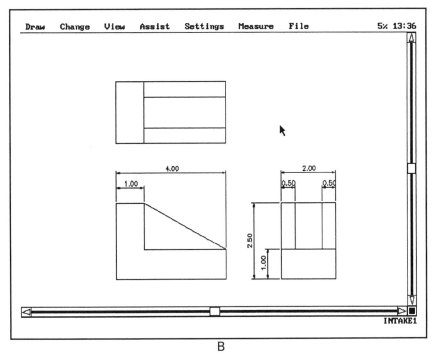

B

Fig. 3-3. The Save As File dialogue box. A–To save a new drawing, point to the box, type the name, and pick the extended OK box. B–Notice that the drawing name you enter now replaces ''(Untitled)'' on the prompt line.

DRAWING1 and DRAWING2 mean. Give your drawings descriptive names. For example, the name INTAKE1 might mean the first design for an intake valve.

A new drawing will be saved to the default disk drive. This is the drive where AutoSketch is stored. To save the drawing to another disk drive, you must enter a drive letter before the name. For example, to save the drawing as INTAKE1 on the B: drive, type B:INTAKE1, Fig. 3-4. NOTE: Not all computers have A:, B:, *and* C: drives as shown. Check to see how many drives your computer has. Also, make sure you have a formatted disk in the drive first, before trying to save a drawing to that drive.

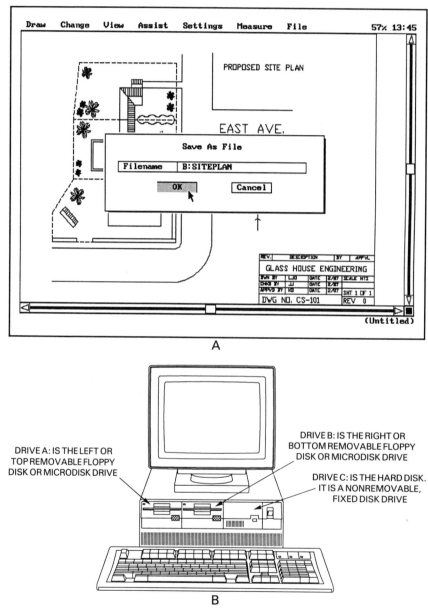

Fig. 3-4. A–To save the drawing to another disk drive, type the drive name (letter and colon) before the filename. B–Most computers have two or three drives.

OPENING A STORED DRAWING

To work on a drawing you have already created and stored on disk, you must load it into memory. Once the drawing is in memory, you can add objects, edit, or otherwise change the drawing. To load a drawing, select the **File** menu and **Open** command. The **Select Drawing File** dialogue box appears, Fig. 3-5. Drawings stored on the current disk drive (shown in the *Directory* box) appear as *icons,* or miniature pictures. To see more icons, pick the scroll bar on the right. You can pick the up or down arrows, or pick the scroll box in the scroll bar. Pick the drawing icon to select a drawing. The drawing name then appears in the *File* box. Pick *OK* at the bottom of the dialogue box to load the drawing. When using Version 3.0, drawings that were created in AutoSketch Version 2.0 will not have icons. However, once you load and then save the drawing, it will have an icon.

The **Select drawing file** dialogue box in AutoSketch Version 2.0 does not have icons, Fig. 3-6. To load a drawing, pick the box next to the drawing name. The drawing name then appears in the *File* box. Pick *OK* at the bottom of the dialogue box to load the drawing.

To see drawings stored on another disk drive, point to the *Directory* box and type in the new drive name (letter followed by a colon), Fig. 3-7. Then, pick the extended *OK* box. The drawings stored on that disk will appear in the file list.

SAVING THE CURRENT DRAWING

As you work on a drawing, save it often. You never know when a power outage will wipe it from memory. Generally, you should select the **Save** command from the **File** menu about every 5 to 10 minutes. AutoSketch does not stop to ask questions; it simply updates the drawing file stored on disk. Your drawing remains on screen to continue editing.

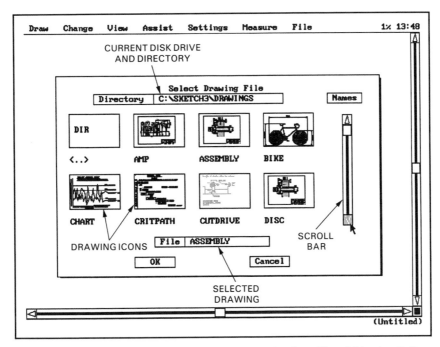

Fig. 3-5. The Select Drawing File dialogue box for AutoSketch Version 3.0.

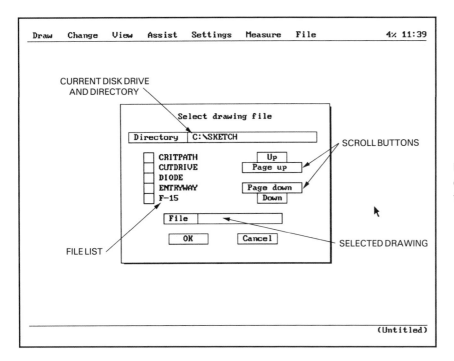

CURRENT DISK DRIVE
AND DIRECTORY

Select drawing file

Directory | C:\SKETCH

SCROLL BUTTONS

CRITPATH   Up
CUTDRIVE   Page up
DIODE
ENTRYWAY   Page down
F-15   Down

FILE LIST

File

SELECTED DRAWING

OK   Cancel

(Untitled)

Fig. 3-6. The Select
drawing file dialogue box
for AutoSketch 2.0.

SAVING DRAWINGS UNDER NEW NAMES

You learned earlier that the **Save As** command allows you to assign a name to a new drawing. This function also lets you save a copy of the current drawing under another name. By doing so, you keep both the original drawing and the revised drawing under separate names. This might be done to save revisions. For example, suppose you created a chart design and named it CHART. Then, you make changes that you also want to keep, but as a different drawing. Select the **Save As** command. The **Save As File** dialogue box appears. Enter a different name, such as NEWCHART, Fig. 3-8. Now you have both versions stored on disk.

SAVING PART OF A DRAWING

AutoSketch Version 3.0 added a powerful filing command, **Part Clip.** Using this command, you can save part of your drawing under a different name. For example, suppose you just drew a complex office plan and want to save just the design of a certain office. To clip part of the drawing, select the **File** menu and **Part Clip** command. The **Part Clip File** dialogue box appears, Fig. 3-9A. Enter the name of the part clip file, pick the *OK* box, and the *OK* at the bottom. The following prompt then appears.

Part Clip   Select object:

You can select objects one by one. You can also pick near, but not on the objects and a Crosses/window box appears. Stretch the box around the objects you want saved. As you select objects, they become dotted on screen, Fig. 3-9B. Continue to pick objects one by one or with a Crosses/window box. When finished, pick another command and the objects will be saved as a drawing.

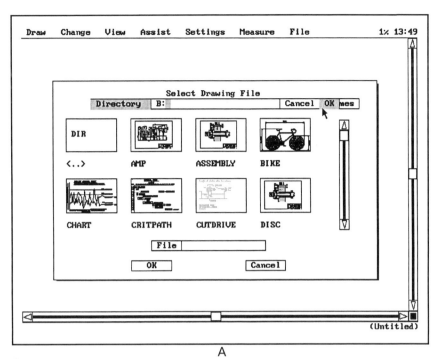

A

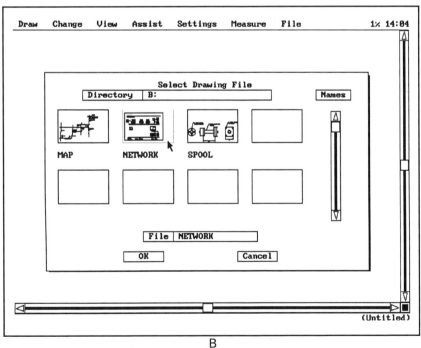

B

Fig. 3-7. A–To see drawings stored on another disk drive, type in the new drive letter followed by a colon in the Directory box and pick OK. B–The drawings stored on that drive then appear in the file list.

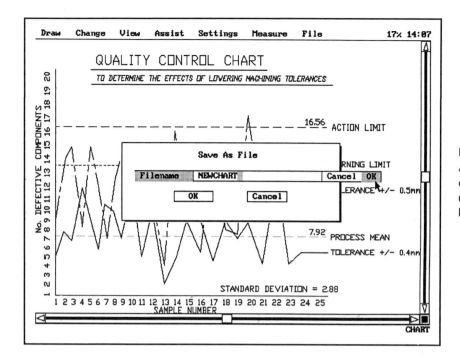

Fig. 3-8. Using the Save As command to save the current drawing CHART under a new name titled NEWCHART.

QUITTING YOUR DRAWING SESSION

When you are finished with AutoSketch, select the **File** menu, and **Quit** command. If you made no changes since the last **Save** command, the drawing screen will immediately clear, you will leave AutoSketch, and the system prompt will appear. If you have made changes since the last **Save** command, a warning will appear. It is the same warning, Fig. 3-2, that appears for the **New** and **Open** commands.

Never turn the computer off to leave AutoSketch. Always select the **Quit** command and return to the system prompt first. Also, once out of AutoSketch, make backup copies of your file disks using DISKCOPY. It is discussed in Chapter 16. If you store drawings on the hard disk, rather than removable floppies or microdisks, you must COPY the drawings to removable file disks to back them up. Again, see Chapter 16.

SUMMARY

The drawings you create using AutoSketch are computer files. The commands to open, save, and start drawings are found in the **File** menu. AutoSketch users without a hard disk load AutoSketch from, and save drawings to, floppy disks or microdisks. Hard disk users can store drawings on removable disks too. Carefully select the disk type according to your computer system. Also, before you can store drawings on removable disks, prepare the disk by formatting.

Most often, you will work with drawing files in this way. First, you start with a blank, untitled drawing screen. After drawing some objects, select the **Save** command to store the drawing under a specific name. Continue to select **Save** about every 5 to 10 minutes. When you are finished for the day, select **Save** and then **Quit** to end your drawing session. To work on the drawing another day, you must load it into memory using the **Open** command. After adding or changing objects, you might want to save the changes as a new drawing. To do so, select the **Save As** command.

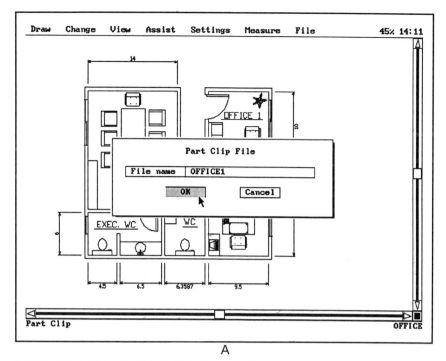

A

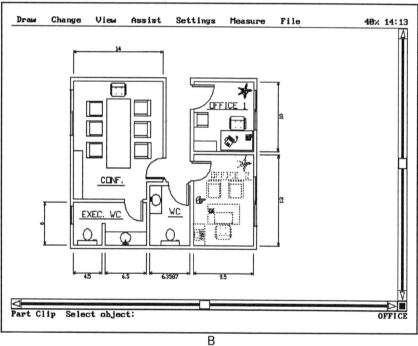

B

Fig. 3-9. A—The Part Clip File dialogue box appears after picking the Part Clip command from the File menu. B—Objects which are to be clipped become dotted on the screen when picked.

NEW TERMS

Drawing file, formatting, **File** menu, **New** command, **Save** command, **Save As** command, **Open** command, file list, **Quit** command.

REVIEW QUESTIONS

Write your answers on a separate sheet of paper. Do not write in this book.
1. If the power goes out, any changes you have made to the drawing on screen are automatically saved. True or false?
2. Hard-disk users save drawings on the hard disk only. True or false?
3. Removable disks can be either _____ or _____ inches in size.
4. Removable disks can be either _____ or _____ density.
5. Formatting is done from the MS-DOS system prompt, before you start AutoSketch. True or false?
6. Give the command to format a disk in drive B:.
7. If the values for "total disk space" and "bytes available on disk" are not the same, what may be the problem?
8. List the six precautions you should take when handling removable disks.
9. The _____ command clears the drawing from screen and memory so that you can begin a fresh drawing.
10. The message "(Untitled)" appears at what two times?
11. You can use up to _____ characters (letters and numbers) to name a drawing.
12. What must you enter to save a new drawing to a disk drive other than the default drive?
13. After choosing **Open**, how do you select a drawing to load into memory?
14. After choosing the **Open** command, how can you see drawings stored on another disk drive?
15. If you have an edited drawing in memory, opening a new drawing will cause a _____ to appear.
16. Generally, you should select the **Save** command from the **File** menu about every _____ to _____ minutes. You never know when a power outage will wipe your drawing from memory.
17. Why might you want to save a drawing under a new name?
18. If you select **Quit** and have made changes since the last **Save** command, a _____ will appear.
19. What guidelines should you follow when naming drawings?

ACTIVITIES

1. Format a new, blank floppy disk or microdisk on which to store drawings. Label the disk with your name and the words "AutoSketch Drawing File Disk."
2. Start AutoSketch and draw several lines. Save this drawing as C3A2 on your newly formatted drawing file disk. Then, clear the current drawing from screen so that the filename "(Untitled)" reappears.
3. Open the file named C3A2. Draw several new lines. Save the revised drawing on your file disk under a new name, C3A3. Leave the original C3A2 unchanged. Then, clear the current drawing from screen so that the filename "(Untitled)" reappears.
4. Load the file named C3A3. Save it under the name C3A4 on the disk drive where AutoSketch files are located. Then, clear the current drawing from screen so that the filename "(Untitled)" reappears.
5. Load the file C3A4 from the disk drive you saved it on in Activity 4.
6. Quit your drawing session without saving any drawing that happens to be on screen.

Chapter 4

DRAWING AND ERASING OBJECTS

After studing this chapter, you will be able to:
- Draw points to mark reference locations.
- Draw single and connected lines.
- Draw circles and arcs.
- Draw curves.
- Draw ellipses.
- Draw boxes filled with patterns.
- Draw polylines.
- Erase one object or several at once.
- Undo and redo your commands.

The purpose of a drawing is to communicate information using graphics. For example, a technical drawing might show details for a product to be manufactured or constructed. An advertisement might show a new product to buy. A chart or graph might show production flow, quarterly sales, or a process sequence. Each of these drawings are composed of one or more objects. *Objects* refer to lines, boxes, polygons, filled regions, circles, arcs, and curves. Each of these items which you can draw are found in the **Draw** menu of AutoSketch, Fig. 4-1.

In this chapter, you will learn how to add objects to your drawing. In doing so, you will pick the size and location of objects freely. This chapter is not concerned with exact size or position. Chapter 5 will discuss how to place objects at precise places or attach them to other objects.

DRAWING POINTS

A *point* marks an exact position on the drawing. It has no size, only location. Points are helpful as a reference for placing other objects. To add a point to the drawing, Fig. 4-2, select the **Draw** menu and the **Point** command. The following prompt will appear:

Point Enter Point:

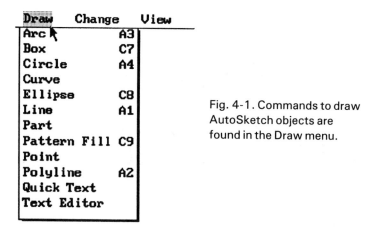

Fig. 4-1. Commands to draw AutoSketch objects are found in the Draw menu.

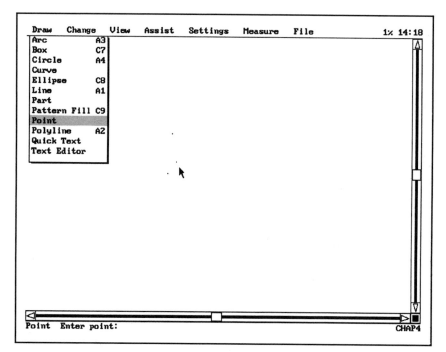

Fig. 4-2. Drawing points. After choosing the Point command, pick locations on the drawing. Dots appear to represent points.

Move your pointer to the desired place on the drawing and pick that spot. A dot will appear on screen to mark the point's location.

DRAWING LINES

A *line* is a straight object drawn by picking two endpoints. To draw a line, select the **Draw** menu and the **Line** command. You could also hold the [Alt] key and press function key [F1]. The following prompt will appear:

Line Enter point:

Locate your pointer and pick the first endpoint of the line. The next prompt that appears is the following:

Line To point:

Move your pointer to place the second endpoint. As you do this, a *rubberband* will appear to stretch out connecting your pointer to the first endpoint, Fig. 4-3. This temporary line helps you locate the second endpoint to place the line. When satisfied with the line's position, pick the second endpoint.

After you place a line, the **Line** command repeats, and asks for another first endpoint. Continue to draw as many single lines as you need. To exit the command, remember that you must select a different drawing or editing command.

AutoSketch does not automatically connect lines together. You could connect lines by carefully picking the endpoint at the end of an existing line. However, you can draw connected lines easier using the **Polygon** command discussed later in this chapter.

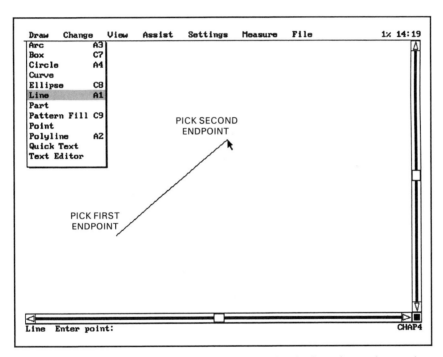

Fig. 4-3. To draw a line, pick the first and second endpoints. As you locate the second endpoint, a ''rubberband'' helps locate the line's position.

DRAWING BOXES

The **Box** command lets you draw rectangles and squares. These shapes are used often on a drawing. They might be the walls of a house or the outline of a computer chip. To draw a box, Fig. 4-4, pick the **Draw** menu and the **Box** command. You can also hold [Ctrl] and press function key [F7]. The following prompt appears:

Box First corner:

Pick one corner of the box. It can be any corner. The next prompt that appears is:

Box Second corner:

Locate the pointer to the opposite corner of the box. As you move the pointer, a temporary box expands and shrinks. This function is similar to the rubberband used when drawing a line. When satisfied with the box's size and position, pick the opposite corner.

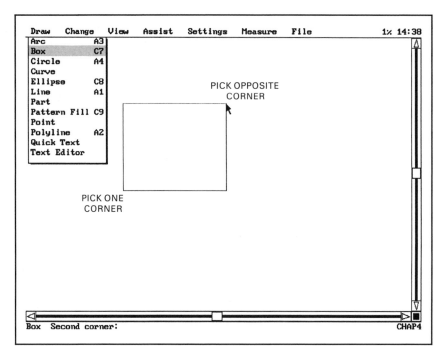

Fig. 4-4. To draw a box, pick opposite corners.

You could draw boxes using the **Line** command. However, the advantage of a box over four lines is that a box is a single object. You only need to pick a box once to erase, move, or copy it. If it were made of four single lines, you would have to pick each line individually.

DRAWING POLYGONS (VERSION 2.0)

A *polygon* is a closed shape made with three or more connected straight lines. The most used polygon is the rectangle, which can be drawn using the **Box** command. The **Polygon** command is used to draw polygons and also connect lines that do not form a closed shape.

To draw a polygon, Fig. 4-5, select the **Draw** menu and the **Polygon** command. You can also hold down the [Alt] key and press [F2]. The following prompt appears:

Polygon First point:

Pick the first point (corner) of your polygon. The next prompt that appears is:

Polygon To point:

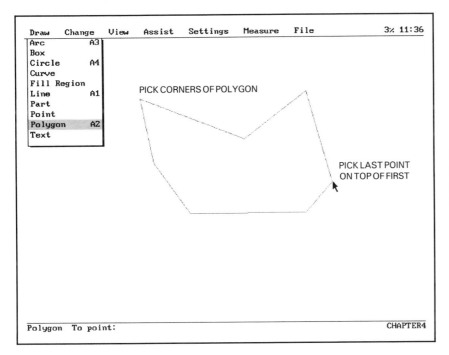

Fig. 4-5. To draw a closed polygon shape, pick the last point on top of the first point.

Pick the second endpoint of the first side of the polygon. This second endpoint becomes the first endpoint of the next line. Continue to pick other corners of the shape. The "Polygon To point:" prompt will reappear each time.

To draw a closed polygon, pick the last point on top of the first point drawn. To draw an open shape, pick any point twice or select another command. Then you will not have a closed polygon, only a series of connected lines. See Fig. 4-6.

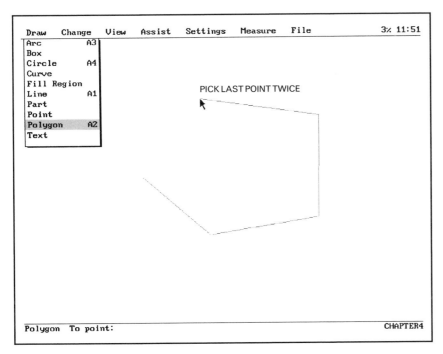

Fig. 4-6. To draw a series of connected lines, use the Polygon command. However, pick twice on the last point, or select another command to complete the object.

An AutoSketch polygon is a single object, whether or not it is closed. You only need to pick a polygon once to erase, move, or copy it. If it were made of single lines drawn with the **Line** command, you would have to pick each line individually.

Regular polygons have equal sides and internal angles. Examples are squares, hexagons, and octagons. AutoSketch does not have a specific command to draw regular polygons. You must enter exact lengths and angles using techniques discussed in Chapter 5.

FILLED REGIONS (VERSION 2.0)

A *filled region* is a closed polygon with a solid color interior. To draw a filled region, Fig. 4-7, select the **Draw** menu and the **Fill Region** command. Drawing a filled region is just like drawing a closed polygon. The first prompt to appear is:

Fill First point:

Pick the first point (corner) of the region. The next prompt that appears is:

Fill To point:

Pick the second corner of the region. Continue to pick other corners of the shape. The "Fill To point:" prompt will reappear each time. When you have picked all of the corners, pick the last point on top of the first. When you do, the interior fills with the current drawing color. Note: A filled region can have no more than 100 points.

AutoSketch treats a filled region as a single object. To select the entire object, pick any edge or cross any portion with a Crosses/window box.

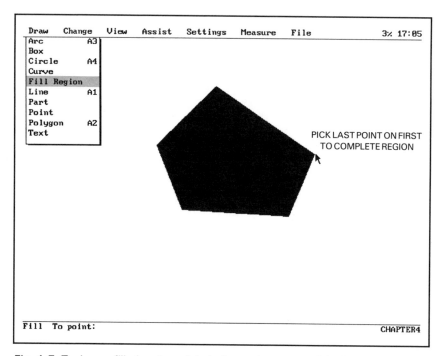

Fig. 4-7. To draw a filled region, pick the last point on top of the first. The interior fills with the current drawing color.

DRAWING CIRCLES

Circles are often used in a drawing to show holes and round objects. The features of a circle are shown in Fig. 4-8. The distance from the center to a place on the circle is called the *radius*. The distance across the circle through the center is the *diameter*. The actual distance a circle travels is called its *circumference*. AutoSketch lets you draw circles by picking the center and a point on the circle.

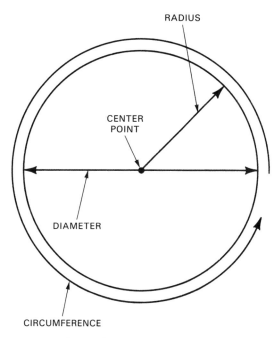

Fig. 4-8. Features of a circle.

To draw a circle, Fig. 4-9, select the **Draw** menu and then the **Circle** command. You can also hold down the [Alt] key and press function key [F4]. The following prompt will appear:

Circle Center point:

Pick the center of the circle. The next prompt that appears is:

Circle Point on circle:

Move the pointer to pick a point on the circle. As you move your pointer, a temporary circle expands or shrinks. This feature lets you see the circle take shape. When satisfied with the circle's size, pick the position.

DRAWING ARCS

Arcs are partial circles. Like circles, they have a center point and radius. However, arcs also have a start point and endpoint, Fig. 4-10. AutoSketch lets you draw arcs by picking the start point, endpoint, and any point along the arc.

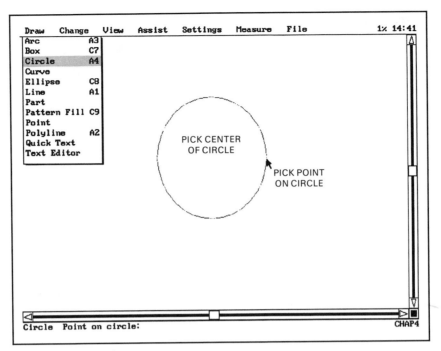

Fig. 4-9. To draw a circle, pick the circle's center and a point on the circle.

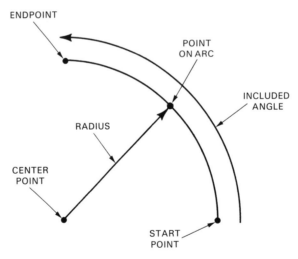

Fig. 4-10. Features of an arc.

To draw an arc, Fig. 4-11, pick the **Draw** menu and the **Arc** command. You can also hold down the [Alt] key and press function key [F3]. The following prompt appears:

Arc Start point:

Pick the starting point of the arc. This will often attach to the endpoint of a line or another object. The next prompt that appears is:

Arc Point on arc:

Now, pick a position that you know will be a part of the final arc. Do not pick either the start or endpoint. The final prompt that appears is:

Arc End point:

Pick the endpoint of the arc. As you move the pointer, a temporary arc moves with your pointer. This feature lets you see the arc's position. When you are satisfied with the arc's size and location, pick the endpoint.

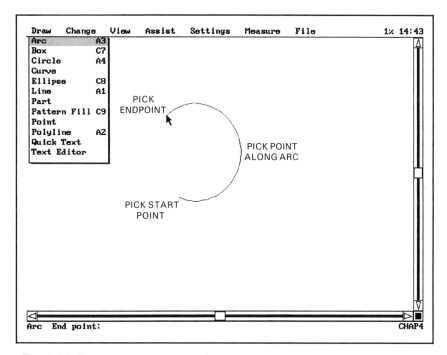

Fig. 4-11. To draw an arc, pick the first endpoint, a point along the arc, and the second endpoint.

DRAWING CURVES

A *curve* is a smoothly bending line. To draw a curve, you pick the start point, points along the curve, and an endpoint. The shape of the curve is guided by *control points*. These are the points you pick between the curve's start and endpoints. Fig. 4-12. The imaginary lines that the points connect make up the *frame*.

Curves are often drawn to show land contours in landscape architecture and map making. They are also used on special occasions in mechanical and architectural drafting.

To draw a curve, select the **Draw** menu and the **Curve** command. The following prompt appears:

Curve First point:

Pick the first point of the curve. The curve will be fixed to the starting point no matter where you pick the control points or endpoint. The next prompt that appears is:

Curve To point:

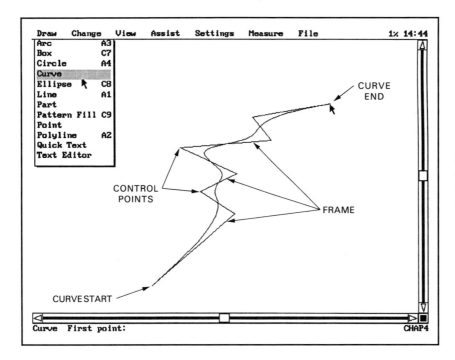

Fig. 4-12. To draw a curve, you pick control points that guide the curve.

At this prompt, begin to pick the points that will control the curve's shape. AutoSketch connects these points to form the curve's *frame*. The closer the points, the closer the curve will follow the frame. See Fig. 4-13.

The actual curve will not appear until you have finished picking control points. When you are finished, pick the same point twice to form an open curve. You could pick the first point again to form a closed curve. You can also pick another drawing or editing command to

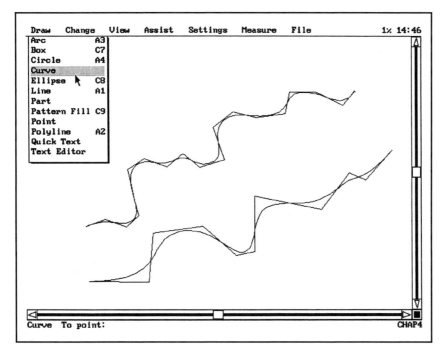

Fig. 4-13. The closer you pick control points that form the frame, the closer the curve follows the frame.

complete the curve. The frame may remain on screen once the curve is drawn. This is determined by the **Frame** command in the **Settings** menu. More information on curves is given in Chapter 12.

DRAWING PATTERN FILLS

A *pattern fill* is a closed polygon filled with a pattern or solid color. The **Pattern Fill** command in Version 3.0 replaces the **Fill Region** command in Version 2.0. When drawing a pattern fill, you must first select the pattern settings.

Selecting Pattern Settings

Pick the **Settings** menu and the **Pattern** command. The **Pattern Settings** dialogue box then appears, Fig. 4-14. Pick the pattern type from the icons that are displayed. Available patterns are shown in the Appendices of this text. The pattern name will appear in the *Active Pattern* box once you pick an icon.

Other Pattern Settings. Several values can be set to change the appearance of patterns, Fig. 4-15. The *Angle for Pattern* setting is the angle at which the pattern is drawn. The *Scale for Pattern* is the relative size the pattern is drawn. The *Boundary*, when checked, draws the pattern boundary. If it is not checked, the pattern is drawn within an invisible boundary.

The *Pattern Alignment Point* is the origin of patterns and should remain at 0 (X coordinate) and 0 (Y coordinate). If you check the *Point* box, AutoSketch prompts you to indicate a new pattern alignment point with the pointer. When you shift the origin of the pattern, its appearance may change. If you change the pattern alignment point, the origins of all patterns, including existing patterns, will be changed.

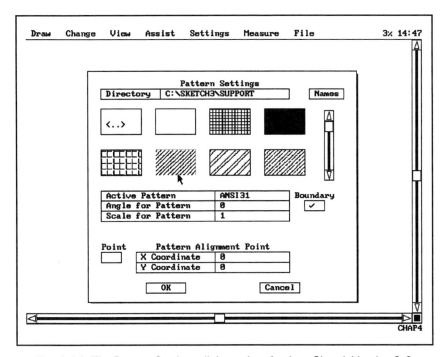

Fig. 4-14. The Pattern Settings dialogue box for AutoSketch Version 3.0.
Additional patterns are accessed using the scroll bar.

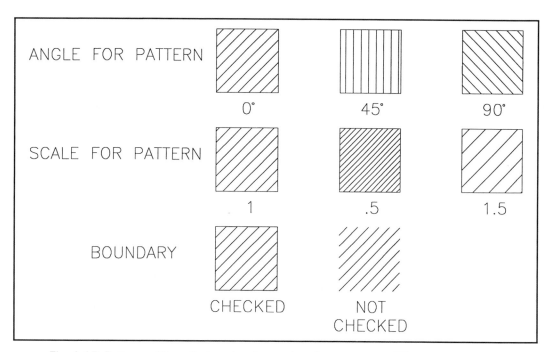

Fig. 4-15. Pattern settings that can be changed to give a pattern a different appearance.

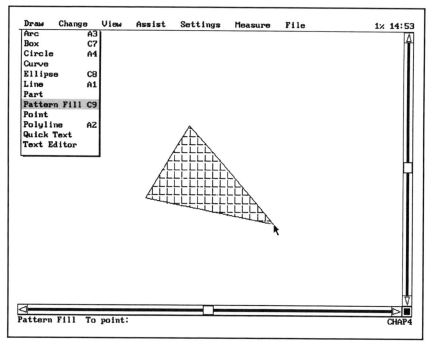

Fig. 4-16. A pattern fill consisting of straight-line segments.

Drawing Pattern Fills with Straight Lines

Pattern-filled shapes can consist of straight lines only, or a combination of straight lines and arcs. To draw a pattern fill consisting of straight-line segments, Fig. 4-16, select the

Draw menu and the **Pattern Fill** command. You can also hold down [Ctrl] while pressing function key [F9]. The first prompt to appear is:

Pattern Fill First point:

Pick the first point of the region. The next prompt that appears is:

Pattern Fill To point:

Pick the second corner of the pattern fill. Continue to pick other corners of the shape. When you have picked all of the corners, pick the last point on top of the first point. The interior then fills with the pattern in the current drawing color. A dialogue box then appears asking whether you wish to *Accept* or *Modify* the shape.

Drawing Pattern Fills with Straight Lines and Arcs

A pattern fill may also consist of straight-line segments and arc segments, Fig. 4-17. You can toggle in and out of Arc Mode by holding down [Ctrl] while pressing [F1], or selecting **Arc Mode** from the **Assist** menu.

You might draw a straight line first. Then, press [Ctrl] and [F1] to access Arc Mode. The point you just picked forms one end of the arc and the "Point on arc:" prompt appears. Pick this point and next the arc segment endpoint to form the arc. You can continue drawing arcs, or you can draw straight lines by pressing [Ctrl] and [F1] to exit Arc Mode.

Note: A pattern-filled object cannot have more than 200 points. In addition, pattern fills take a long time to display. You may choose to select **Fill** from the **Assist** menu so that patterns are not displayed. (They still exist, but are simply invisible.) Finally, AutoSketch

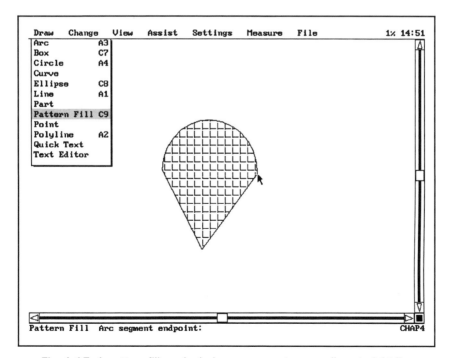

Fig. 4-17. A pattern fill can include arc segments, as well as straight-line segments.

considers pattern fill a single object. You can erase, move, copy, and perform other editing commands on the object with a single pick.

DRAWING POLYLINES

A *polyline* is a single object consisting of connected lines and arcs. A polyline can have thickness and be either solid or pattern filled, unlike standard lines and arcs. See Fig. 4-18. The **Polyline** command in Version 3.0 replaces the **Polygon** command in Version 2.0. The first step to take when drawing a polyline is to select the polyline settings.

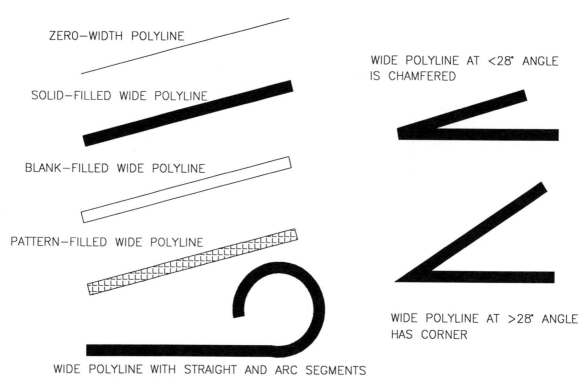

ZERO—WIDTH POLYLINE

SOLID—FILLED WIDE POLYLINE

BLANK—FILLED WIDE POLYLINE

PATTERN—FILLED WIDE POLYLINE

WIDE POLYLINE WITH STRAIGHT AND ARC SEGMENTS

WIDE POLYLINE AT <28° ANGLE IS CHAMFERED

WIDE POLYLINE AT >28° ANGLE HAS CORNER

Fig. 4-18. Examples of how the appearance of polylines can be altered.

Selecting Polyline Settings

To select the polyline settings, pick the **Settings** menu and the **Polyline** command. The **Polyline** dialogue box appears, Fig. 4-19. Set the *Polyline Width*. A zero-width polyline has the same thickness as a line drawn with the **Line** command. Check whether you want a wide polyline that is filled solid, left blank, or filled with a pattern. To change the pattern, pick the *Change Pattern* box. When finished, pick *OK*.

Drawing Polylines

Select the **Draw** menu and the **Polyline** command to draw a polyline, Fig. 4-20. You can also hold down [Alt] while pressing [F2]. The first prompt to appear is:

Polyline First point:

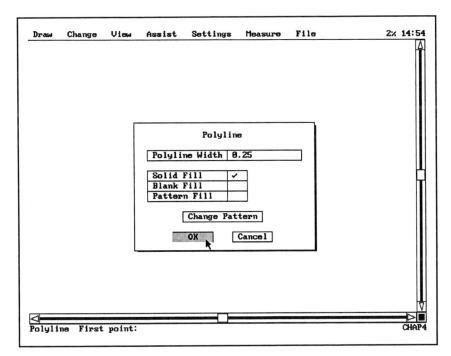

Fig. 4-19. The Polyline dialogue box. When Change Pattern is picked, the Pattern Settings dialogue box is accessed.

Pick the first point of the polyline. The next prompt that appears is:

Polyline To point:

Pick the second point of the polyline. You can continue to draw straight polyline segments by picking additional points. If you have selected a solid or patterned interior, each segment of a wide polyline fills as it is completed.

Adding Arc Segments. Arc segments of the polyline are drawn by toggling in and out of Arc Mode. Arc Mode is accessed by pressing [Ctrl] and [F1], or by selecting **Arc Mode** from the **Assist** menu. The previous point you picked forms one end of the arc and the "Polyline Point on arc:" prompt appears. Pick this point and the arc segment endpoint to form the arc. You can then continue drawing arcs, or you can draw straight polyline segments by pressing [Ctrl] and [F1] to exit Arc Mode.

Completing the Polyline. There are two ways to complete the polyline. You can either pick the first point again to form a closed polyline, or pick the last point twice to form an open polyline.

Note: You are limited to 200 points when drawing a polyline. This includes endpoints, and points along an arc segment. If you surpass 200 points, AutoSketch automatically ends the polyline. In addition, you may choose to select **Fill** from the **Assist** menu so that patterns are not displayed. This speeds up redraw time. Finally, AutoSketch considers polylines a single object. This allows you to erase, move, copy, and perform other editing commands by picking the polyline once.

DRAWING ELLIPSES

Another command introduced with AutoSketch Version 3.0 is **Ellipse.** An *ellipse* is formed when a circle is viewed at an angle. It is defined by a center, major axis, and minor

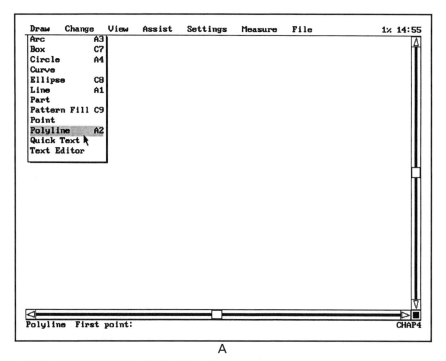

A

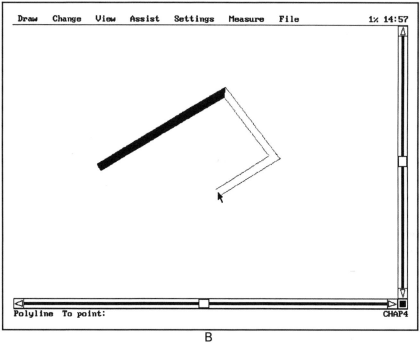

B

Fig. 4-20. A–When Polyline is picked, AutoSketch prompts for the first point of the polyline. B–As additional points are picked, the sections fill with the selected color or pattern, or are left blank.

axis, Fig. 4-21. An ellipse also has two focal points. AutoSketch allows you to draw ellipses using three methods. Pick the **Settings** menu and **Ellipse** command to open the **Ellipse Input Format** dialogue box and pick the method, Fig. 4-22.

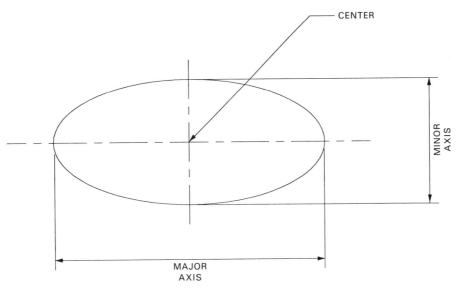

Fig. 4-21. Parts of an ellipse.

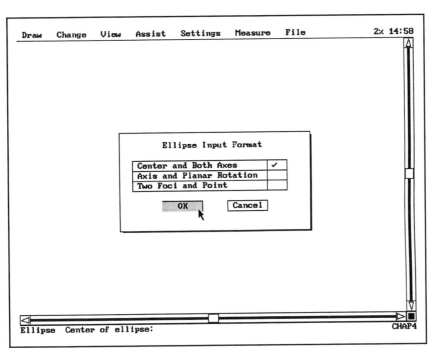

Fig. 4-22. The method used to construct an ellipse is selected from the Ellipse Input Format dialogue box.

Drawing Ellipses by Center and Axes

The default method for drawing ellipses with AutoSketch is by picking the center and one endpoint of each axis. Pick the **Draw** menu and **Ellipse** command, Fig. 4-23. You can also hold down [Ctrl] while pressing [F8]. The first prompt to appear is:

Ellipse Center of ellipse:

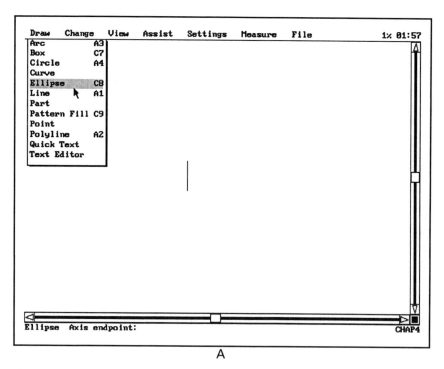

A

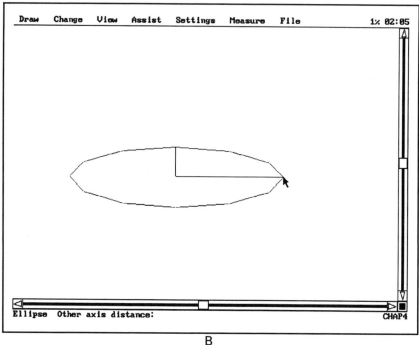

B

Fig. 4-23. Drawing an ellipse using the center and axes. A—Pick the center and endpoint of one axis. B—The ellipse expands as you move the pointer to pick the other axis endpoint.

Pick the center point of the ellipse. The next prompt that appears is:

Ellipse Axis endpoint:

Pick one axis endpoint of the ellipse. The next prompt that appears is:

Ellipse Other axis distance:

The ellipse expands as you move the pointer away from the ellipse center. When you are satisfied with the size, press the Pick button. You could also enter an exact distance. However, you cannot rotate the ellipse while sizing it.

Drawing Ellipses by Axis and Planar Rotation

This method allows you to select an angle at which to view a circle. The view you see is an ellipse. An ellipse is drawn using this method by first picking *Axis and Planar Rotation* from the **Ellipse** command of the **Settings** menu. Next, pick the **Draw** menu and **Ellipse** command. You can also press the keys [Ctrl] and [F8] to access the Ellipse command. The first prompt to appear is:

Ellipse Center of ellipse:

Pick the center point of the ellipse. The next prompt that appears is:

Ellipse Axis endpoint:

Pick one axis endpoint of the ellipse. The next prompt that appears is:

Ellipse Rotation around major axis:

You can enter an exact viewing angle at this prompt, Fig. 4-24. You can also move the pointer away from horizontal to change the angle. Pick the point when you are satisfied with the ellipse size.

Drawing Ellipses by Two Foci and Point

This method allows you to pick the two foci points and a point on an ellipse. To draw an ellipse by this method, first pick *Two Foci and Point* from the **Ellipse** command of the **Settings** menu. Next, pick the **Draw** menu and **Ellipse** command. You can also press the [Ctrl] and [F8] keys. The first prompt to appear is:

Ellipse First focus of ellipse:

Pick the first focus point of the ellipse. The next prompt that appears is:

Ellipse Second focus:

Pick the second focus point of the ellipse. The next prompt that appears is:

Ellipse Point on ellipse:

The ellipse expands and contracts as you move the pointer away from the foci points. Pick the point when you are satisfied with the ellipse size. See Fig. 4-25.

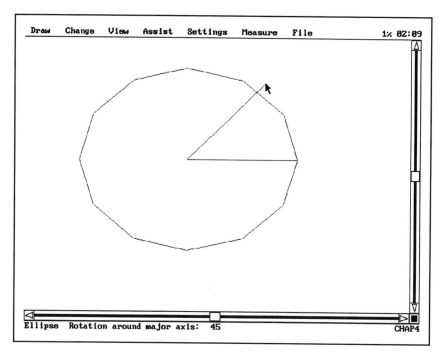

Ellipse   Rotation around major axis: 45   CHAP4

Fig. 4-24. An exact rotation angle can be achieved using the axis and planar
rotation method for constructing an ellipse.

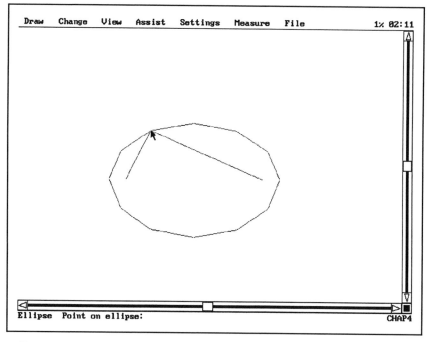

Ellipse   Point on ellipse: CHAP4

Fig. 4-25. Two foci points and a point on the ellipse can be used to create an
ellipse.

ERASING OBJECTS

Everything you draw will not be right the first time. Sometimes, it is necessary to erase one
or more objects. To do so, pick the **Change** menu, Fig. 4-26, and then the **Erase** command.

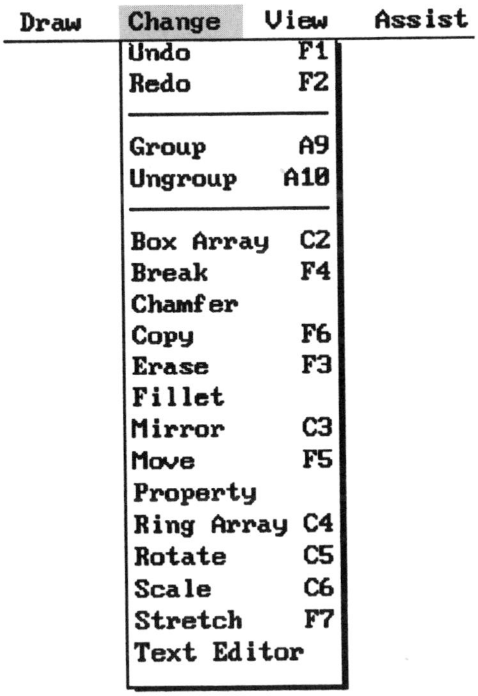

Draw	Change	View	Assist

```
Undo        F1
Redo        F2

Group       A9
Ungroup     A10

Box Array   C2
Break       F4
Chamfer
Copy        F6
Erase       F3
Fillet
Mirror      C3
Move        F5
Property
Ring Array  C4
Rotate      C5
Scale       C6
Stretch     F7
Text Editor
```

Fig. 4-26. Change menu.

You can also press function key [F3]. The pointer will change from an arrow to a hand. The following prompt will also appear:

> Erase Select object:

You can select objects one at a time or several at a time using AutoSketch's Crosses/window box function.

Picking Single Objects

It is easy to erase single objects. Locate the hand's finger over the object to erase and press the pick button on your pointing device, Fig. 4-27. The object will disappear from the screen.

Picking Multiple Objects

You can select several objects at once using AutoSketch's *Crosses/window box* function. This function lets you pick corners of a box around the objects to erase. AutoSketch uses this mode if you miss picking an object or purposely pick an empty area of the drawing. Once you pick an empty area, the following prompt appears.

> Erase Crosses/window corner:

Locate the opposite corner of the box away from the first corner. (The first corner is fixed where you originally picked.) You can drag the box's corner to expand or shrink the box around the objects to erase. There are two ways to select objects with the box:
- If you move the pointer to the right of the first corner, a solid line box appears. This is the *Window box*. Only those objects entirely within the box will be erased. See Fig. 4-28.
- If you move the pointer to the left of the first corner, a dotted box appears. This is the *Crosses box*. All objects within *and* crossing the box are erased. See Fig. 4-29.

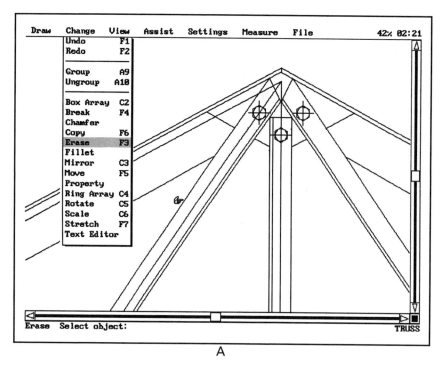

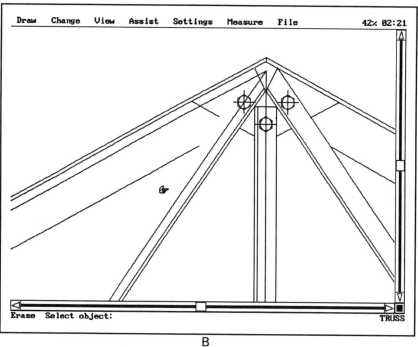

Fig. 4-27. Erasing an object. A–Locate the finger over and pick the object to erase. B–Once you pick the object, it disappears.

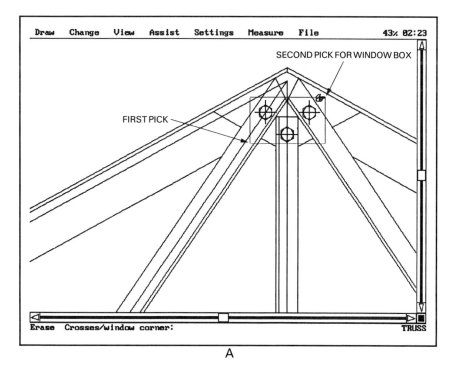

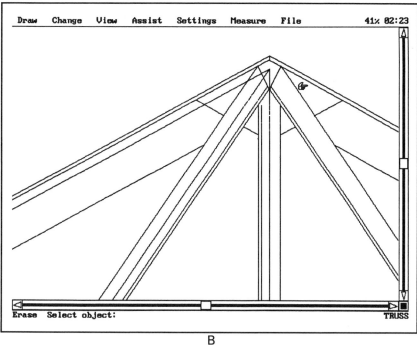

Fig. 4-28. Erasing several objects with the Window box. A—Pick opposite corners, from left to right, of a box around the objects. B—Only those objects entirely within the box are erased.

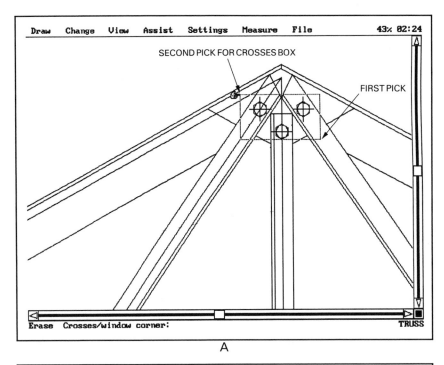

A

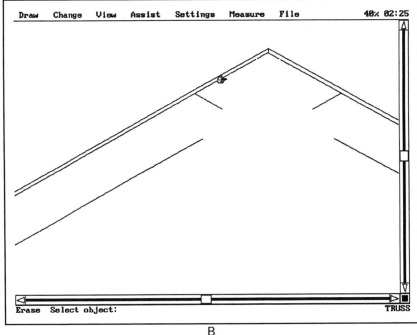

B

Fig. 4-29. Erasing several objects with the Crosses box. A–Pick opposite corners, from right to left, of a box around the objects. B–Those objects within and crossing the box are erased.

By carefully choosing your first point, you can use either the Window box or Crosses box. These same selection techniques are used for other editing commands, such as **Move** and **Copy, Break** or **Chamfer.**

UNDOING AND REDOING YOUR COMMANDS

AutoSketch forgives your mistakes with the **Undo** command. You can reverse the effect of any previous drawing or editing function. For example, suppose you accidentally erased a line. To restore it, select the **Change** menu and the **Undo** command. You can also press function key [F1].

Select **Undo** once for every command you want to undo. This happens in reverse order. If necessary, you can step back one command at a time all the way to the beginning of your drawing session.

NOTE: You cannot undo tasks done in a previous drawing session. If you back up to the beginning of your drawing session, the **Undo** command will be grayed out and you cannot select it.

How **Undo** works depends on how you chose the previous command. For example, suppose you just erased several objects within a window box. Using **Undo** once will replace all those objects. However, suppose you erased several objects one at a time. In this case, you would need to select **Undo** for each individual object that you erased to replace them on screen.

If you accidentally undo too many steps, select **Redo** from the **Change** menu. You can also press function key [F2]. This command reverses the effects of an undo. You can step back through the undo commands issued. If you have not used the **Undo** command, **Redo** will be grayed out.

SUMMARY

AutoSketch allows you to create a wide variety of drawings. However, even the most complex drawing is simply an assortment of objects. AutoSketch objects include points, lines, boxes, polygons, circles, arcs, and curves. All of these items are found in the **Draw** menu. This chapter showed only how to add objects to the drawing, not how to place them in exact locations. Chapter 5 will discuss how to draw precisely.

While creating drawings, you are likely to make at least a few mistakes. If the action you just completed did not turn out right, select **Undo.** If you need to remove objects from the drawing, use **Erase.** You can erase single objects or collect several using the Crosses/window box function.

NEW TERMS

Objects, **Draw** menu, point, **Point** command, line, **Line** command, rubberband, box, **Box** command, polygon, **Polygon** command, regular polygon, circle, **Circle** command, radius, diameter, arc, **Arc** command, curve, **Curve** command, control points, frame, Crosses box, Window box, **Undo** command, **Redo** command.

REVIEW QUESTIONS

Write your answers on a separate sheet of paper. Do not write in this book.

 1. Lines, boxes, points, circles, polygons, arcs, and curves that you add to the drawing are called _____.
 2. A _____ marks an exact location on the drawing. It appears as a dot on the screen.
 3. What keyboard keys can you press to perform the **Line** command?
 4. As you locate the second endpoint of a line, a _____ will appear to stretch out. It helps position the line.
 5. Since commands repeat, you must_____ to exit a command.
 6. AutoSketch automatically connects lines together. True or false?
 7. To draw a rectangle after choosing the **Box** command, you must _____.
 8. The AutoSketch **Polygon** command allows you to draw open connected lines as well as closed polygon shapes. True or false?
 9. _____ polygons have equal sides and internal angles.
10. AutoSketch lets you draw circles by picking the _____ and _____.
11. Using AutoSketch, you can draw an arc by picking the center, start point, and endpoint. True or false?
12. The shape of a curve is guided by _____.
13. A curve will not appear until you finish picking points that form the curve's frame. True or false?
14. To form a closed curve shape, you must _____.
15. When checked, the Pattern Fill *Boundary* setting draws a line around the perimeter of the pattern. True or false?
16. What key combination do you press to enter Arc Mode?
17. A zero-width polyline has the same thickness as what standard objects?
18. What command is used to set the thickness of a polyline?
19. Which ellipse drawing method allows you to set the angle at which a circle is viewed?
20. An erased object cannot be restored. True or false?
21. What must you do to invoke the Crosses/window box function to select objects to erase?
22. Describe how you determine whether the Crosses box or Window box is used to select objects.
23. Only those objects entirely within a Window box are erased. True or false?
24. Only those objects entirely within a Crosses box are erased. True or false?
25. You can step backwards through commands issued during your drawing session using the _____ command.

ACTIVITIES

Here is a mixture of drawing activities to develop your skill with drawing commands. Save your AutoSketch drawings on your file disk, not on the program disk. Clear the previous drawing from screen and memory using **New** before completing each activity. Commands for both Version 2.0 and Version 3.0 are given.

 1. Start AutoSketch and complete the following tasks to create the following drawing. Refer to the illustration as you follow each step exactly as given.
    A. Place several points on the drawing.
    B. Draw a rectangle using the **Line** command four times.

C. Draw a rectangle using the **Polyline** or **Polygon** command. Be sure to connect the last point on top of the first.
D. Draw a filled rectangle using the **Pattern Fill** or **Fill Region** command.
E. Draw a rectangle using the **Box** command. Note how much easier it is to create a rectangle using this method.
F. Using the **Polyline** or **Polygon** command, draw an open shape made of a series of connected lines.
G. Add a circle to your drawing.
H. Draw an arc that connects as close as possible to one side of a rectangle.
I. Draw two curves. Make one an open curve. Make the other a closed curve by picking the last point on top of the first point.
J. Draw ellipses using each method.
K. At this time, save the drawing on your file disk, using the name C4A1.

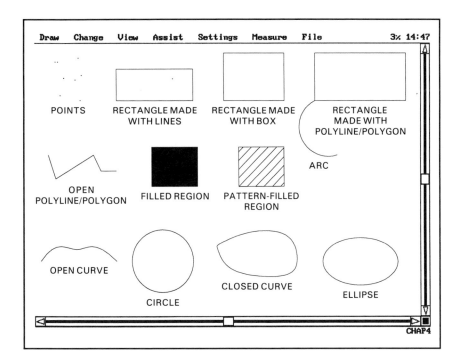

2. If your drawing from Activity 1 is not on screen, open it. Then, complete the following tasks.
   A. Erase the rectangle made using the **Box** command. Pick exactly on the object. You should be able to delete it with one pick.
   B. Erase the rectangle made using the **Line** command. Note how you must erase each individual line to erase the rectangle.
   C. Erase the remaining objects in the drawing. Select them by using either the Window box or Crosses box.
   D. Select **Undo** as many times as needed to restore all the objects you drew.
   E. Select **Redo** to step through your drawing session until no objects remain on screen.
   F. Clear the drawing without saving it.

3. Select and draw five of the objects shown below. Fill the tinted regions with a color and/or pattern of your choice.

4. Create a landscape design like that shown in the illustration. Do not be concerned with making the drawing perfect. Just get a feel for adding objects to a drawing. Save your drawing as C4A4.

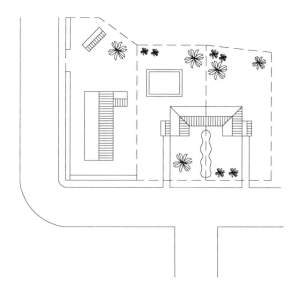

5. Think of a product you would like to invent or see built. Put some thought into the design. Then, use AutoSketch to make some rough sketches of your ideas. When finished, save the drawing as C4A5. Also, save the drawing under a special name you will remember easily.

Chapter 5

DRAWING PRECISELY

After studying this chapter, you will be able to:
- Explain how the Cartesian coordinate system is used to locate objects accurately.
- Type in absolute, relative, and polar coordinate values to place objects and enter distance.
- Identify AutoSketch functions that help you draw precisely with a mouse or digitizer.
- Describe the Grid and set the grid spacing.
- Explain the purpose of Snap and set the snap spacing.
- Use Attach modes to connect new objects to existing objects.
- Use the orthogonal mode to draw perfect horzontal and vertical lines.
- Set the color and linetype assigned to newly drawn objects.

In Chapter 4, you learned how to place objects in a drawing. You were able to place these objects freely with the pointer, without regard to their size or location. Most designs, such as technical drawings, require that you draw objects using exact measurements. This chapter shows you how to enter exact distance and size values using your keyboard and/or mouse. Drawing aids, such as the snap grid and attach modes, are also covered. In addition, this chapter also shows how to set the color and linetype for objects you add to the drawing.

CARTESIAN COORDINATE SYSTEM

Chapter 1 stated that CAD systems are much more accurate than manual drawing. You might wonder how AutoSketch can make your drawings so accurate. The answer is that AutoSketch and all CAD programs use a standard method of point location called the Cartesian coordinate system.

Locating Points on the Cartesian Coordinate System

The *Cartesian coordinate system* consists of two axes at 90 degrees to each other, Fig. 5-1. The horizontal axis is the *X axis*. The vertical axis is the *Y axis*. The intersection of the two axes is the *origin*. The location of any point or object can be found by measuring distance, in units, along the axes. You might think of each unit as an inch or a millimeter.

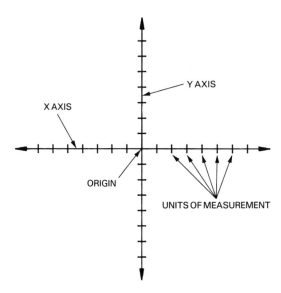

Fig. 5-1. The Cartesian coordinate system.

TYPING IN POINT LOCATIONS

There are three ways to enter point locations and distance using the keyboard; you can type in absolute, relative, or polar coordinate values. Absolute coordinates measure distance from the origin. Relative and polar coordinates measure distance from the previous point. Whenever AutoSketch prompts for location of a point, you can type in coordinates instead of using the pointer.

Absolute Coordinates

Absolute coordinates mark an exact position measured from the origin of the Cartesian coordinate system. (AutoSketch aligns the origin of the coordinate system with the lower-left corner of your screen.) The location is given with a coordinate pair, written as (X,Y). The X value is the distance from the origin along the X axis. The Y value is the distance from the origin along the Y axis. When entering absolute coordinate values in AutoSketch, you do not use the opening or closing parentheses.

Drawing with Absolute Coordinates. An example of drawing a line using absolute coordinates is shown in Fig. 5-2. After choosing the **Line** command, you might enter the following values.

Line Enter point: **2,2**

Line To point: **10,7**

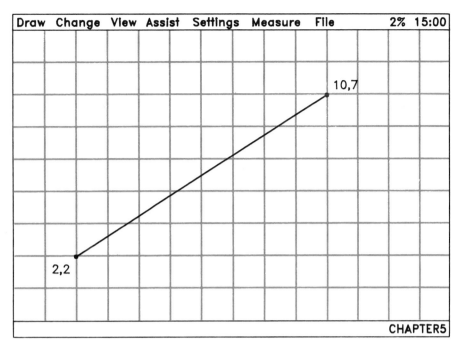

Fig. 5-2. Line drawn by entering absolute coordinates.

You must separate the X and Y coordinate values with a comma. Press the [Enter] key, sometimes labeled [Return], after typing in the values. The line appears on screen after you press the [Enter] or [Return] key.

Format for Entering Coordinate Values

There are two ways to enter coordinate values. You can type values in decimal format or in architectural format.

Decimal Format. If each unit of the coordinate system refers to a metric unit, enter decimal values. For example, if each unit equals a centimeter, you might enter the coordinate pair (5.05,4.15) to locate a point. You can also enter decimal values to measure in inches. For example, the absolute coordinate pair (2.5,2.5) defines a point two and one-half inches away from the origin along both the X and Y axes. You can use up to seven digits behind the decimal point (0.0000000) for greater precision.

Architectural Format. You can also enter coordinate values in architectural units beginning with Version 2.0 of AutoSketch. Architectural units are expressed in feet and inches. For example, you might enter the absolute coordinate pair (3'-2 1/2",4'-3 1/4") to locate one corner of a house floor plan. You can also enter just inches, such as (5 1/4",6 7/8"), or just fractions, such as (1/2",3/4"). The rules when entering architectural units are:

- Use an apostrophe when you specify feet values.
- Separate the foot from inch units with a dash.
- Separate fractions of an inch from whole inches with a space.
- Separate the numerator and denominator of a fraction with a slash.
- The denominator of the fraction must be a power of 2, up to 1024. The following denominators are used most often: 2, 4, 8, 16, 32, and 64.
- Enter a quotation mark after inch values.

NOTE: You cannot mix decimal units and architectural units in the same entry. For example, AutoSketch will not accept the coordinate pair (5.25,5 1/2″). A dialogue box will appear saying "Bad Point Specification." Either change the 5.25 to 5 1/4″ or change the 5 1/2″ to 5.5 so that AutoSketch will accept the coordinate.

Relative Coordinates

Relative coordinates measure position from the previous point. The previous point could have been typed at the keyboard or picked using your pointing device. A relative coordinate is written in AutoSketch as R(X,Y). The X value is the distance from the previous point measured along the X axis. The Y value is the distance from the previous point measured along the Y axis. When entering relative coordinates, you must use the opening and closing parentheses.

Drawing with Relative Coordinates. Here is an example of drawing a line using both absolute and a relative coordinate, Fig. 5-3. First select the **Line** command. Place the first endpoint using your pointing device, or type an absolute coordinate as is done here.

Line Enter point: **2,2**

At the next prompt, enter a relative coordinate. See Fig. 5-3 as you enter the following value.

Line To point: **R(9,5)**

This value places the second endpoint nine units to the right and five units above the first endpoint of the line. Simply stated, the absolute coordinate tells where you want to start. The relative coordinate tells how many steps (units) to take in each direction.

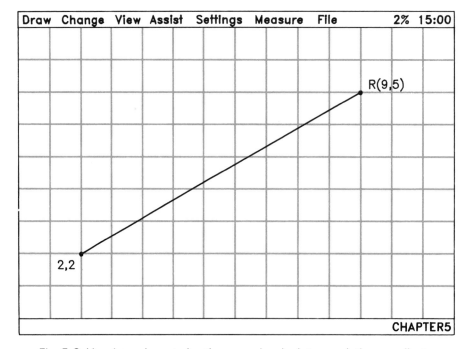

Fig. 5-3. Line drawn by entering the second endpoint as a relative coordinate.

You can enter relative coordinates in architectural format as well as decimal format. For example, you might enter the relative coordinate R(3 1/2″,1′-5 1/8″). This format allows you to easily work on architectural drawings that are measured in feet and inches. Architectural drafters frequently use relative coordinates in architectural format to lay out wall lengths.

Polar Coordinates

Polar coordinates measure position by distance from the previous point and angle from the X axis. The previous point could have been typed at the keyboard or picked using your pointing device. A polar coordinate is written in AutoSketch as P(D,A). The D value is the Distance from the previous point. The A value is the Angle measured counterclockwise from the X axis, Fig. 5-4. When entering polar coordinates, you must use the opening and closing parentheses.

Drawing with Polar Coordinates. Here is an example of drawing a line using an absolute coordinate for the first endpoint, and a polar coordinate for the second endpoint. See Fig. 5-5. First, select the **Line** command. You could place the first endpoint using your pointing device, or type an absolute coordinate as is done here.

Line Enter point: **2,2**

At the next prompt, enter a polar coordinate. See Fig. 5-5 as you enter the following value.

Line To point: **P(8.00,35)**

The polar coordinate makes the line 8 units long at a 35 degree angle from the X axis. Simply stated, the absolute coordinate tells where you want to start. The polar coordinate tells how far you want to go and in what direction.

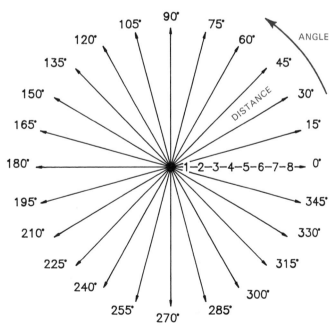

Fig. 5-4. The angle (A) value of a polar coordinate is the angle measured counterclockwise from the X axis. The distance (D) is measured from the previous point.

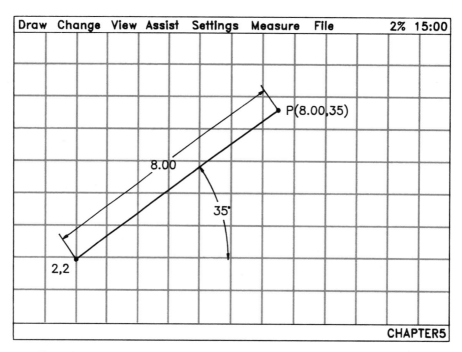

P(8.00,35)

8.00

35°

2,2

CHAPTER5

Fig. 5-5. Line drawn by entering the second endpoint as a polar coordinate.

You can enter polar coordinates in architectural format as well as decimal format. This can be very helpful when laying out a plot plan. For example, you might locate the corner of a property line with the polar coordinate P(80'-6 1/2",37). Note that the angle value, 37 degrees, is a single number without any marks behind it.

Combining Absolute, Relative, and Polar Coordinates

You will probably use all three types of coordinates–absolute, relative, and polar–on any given drawing. In fact, it is best to combine several methods along with using your pointer to pick locations. Type in coordinates when you know exact position, or how far you need to travel from your current position. Use the pointer to locate a position on another object quickly. Later in this chapter, you will learn how to draw accurately using the pointer.

When to Use Relative Coordinates. Relative coordinates are handy when you are drawing horizontal and vertical lines at a known distance. For example, suppose you are drawing the wall of a house plan. After selecting the **Polygon** command, pick one corner of the house using the pointer. Then, to draw a horizontal wall 9 feet long, enter R(9'-0",0) at the "Line To point:" prompt.

Relative coordinates also let you enter negative values to move left or down. For example, enter R(-5,0) to locate a point five units to the left of the previous point. Enter R(-2,-5) to locate a point two units to the left and five units down from the previous point. Fig. 5-6 shows how to draw a rectangle using one absolute and four relative coordinates. Note that both positive and negative values are entered.

When to Use Polar Coordinates. You will probably use polar coordinates more than any other keyboard entry method. You can draw lines in any direction and at any distance. In addition, to draw horizontal and vertical lines, simply enter 0, 90, 180, or 270 degree angles.

Polar coordinates can also be used to enter the radius of a circle. This is more precise than "eyeballing" the size. At the "Circle Point on circle:" prompt, enter the distance value as the radius. You can enter any angle value, but 0 is the easiest to remember. Here is an example of drawing a circle with two types of coordinates. Use an absolute coordinate to locate the circle's center. Then, enter a polar coordinate to give the radius.

Circle Center point: **2,2**

Circle Point on circle: **P(3,0)**

This sequence draws a three unit radius circle with the center two units to the right and two units above the drawing origin.

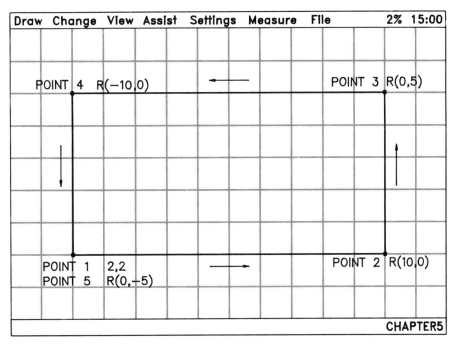

Fig. 5-6. Drawing a rectangle using relative coordinates. You will enter both positive and negative X and Y values.

DRAWING AIDS FOR POINTER INPUT

In Chapter 4, you learned that it is easy to use the pointer to draw objects. You can see the pointer's position on screen and quickly find where an object will be placed. You can also "drag" objects to size. However, your ability to draw accurately with the pointer depends on the display's resolution and your skills in handling the input device. It is important that lines that should meet, do so precisely. Even if two objects that should meet are .001 inch apart, this could impair the design.

AutoSketch provides *drawing aids* that help you use the pointer to locate position more accurately. There are five types of drawing aids: Coordinate display, visible Grid, invisible Snap grid, Attach modes, and Orthogonal mode. These functions are toggle modes, meaning that they are either on or off. You turn them on and off in the **Assist** menu, Fig. 5-7. A check mark appears next to the option when it is on.

ON-SCREEN COORDINATE DISPLAY

When using the pointer to draw, it is helpful to have a readout of the location of the pointer. When you turn on the **Coords** mode, two things happen, Fig. 5-8.
- The absolute coordinate position of the pointer appears on the prompt line.
- When drawing a line, the polar coordinate value showing the position of the pointer replaces the memory meter.

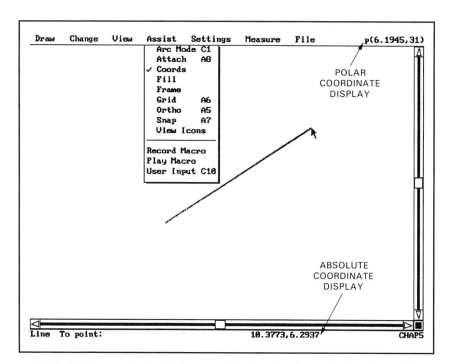

Fig. 5-7. Drawing aids are found in the Assist menu.
A check mark appears next to drawing aids that are
turned on.

Fig. 5-8. The coordinate display, set with Coords, shows the location of the
pointer in absolute coordinates and polar coordinates.

The displayed values are called *running coordinates* because the readouts constantly change to reflect the pointer's position. The display will read in decimal units only. NOTE: When using certain editing commands, such as **Scale** and **Rotate,** the coordinate readout will disappear so that other readouts can appear.

GRID DISPLAY

A *grid* is a pattern of dots on screen used much like graph paper. See Fig. 5-9. The grid pattern lets you see distance between points of the Cartesian coordinate system. When adding an object, such as a line, circle, or box, you can use the grid to locate position. The grid does not control the movement of the pointer. The grid is only used as a visual reference.

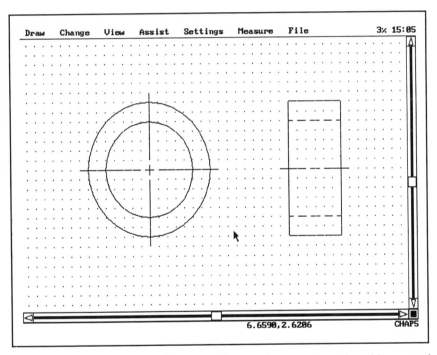

Fig. 5-9. A grid is a pattern of dots used like graph paper. Here, the grid was used to help draw front and side views of a bearing.

Setting Grid Spacing
The spacing between grid dots is set by picking the **Settings** menu, and then the **Grid** command. The **Grid** dialogue box appears, Fig. 5-10.

Grid Settings. The *X spacing* is the horizontal distance between grid dots. The *Y spacing* is the vertical distance between grid dots. The default value for X and Y spacing is 0. Enter a value opposite *X spacing* and pick the extended *OK* box. When you set the X spacing, the Y spacing assumes the same value. However, you can enter a different *Y spacing* value, if necessary. When finished, pick *OK* at the bottom of the dialogue box. You can reset the spacing at any time during your drawing session.

Guidelines for Grid Spacing. Here are some guidelines for setting the grid spacing.
- The X and Y spacing is usually the same value.
- Grid spacing does not have to be in whole units. You may want grid dots spaced every .25 or .5 unit.
- The distance between grid dots can be large or small. The grid spacing depends on the size of the objects to be drawn. The distance between grid dots for a detailed drawing could be small–.125, or 1/8″ in architectural format. If the drawing is large or simple, space the grid dots further apart.
- Setting the distance too small will blur the grid or prevent it from appearing at all. If the grid spacing is too close, AutoSketch displays a dialogue box saying "Grid is too dense to display."
- If you set the grid spacing to 0, but turn on the grid, the spacing will be the same as the Snap grid.
- The grid is offered for your reference; set the spacing how it will help you best.

Turning the Grid On and Off

Pick the **Assist** menu and **Grid** command to turn on and off the grid display. You can also hold down [Alt] and press function key [F6]. The grid can also be turned on and off when setting the spacing. Pick the box opposite *Grid* in the **Grid** dialogue box so that it shows *On* or *Off*. See Fig. 5-10. NOTE: AutoSketch allows you to turn the grid off when you set a spacing too dense to display.

Guidelines for Displaying the Grid. Use the grid only when it is useful. Sometimes the grid dots make the drawing look cluttered. NOTE: The visible grid is not a permanent part of the drawing. Even if the grid is on when you plot the drawing to paper, the grid dots are not plotted.

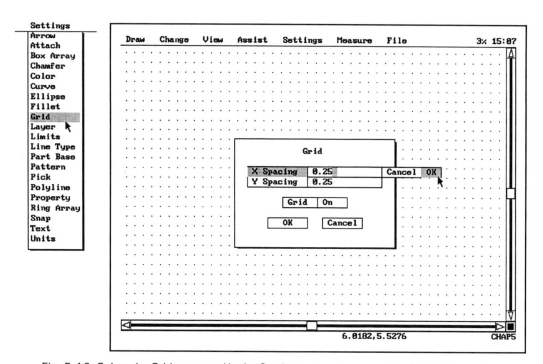

Fig. 5-10. Select the Grid command in the Settings menu to access the Grid dialogue box.

SNAP GRID

A grid does not control the pointer; it is only a visual reference. This is why AutoSketch offers an invisible *Snap grid*. When Snap is turned on, a small crosshair, like a plus (+) mark, jumps along beside your pointer, Fig. 5-11. The crosshair moves in precise increments measured by the snap spacing. Any point you pick is placed at the crosshair. This lets you pick locations in very precise measurements.

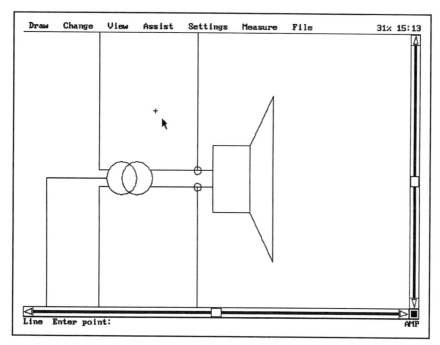

Fig. 5-11. When Snap is on, a crosshair jumps along beside your pointer. It moves in increments set in the Snap dialogue box.

Setting Snap Spacing

Pick the **Settings** menu and then the **Snap** command to set the snap spacing. The **Snap** dialogue box appears. It looks and works exactly like the **Grid** dialogue box, Fig. 5-12.

Snap Settings. The *X spacing* is the horizontal distance between the snap grid. The *Y spacing* is the vertical distance between the snap grid. The default value for X and Y spacing is 1. When you set the X spacing, the Y spacing assumes the same value. Although the X and Y spacing is usually the same, you can set different values if needed. You can reset the snap spacing at any time during your drawing session.

Guidelines for Snap Spacing. Here are some guidelines for setting the grid spacing.

- The snap spacing is often the same as the grid spacing. However, they can be entirely different values.
- If the snap spacing is not the same value as the grid spacing, it is usually set to evenly divide the grid spacing. For example, if the grid spacing is 1, the snap spacing might be .25. In this example, there are four snap locations for every grid point.
- Set the grid spacing to 0 and turn on the grid to display the grid spacing that is the same as the snap spacing.

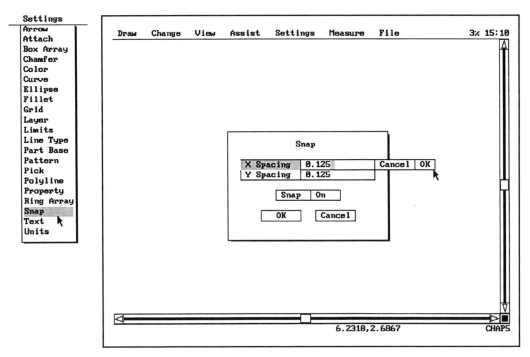

Fig. 5-12. Select the Snap command in the Settings menu to set the Snap spacing in the Snap dialogue box.

NOTE: Set the grid and snap spacings wisely. For example, many users set the snap spacing to the smallest distance needed to create the drawing. Suppose the size and spacing of most objects is .25, .5, and .75. Set the snap spacing to .25. Then, all distances you need to move or draw with the pointer are multiples of the snap spacing. The visible grid could be set at .5 to show half units or 1 to show whole units of the coordinate system.

Turning Snap On and Off

You can turn on snap by selecting the **Assist** menu and then the **Snap** command. A check mark appears next to the option. You can also hold down [Alt] and press function key [F7]. Another way to turn snap on and off is when you set the snap spacing. Pick the box opposite *Snap* in the **Snap** dialogue box so that it shows *On* or *Off*. See Fig. 5-12.

Guidelines for Using Snap. The invisible snap grid can be turned on and off at any time. Turn snap on when needed for drawing help. Remember, with snap on, you cannot freely digitize locations other the snap spacing. If you want to place a point freely, you must turn snap off. Also, turn snap off when it interferes with picking an object to erase or edit.

ATTACHING TO OBJECTS

Attach is a drawing aid that helps you connect to places on existing objects. Attach is needed because objects tend to look jagged on the display screen. This makes it difficult to precisely connect objects. If you pick close to an object to draw or edit when Attach is on, the pointer will "attach" to one of eight places, Fig. 5-13:
- Center. The center of a circle, arc, or ellipse.

- End Point. The nearest endpoint of a line, box, pattern fill, arc, polyline/polygon, or curve frame.
- Intersect. The place at which two objects intersect.
- Midpoint. The midpoint of a line, arc, pattern fill, polyline/polygon, or curve frame.
- Node Point. A point, or the endpoint of a text string.
- Perpendicular. A line or polyline you draw will attach perpendicular (90 degrees) to the object you pick. Perpendicular Attach will be discussed in greater detail in Chapter 12.
- Quadrant. Quadrant of a circle, arc, or ellipse. Quadrant refers to the 0, 90, 180, and 270 degree positions.
- Tangent. The tangent point of a circle, arc, or ellipse. A line that is tangent touches a circle, arc, or ellipse at only one point.

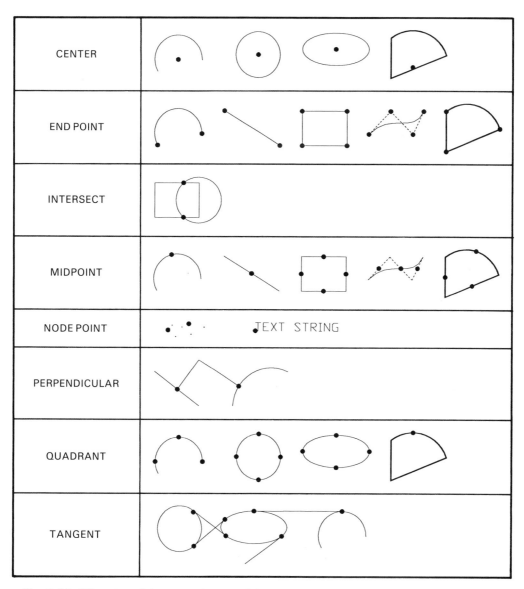

Fig. 5-13. When Attach is on, a point you pick close to an object will "attach" to one of eight places. The location depends on the object type and which Attach modes are turned on.

Setting the Attach Options

You can turn on any combination of Attach options. Pick the **Settings** menu and then the **Attach** command. The **Attachment Modes** dialogue box then appears, Fig. 5-14. Pick the box opposite the attachment modes you want turned on. AutoSketch looks in the area where you pick, until it finds the first match with more than one attachment mode on. There is one exception. Most Attach modes override the Center mode. You must turn off other modes to use Center.

Turning Attach On and Off

Attach is a toggle function; you can turn it on or off at any time, even in the middle of a drawing command. Hold down [Alt] and press function key [F8], or select the **Assist** menu and then the **Attach** command. A check mark appears when Attach is on. Another way to turn Attach on and off is in the **Attachment Modes** dialogue box. See Fig. 5-14.

Using Attach

You must pick very close to the object on screen for Attach to work. Otherwise, the point picked will be placed freely, and not be connected to the object. For example, suppose the Center mode is On and you are drawing a line to the center of a circle. Locate your pointer on the circle and pick it. The endpoint of the line will jump to the circle's center.

How close to the object you must pick varies according to your display and the Pick distance value. In Chapter 7, you will learn how to set this value to make it easier to use Attach. Remember that AutoSketch looks for the first Attach it can find. For example, suppose both the End point and Midpoint modes are on and you pick a line. AutoSketch will lock onto the midpoint or endpoint, whichever is closer.

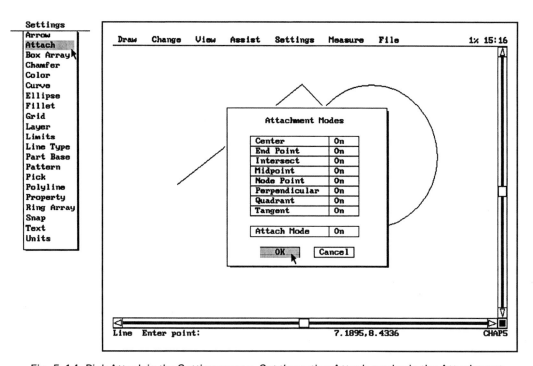

Fig. 5-14. Pick Attach in the Settings menu. Set the active Attach modes in the Attachment Modes dialogue box.

ORTHOGONAL MODE

Many lines you draw must be either horizontal or vertical. Many times it is difficult to draw lines or move objects perfectly horizontal or vertical. AutoSketch helps you with the orthogonal mode using the **Ortho** command. *Orthogonal* means perpendicular, or at right angles. When the orthogonal mode is on, it allows you to draw and edit only horizontally and vertically, Fig. 5-15.

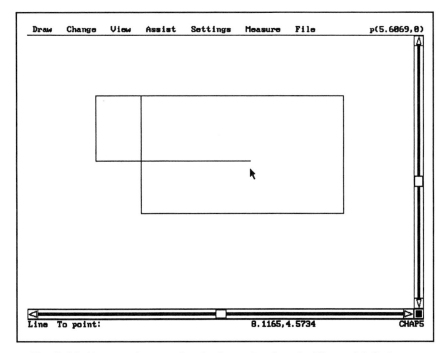

Fig. 5-15. You can draw perfect horizontal and vertical lines with Ortho on.

Turning Ortho Mode On and Off
You can turn on Ortho mode by selecting the **Assist** menu and the **Ortho** command. A check mark appears next to it. You can also hold down [Alt] and press function key [F5] to turn the orthogonal mode on and off.

LAST POINT SYSTEM VARIABLE

Whenever you pick a point, AutoSketch stores its location in memory as a *system variable.* You can recall that value by entering "/lpoint" to attach to the previous point.

Using /lpoint
Suppose you just drew a line. Now, you need to connect the first endpoint of a new line to the place where you ended the previous line. Instead of using an Attach mode, enter the following value:

Line Enter point: **/lpoint**

This method is easier to use than Attach. Also, there are times when the only method to find the previous point is /lpoint. This occurs when you pick a location without using the **Snap** or **Attach** commands.

SETTING COLORS AND LINETYPES

AutoSketch lets you draw in color, using a variety of line patterns, or linetypes. You will use different colors and linetypes depending on your application for AutoSketch. For example, a graphic designer might use various colors and linetypes to draw an advertisement.

In technical drafting, color and linetype are selected to give objects certain meanings. A solid, black line might outline the shape of an object. A dashed, yellow line might represent a hidden edge of an object. The meaning of different linetypes is called the *alphabet of lines*. This standard was developed to distinguish lines by style so that drawings are easier to read. Selecting color and linetype for technical drafting is discussed in Chapter 11.

Setting Object Linetype

The *linetype* refers to the line style of objects. It may be solid, dashed, or a combination of solid and dashed segments. When you first start AutoSketch, the default linetype is solid. To specify a new linetype, pick the **Settings** menu and **Line Type** command. The available linetypes appear in the **Drawing Line Type** dialogue box, Fig. 5-16.

Many of the names reflect the names given in the alphabet of lines for technical drafting–hidden, center, phantom, and border. Pick the box opposite the linetype you want to draw. A check mark will appear. Then, pick *OK* at the bottom to close the dialogue box. All new

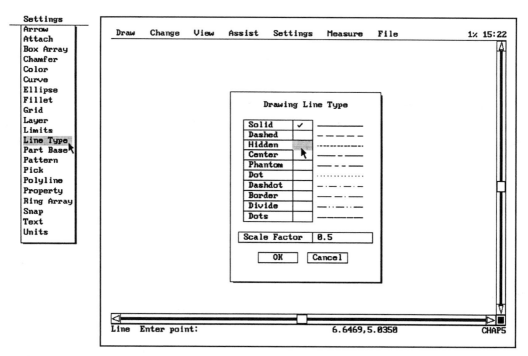

Fig. 5-16. Select the Line Type command in the Settings menu to open the Drawing Line Type dialogue box. Pick the box opposite the linetype you need.

objects (other than wide polylines) will have the new linetype after setting a different line-type. All existing objects will remain the same.

The *scale factor* in the **Drawing Line Type** dialogue box refers to how often the line pattern repeats. The default scale factor is .5. Experiment with different scale factors to see how the line appears. If you plan to plot a drawing on large C- or D-size paper, consider increasing the scale factor to .75 or 1. Resetting the scale factor affects all objects, including those already drawn.

Setting Object Color

It is helpful to assign colors to objects, especially if your system has a color display. Pick the **Settings** menu and **Color** command to specify a new color. The available colors appear in the **Drawing Color** dialogue box, Fig. 5-17. Pick the box opposite the desired color. A check mark will appear. The color code (numerical value for the color) will also appear in the *Color Number* box. Pick *OK* at the bottom to close the dialogue box. All newly drawn objects will have the new color. Filled regions will be filled with the new color. All existing objects will remain the same color.

Guidelines for Using Color. Separating details by color helps identify different parts of the drawing. You can use color for illustration as well as for technical drafting. Creative designs entertain; technical drawings communicate. For example, if you are doing a land-scape design, make all shrubbery green and bricks red. A technical drawing, on the other hand, might have all text in blue and dimensions in green.

Even if you have a monochrome display, you may still want to set colors. When you plot the drawing to a pen plotter, the object's color determines which pen is used. The actual pens may have different ink colors or different tip widths. In technical drafting, you must use pens

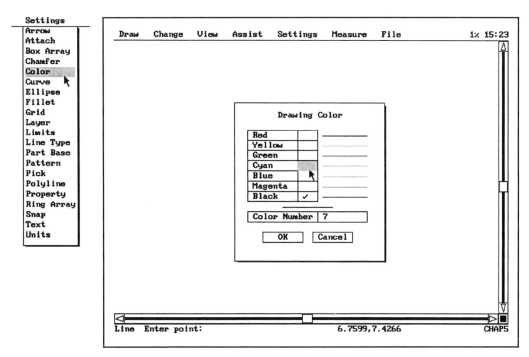

Fig. 5-17. Select the Color command in the Settings menu to set the drawing color in the Drawing Color dialogue box.

with different tip widths. You can have the plotter select different pens according to line width by making objects different colors.

NOTE: There is only one limitation. If you have a monochrome display and a single-color hardcopy device, the color command is of little use.

SUMMARY

Most designs require that you draw objects at precise locations using exact dimensions. AutoSketch provides precision drawing aids the let you type in coordinate values and pick precise points with your mouse or digitizer.

AutoSketch and all other CAD systems use a standard method of point location called the Cartesian coordinate system. You can type in absolute, relative, and polar coordinate values whenever AutoSketch asks for a point. Absolute coordinates measure distance from the origin. Relative and polar coordinates measure distance from the previous point.

AutoSketch provides several helpful drawing aids to help you draw accurately with the pointer. Two aids that work well together are Grid and Snap. A grid is a pattern of dots on screen used much like graph paper. The grid alone does not control movement of the pointer. Turn on an invisible snap grid to draw objects in precise increments. The snap spacing can be the same as the grid spacing, or a different value.

Another useful drawing aid is Attach. It helps you connect to existing objects. When Attach is on, a point you pick close to an object will "attach" to one of eight places. This can be a center, endpoint, intersection, midpoint, node point, perpendicular, quadrant, or tangent. You can make sure that objects meet precisely by using Attach.

The remaining three drawing aids are Coords, Ortho, and /lpoint. Coords displays the absolute coordinate location of the pointer on the prompt line when it is turned on. Ortho lets you draw only horizontally or vertically. A new object is connected to the previous point by entering /lpoint on the prompt line rather than using the pointer or coordinates.

AutoSketch lets you draw in color, and with a variety of linetypes. You will use different colors and linetypes depending on your application for AutoSketch. The proper color and linetype is especially important in technical drafting. Each line you draw has a certain meaning. In addition, when you plot the drawing to a pen plotter, the object's color determines which pen is used.

NEW TERMS

Cartesian coordinate system, X axis, Y axis, origin, absolute coordinates, relative coordinates, polar coordinates, drawing aids, **Coords** mode, **Grid** command, grid spacing, **Snap** command, **Attach** command, attachment modes, **Ortho** command, system variable, /lpoint, alphabet of lines, **Line Type** command, linetype, scale factor, **Color** command, color code.

REVIEW QUESTIONS

Write your answers on a separate sheet of paper. Do not write in this book.
1. AutoSketch and other CAD systems use a standard method of point location called the
_____.

2. The X and Y axes meet at the _____.
3. When can you type in coordinate values?
4. In AutoSketch, an absolute coordinate value is written as _____.
5. In AutoSketch, a relative coordinate value is written as _____.
6. In AutoSketch, a polar coordinate value is written as _____.
7. Relative and polar coordinates measure distance from _____.
8. Explain why you might use several point entry methods during a drawing session.
9. What polar coordinate value could you enter at the "Circle Point on Circle:" prompt to draw a 4 unit diameter circle?
10. Functions that help you draw accurately with the pointer using your mouse or digitizer are typically called _____.
11. A readout of the pointer's location on screen is displayed by selecting _____ from the **Assist** menu.
12. AutoSketch's visible Grid restricts your pointer's movement to precise increments. True or false?
13. Define X spacing and Y spacing as they apply to the **Grid** and **Snap** commands.
14. The grid dots automatically appear on screen after you set the grid spacing. True or false?
15. Describe two guidelines that determine what values you enter for the grid and snap spacing.
16. When Snap is on, a point you pick will be placed at the tip your pointer arrow. True or false?
17. Name the times when you would turn Snap on, and when you would have it off.
18. List the eight locations where Attach helps you to connect.
19. Why do some Attach modes need to be turned off so that others will work?
20. The Ortho mode restricts your drawing to what two directions?
21. A new point is connected to the previous point entered by typing the system variable _____ on the prompt line.
22. Why is the color and linetype of an object important in technical drafting?
23. The setting that determines how often a line pattern repeats is _____.
24. In what two ways can you specify the drawing color in the **Drawing Color** dialogue box?
25. When is the **Color** command of little use to the drafter?

ACTIVITIES

Here is a mixture of drawing activities to develop your skill in drawing precisely. There are an assortment of written and drawing activities. Place your answers on a separate sheet of paper. Save your AutoSketch drawings on your file disk, not on the program disk.

1. Draw a Cartesian coordinate system similar to the one shown here. Place a dot on the Cartesian coordinate axes to locate points P1 through P10. The values are given as absolute Cartesian coordinates.

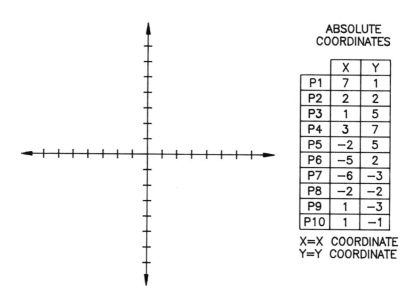

ABSOLUTE COORDINATES

	X	Y
P1	7	1
P2	2	2
P3	1	5
P4	3	7
P5	-2	5
P6	-5	2
P7	-6	-3
P8	-2	-2
P9	1	-3
P10	1	-1

X=X COORDINATE
Y=Y COORDINATE

2. Record the absolute X and Y Cartesian coordinate values for the points labeled P1 through P10.

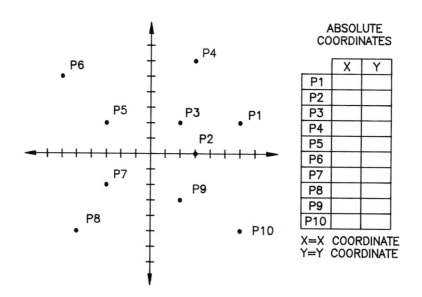

ABSOLUTE COORDINATES

	X	Y
P1		
P2		
P3		
P4		
P5		
P6		
P7		
P8		
P9		
P10		

X=X COORDINATE
Y=Y COORDINATE

3. Given point P1 at (2,2) on AutoSketch's drawing screen, list the relative X and Y coordinate values to travel point to point, from point P2 through P10. The gray lines show units of the Cartesian coordinate system.

Draw	Change	View	Assist	Settings	Measure	File	2% 15:00

P7

P8   P9

P6

P10

P4

P2

P1   P5

P3

CHAPTER5

FROM	TO	X	Y
P1	P2		
P2	P3		
P3	P4		
P4	P5		
P5	P6		
P6	P7		
P7	P8		
P8	P9		
P9	P10		
P10	P1		

X=X DISTANCE
Y=Y DISTANCE

4. Create a polar coordinate system similar to the one shown here. Place a dot to show angle and distance for each of the polar coordinates. Measure all of the points from the center.

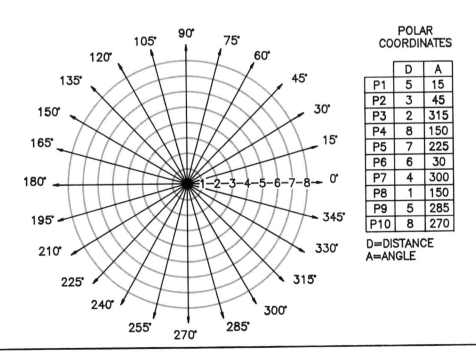

POLAR
COORDINATES

	D	A
P1	5	15
P2	3	45
P3	2	315
P4	8	150
P5	7	225
P6	6	30
P7	4	300
P8	1	150
P9	5	285
P10	8	270

D=DISTANCE
A=ANGLE

5. Given point P1 at (0,0), list the relative polar coordinate values to travel point to point, from points P2 through P4.

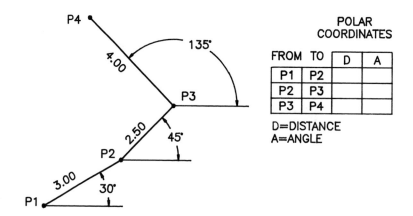

POLAR COORDINATES

FROM	TO	D	A
P1	P2		
P2	P3		
P3	P4		

D=DISTANCE
A=ANGLE

6. Given the dimensioned drawing with P1 at (0,0), identify the absolute coordinates of the points labeled P2 through P5.

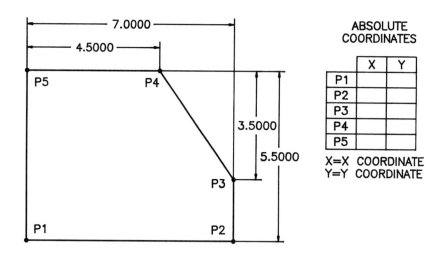

ABSOLUTE COORDINATES

	X	Y
P1		
P2		
P3		
P4		
P5		

X=X COORDINATE
Y=Y COORDINATE

7. Given the dimensioned drawing in Activity 6 with P1 at (0,0), list the relative X and Y coordinate values to travel point to point.

RELATIVE COORDINATES

FROM	TO	X	Y
P1	P2		
P2	P3		
P3	P4		
P4	P5		
P5	P1		

X=X DISTANCE
Y=Y DISTANCE

8. Given the dimensioned drawing with P1 at (0,0), identify the coordinates of the points labeled P2 through P4. Use polar coordinate values.

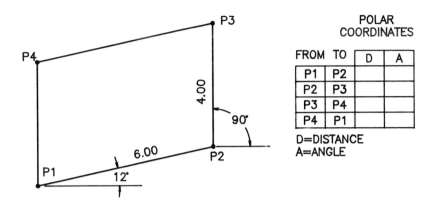

FROM	TO	D	A
P1	P2		
P2	P3		
P3	P4		
P4	P1		

D=DISTANCE
A=ANGLE

9. Clear any drawing from screen using **New.** Set the X and Y Grid spacing at .5 units and turn on the grid. Set the X and Y Snap spacing at .25 units and turn on Snap. Use the Grid and Snap, and draw the object shown with your pointer. Use the **Pattern Fill** command or **Fill Region** command for the solid color. Save the drawing as C5A9. Try drawing the same object (except the circle) using zero-width and wide polylines. (Hint: You will need to reset the Snap setting.)

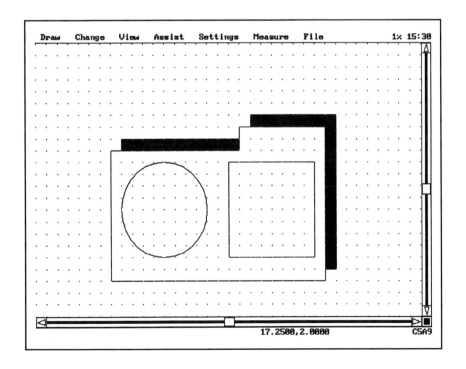

10. Clear any drawing from screen using **New** and turn off Grid or Snap. Draw the objects in the order shown, from screen A to E. Use the Attach modes to connect the objects. Save the drawing as C5A10.

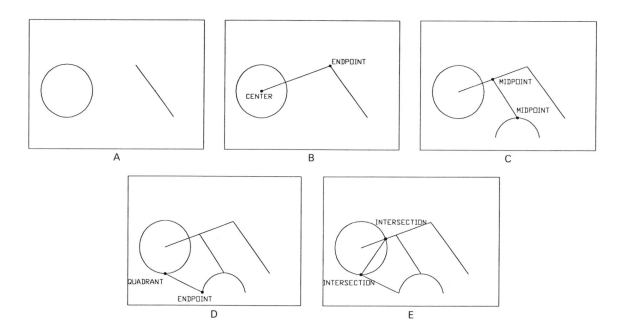

11. Clear any drawing from screen using **New** and turn off Grid or Snap. Draw the objects in the order shown, from screen A to D. Use the Attach modes to connect the objects. Draw the objects with the linetype shown. Save the drawing as C5A11.

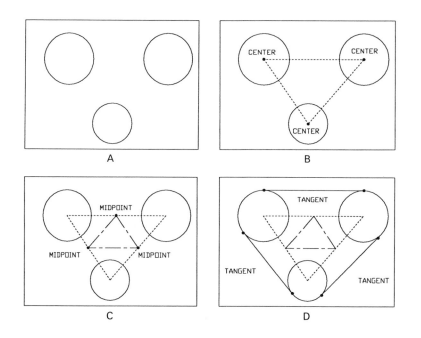

12. Clear any drawing from screen using **New** and turn off Grid or Snap. Draw a line. Then, draw a circle by picking the center and a point on the circle. Connect a new line from where you picked the circle's size to the endpoint of the line using the /lpoint system variable. Save the drawing as C5A12.

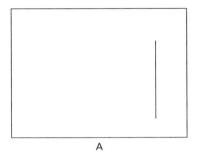

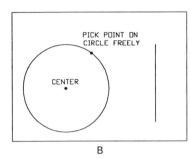

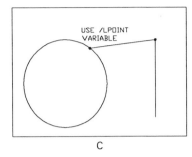

A   B   C

13. Clear any drawing from screen using **New.** Use Ortho mode to draw horizontal lines using all linetypes offered by AutoSketch. In addition, draw the lines using every color, even if you do not have a color monitor. Save the drawing as C5A13.

14. Draw four concentric circles (circles that share the same center point). Make the smallest circle 1 unit in diameter. Increase the diameter one unit for each larger circle. Save the drawing as C5A14.

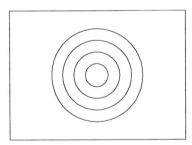

15. Draw a 3 unit square box. Without typing coordinates, Grid, or Snap, draw a circle inside the square so that the circle touches all four sides. How did you do it? (Hint: You will have to draw one extra line and erase it later.) Save the drawing as C5A15.

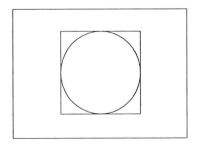

16-17. For each activity, clear any drawing from screen using **New.** Then, draw the objects shown in Activities 6 and 8 by typing in coordinates. Save the drawings as C5A16 and C5A17.

18-24. For each activity, draw the design or object shown using drawing aids. Grid and Snap are especially useful. Undimensioned drawings should fill the screen, but look proportional. Draw the dimensioned drawings using exact measurements, either by typing in coordinates or using your pointer with drawing aids. Save the drawings using the Activity file names given underneath.

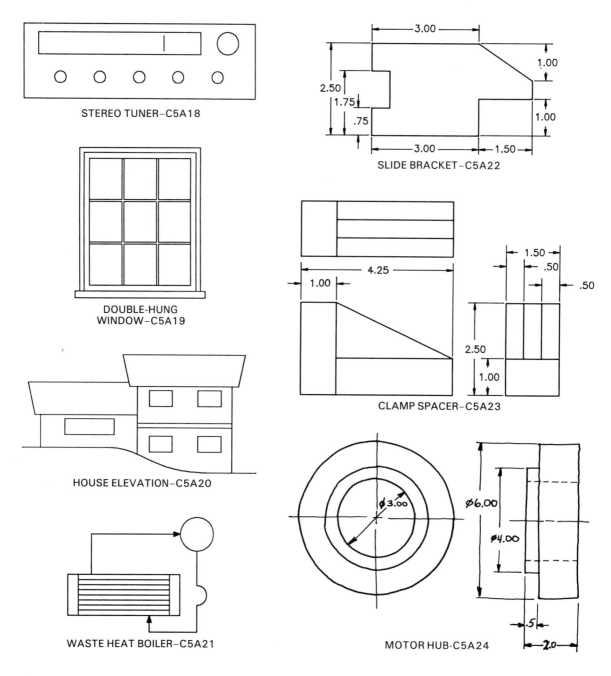

STEREO TUNER–C5A18

DOUBLE-HUNG
WINDOW–C5A19

HOUSE ELEVATION–C5A20

WASTE HEAT BOILER–C5A21

SLIDE BRACKET–C5A22

CLAMP SPACER–C5A23

MOTOR HUB-C5A24

25. In Chapter 4, you made rough sketches of a product you would like to invent or see built. Recall the drawing named C4A5. Refine your design using precise measurements. When finished, save the drawing as C5A25.

Chapter 6

EDITING OBJECTS

After studying this chapter, you will be able to:
- Describe the process of editing.
- Identify ways to select one or several objects to edit.
- Move one or several objects to a new location.
- Copy one or several objects.
- Rotate one or several objects.
- Remove a portion from an object.

Editing is the process of changing objects you have drawn. You will probably spend more time editing drawings than you will creating them. Drafting departments spend vast amounts of time editing because most designs pass through many revisions before they are complete. As one drafter said, "There may be one way to create a line, but there are 100 ways to change it." The benefit of AutoSketch is that editing is made quite easy.

AutoSketch provides a variety of editing functions to suit every situation. You can erase, move, copy, break, rotate, mirror, stretch, and scale one or several objects at once. You can also change an object's properties (color and linetype). The commands to do these tasks are found in the **Change** menu, Fig. 6-1. This chapter covers basic editing commands. Chapter 7 covers more advanced editing techniques.

CHOOSING OBJECTS TO EDIT

In traditional drafting, you use an eraser to make changes. AutoSketch does not have an eraser. Instead, you select an editing command and then select the objects to edit. Chapter 4 told you how to select objects to **Erase.** You will use these same selection techniques. When you select an editing command from the **Change** menu, the pointer changes from an arrow to a hand. Plus, the following prompt appears:

Command Select object:

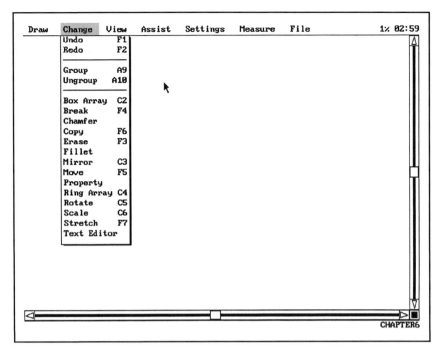

Fig. 6-1. Editing commands are found in the Change menu.

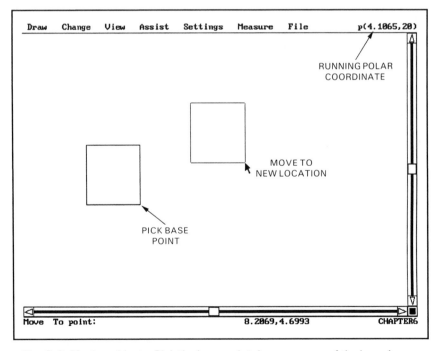

Fig. 6-2. Moving objects. Pick the base point, here a corner of the box. As you drag the object to a new location, notice that the pointer ''pulls'' the base point to move the object.

Now, you can "grab" an object with the hand, or select several at once using the *Crosses/window box* function. To select one object, locate the hand's finger over the object and pick it. To select several objects, pick near, but not on, the objects to choose. Make sure you do not select any single object. The following prompt then appears:

Command Crosses/window corner:

Your hand pointer now drags a selection box around on screen. Locate the opposite corner of the box away from the first corner, and around the objects to edit. If you drag the box to the right, a solid box appears. This is the *Window box*. Only those objects entirely within the box are selected. If you drag the box to the left, a dotted box appears. This is the *Crosses box*. All objects within *and crossing* the box are selected. See Figs. 4-28 and 4-29.

Once you select the object(s), AutoSketch usually prompts you to perform another action. You might have to pick a location, or type in the size, distance, or another value. Remember to always look at the prompt line after you enter a command. AutoSketch will tell you what information to enter or action to perform.

MOVING OBJECTS

The **Move** command lets you move objects to a new location on the drawing. You must select the objects and then two points. To move objects, Fig. 6-2, select the **Change** menu and **Move** command. You can also press function key [F5]. The following prompt appears:

Move Select object:

Pick the object to move, or select several with the Crosses/window box. The next prompt that appears is:

Move From point:

This first point you pick is a *base point*. The pointer will hold on to this "base" to drag the objects around on screen. You can use an Attach mode to place the base point at a precise place. For example, you might want to drag the objects using the end of a line or center of a circle. The next prompt that appears is:

Move To point:

This second point tells where to move the objects. The easiest way to move objects is to drag them across the screen. As you move the pointer, a ghost image of the objects moves along. The ghost image helps you pull the objects to their new location. You can use Snap or Attach options to position the objects precisely. Also, notice that when you have Coords mode on, the memory meter is replaced by a running polar coordinate.

You do not have to drag the objects to their new location. If you know exact distance, enter coordinates at the second "Move To point:" prompt. Here is an example of moving objects by a polar coordinate.

Move To point: **P(3,30)**

This entry tells AutoSketch to move the objects 3 units away at a 30 degree angle, Fig. 6-3. Remember to press the [Enter] or [Return] key after typing in coordinates.

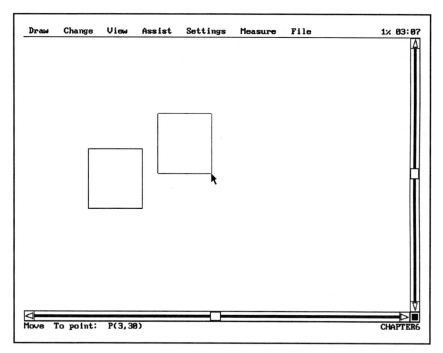

Move To point: P(3,30)   CHAPTER6

Fig. 6-3. When you know exact distance and direction to move objects, enter a
relative or polar coordinate. Here a polar coordinate was used.

COPYING OBJECTS

The **Copy** command is one of the most used functions of a CAD system. As stated in
Chapter 1, you should never draw the same item twice when using CAD. Instead, copy the
shape. AutoSketch's **Copy** command works exactly like **Move**, only the original objects are
left unchanged.

To copy objects, Fig. 6-4, pick the **Change** menu and the **Copy** command. You can also
press function key [F6]. The following prompt appears:

Copy Select object:

Select an object to copy, or select several with the Crosses/window box. The next prompt
to appear is:

Copy From point:

Pick the base point. The pointer will hold onto this "base" to drag the copy around on
screen. For accuracy, use an Attach mode or Snap to place the base point. The next prompt
that appears is:

Copy To point:

This second point tells where to place the copy. The easiest way to place the copy is to drag
it across the screen. A ghost image of the objects moves along with the pointer. Position the
image and then pick that location. You can use Snap or Attach to position the objects
precisely. You can also enter relative or polar coordinate values to place the copy an exact
distance away.

The **Copy** command is useful when you have many identical shapes in your drawing. Draw only one, and then copy it wherever needed. You can also use the **Copy** command to experiment with designs. For example, suppose you want to alter some part of your drawing. Make a copy and work on the copy rather than the original. If you like the revised shape, erase the original. If you don't like your changes, simply erase them. Because you worked on a copy, the original is left unchanged.

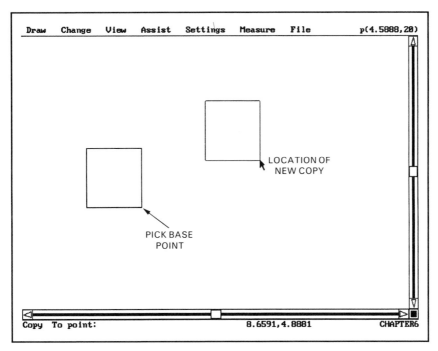

Fig. 6-4. Copying objects. Pick the base point and drag the copy to its location. Here, a copy is ''pulled'' into place. Remember, you can also type in a coordinate to place the copy.

ROTATING OBJECTS

The **Rotate** command is used to rotate one or several objects. It can be used to position shapes at precise angles. To rotate one or several objects, select the **Change** menu and then the **Rotate** command. You can also hold down [Ctrl] and press function key [F5]. The following prompt appears:

Rotate Select object:

Select the object to rotate, or select several with the Crosses/window box. The next prompt that appears is:

Rotate Center of rotation:

Pick the center of rotation around which the objects should rotate. The position of this point is important, Fig. 6-5. If a shape must rotate around a circle's center point, use an

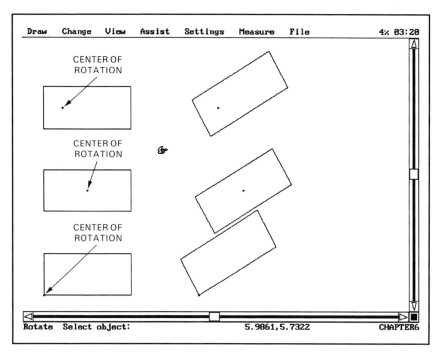

Fig. 6-5. Objects rotate about a center point you pick. Notice how the rectangle rotates depending on where the center point was chosen.

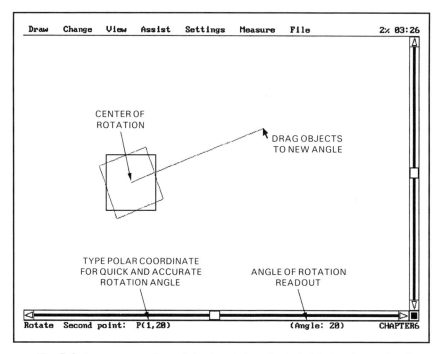

Fig. 6-6. As you move the pointer to rotate selected objects, the angle of rotation appears on the prompt line. You could also type in a polar coordinate as is done here.

Attach mode to pick the center. If a shape is rotated around a corner use Attach here, too. You may have to turn Snap off; otherwise, the center you pick will align with a snap point. The next prompt that appears is:

Rotate Second point:

The second point you pick determines the angle of rotation. Move your pointer around to drag the objects around the pivot point. Notice that a ghost image rotates with your pointer. Also, a readout on the prompt line shows the angle of rotation, Fig. 6-6. If the angle is important, move your pointer until the correct angle (in degrees) appears. If the exact angle is not important, move your pointer until the object(s) appear correct. Then press the pick button. If the Ortho mode is on, the pointer can only select angles of 0, 90, 180, and 270 degrees. Also, if Snap is on, the pointer will move only in snap increments.

An easier way to enter an exact rotation angle is by typing a polar coordinate. Enter the angle you want. Use a distance value of 1.

Rotate Second point: **P(1,45)**

This entry would rotate the objects 45 degrees counterclockwise. Remember to press the [Enter] or [Return] key after typing the coordinate. Notice that in Fig. 6-6 a polar coordinate was entered to rotate the object 20 degrees.

BREAKING OBJECTS

The **Break** command lets you remove a portion of an object. You can remove a section from a line to form two lines. You can remove a section from a circle to form an arc. To break an object, select the **Change** menu and **Break** command. You can also press function key [F4]. The following prompt appears:

Break Select object:

Only one object can be broken at a time. Notice that after you pick it, it becomes dotted on screen. Now, you must pick two *break points*. The next two prompts that appear are:

Break First break point:

Break Second break point:

Pick two points that define the portion to remove. You can also pick the second point beyond the object to trim it. See Fig. 6-7 for several examples of using the **Break** command. The illustration also shows how **Break** affects different objects.

Drawing aids, such as Snap and Attach, can affect where the break points are placed. If they cause the object to be broken incorrectly, select **Undo**. Then, turn Attach and Snap off in the **Assist** menu and try again.

You can break any AutoSketch object, except dimensions, text, and filled regions. CAUTION: When breaking a circle, the portion removed is counterclockwise from the first to second break point. If you select them in the wrong order, you can get some odd results. Notice in Fig. 6-7 the two ways a circle is broken. An ellipse breaks the same way.

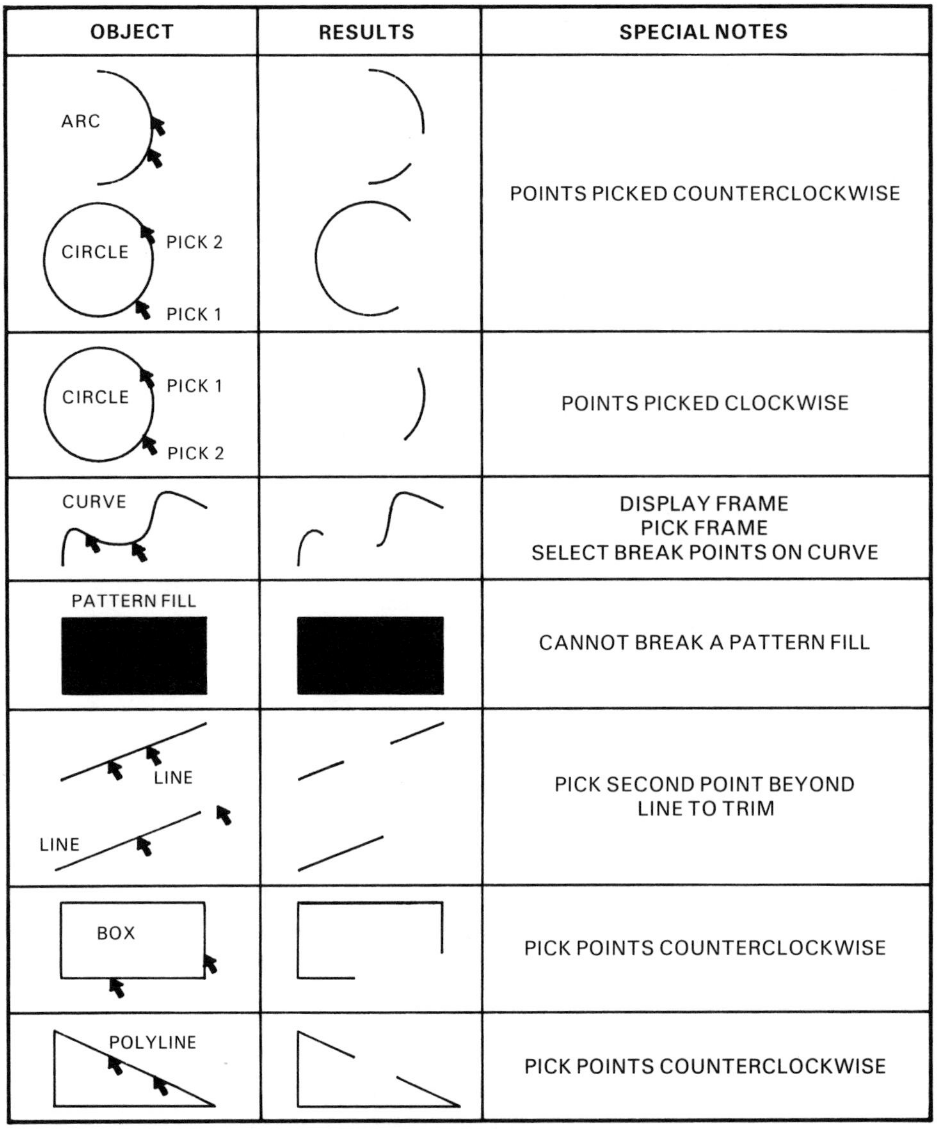

OBJECT	RESULTS	SPECIAL NOTES
ARC / CIRCLE PICK 2 / PICK 1		POINTS PICKED COUNTERCLOCKWISE
CIRCLE PICK 1 / PICK 2		POINTS PICKED CLOCKWISE
CURVE		DISPLAY FRAME PICK FRAME SELECT BREAK POINTS ON CURVE
PATTERN FILL		CANNOT BREAK A PATTERN FILL
LINE / LINE		PICK SECOND POINT BEYOND LINE TO TRIM
BOX		PICK POINTS COUNTERCLOCKWISE
POLYLINE		PICK POINTS COUNTERCLOCKWISE

Fig. 6-7. Objects break differently, and sometimes not at all. Review these examples.

SUMMARY

Editing is the process of changing objects you have drawn. You will probably spend more time editing drawings than you will creating them. AutoSketch provides a variety of editing functions to suit every situation. This chapter told you how to move, copy, rotate, and break objects. Chapter 7 will cover how to mirror, stretch, scale, and change the properties (color and linetype) of objects.

CAD systems, such as AutoSketch, do not have an "eraser." Instead, you must select objects to edit. You can pick one object at a time or select several at once with the Crosses/window box.

The **Move** and **Copy** commands are very similar. First, select the objects. Then, pick or enter a reference point. Finally, pick a position or enter a coordinate to tell where to move the objects. The difference between these two commands is that the **Copy** command leaves the original objects in place and makes a copy.

The **Rotate** command is used to turn one or several objects to a new angle. To rotate a shape, first select the objects that make up the shape. Then, pick the center of rotation around which the objects will rotate. Finally, move your pointer around to rotate the objects and pick a location when the correct angle appears on the prompt line. You can also enter a polar coordinate.

The **Break** command lets you remove a portion of an object. Only one object can be broken at a time. After choosing this command, pick the object to break. Then pick the two break points. The portion of the object between the two points is removed. Remember that when breaking a circle, ellipse, or polyline the portion removed is counterclockwise from the first to second break point.

NEW TERMS

Editing, Crosses/window box, **Move** command, base point, **Copy** command, **Rotate** command, center of rotation, **Break** command, break points.

REVIEW QUESTIONS

Write your answers on a separate sheet of paper. Do not write in this book.
1. The process of changing objects you have drawn is known as _____.
2. You will probably spend more time creating drawings than you will editing them. True or false?
3. AutoSketch's editing commands are found in the _____ menu.
4. In traditional drafting, you use an eraser to make changes. With AutoSketch, what must you do to edit objects?
5. When given the prompt, "Command Select object:," how do you select only one object?
6. Describe how AutoSketch determines whether a Window box or Crosses box is used to select objects to edit.
7. After selecting objects to move, the first point you pick is the _____.
8. When moving objects, how does AutoSketch help you "pull" the objects to their new location?
9. When specifying the distance to move objects or place a copy, you can type in _____ as well as pick position with the pointer.
10. AutoSketch's **Copy** command works exactly like **Move**, except that the original objects are _____.
11. After selecting objects to rotate, you must pick a _____ around which the objects will rotate.
12. When rotating objects, what two methods can you use to determine the angle of rotation?
13. When you select an object to break, it becomes _____ on screen.
14. After picking an object to break, you must pick two _____.
15. When breaking a circle, the portion removed is clockwise from the first to second break point. True or false?

ACTIVITIES

Here is a mixture of drawing activities to develop your skills with editing commands. Use drawing aids such as Grid, Snap, and Attach to your advantage, unless the directions tell otherwise. Save your AutoSketch drawings on your file disk, not on the program disk. Clear the previous drawing from screen and memory using **New** before starting each activity.

1. Draw four circles, where three of them cross a center circle. Erase two circles (those dotted) at one time by selecting them within a Window box. Save the drawing as C6A1.

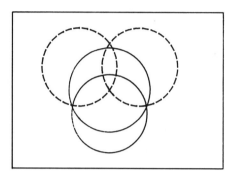

2. Draw a triangle using the **Line** command and Attach mode Endpoint. Move one line 3 units to the right and 3 units up. (Hint: type in relative Cartesian coordinates.) Then, move the two remaining lines at the same time to make the triangle again. (Hint: You can type coordinates or use Attach to reconnect the triangle properly.) Save the drawing as C6A2.

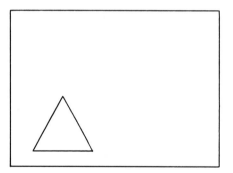 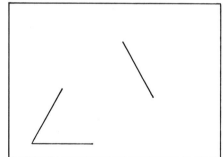

3. With the drawing from Activity 2 still on screen, copy the triangle three times as shown. A corner of each copy should connect to the midpoint of a side of the original triangle. (Hint: use the Attach modes Midpoint and Endpoint.) Save the drawing as C6A3.

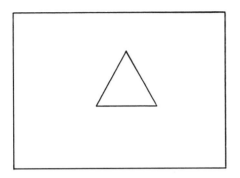 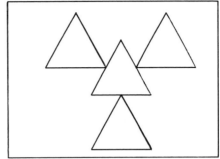

4. Do not use a Grid or Snap, but do use Ortho for this activity. Draw two intersecting roads using horizontal and vertical lines. Break the lines to complete the intersection. Save the drawing as C6A4.

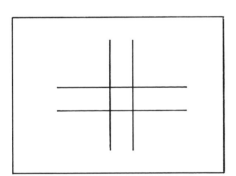 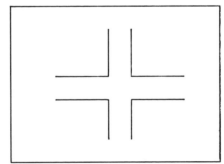

5. Set both the Grid and Snap spacing at .5. Draw the rectangle and the circle to the size shown in the left illustration. Copy the circle as needed to complete the drawing shown in the right illustration. How many times did you need to use the **Copy** command? Save the drawing as C6A5.

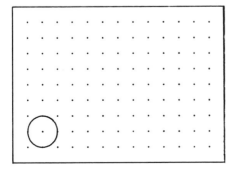 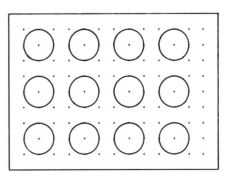

6. Draw two boxes approximately the same size and place them end-to-end. Rotate the left box 90 degrees (one-quarter turn) by picking a corner as the center point. Rotate the right box by picking a center of rotation near the center of the box. Note how the two boxes rotate differently depending on where the center point is chosen. Save the drawing as C6A6.

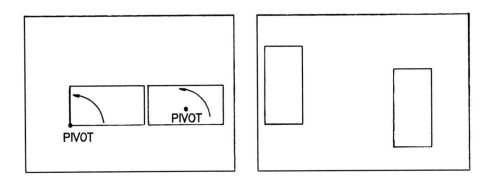

7. AutoSketch does not allow you to draw an arc by picking a center point. However, you can draw a circle and break it into an arc. Doing so gives you another method to draw arcs. This activity shows you how to draw an arc at the end of two parallel lines.

   Use Snap to draw two horizontal lines of equal length. Then turn off the Grid and Snap for the remainder of this activity. Draw a third line connecting the endpoints of the two horizontal lines. Draw a circle, placing the center at the midpoint of the vertical line. See the left illustration. Pick the point on the circle as the endpoint of one horizontal line. Break the circle that passes between the two horizontal lines to leave an arc. Erase the vertical line. Save the drawing as C6A7.

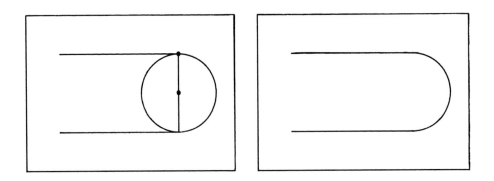

8. Using Snap, draw a 3 unit diameter circle and 3 unit square box at different locations on screen. Now, turn Snap off. Use Attach modes to move the circle into the box so that it touches all four sides exactly. How did you do it? Save the drawing as C6A8.

9. Set the Grid and Snap spacing at .5. Draw the two circles as shown. Use the commands needed to create six copies at equal 60 degree angles as shown. Save the drawing as C6A9. Ask your instructor for help if you have problems with this activity.

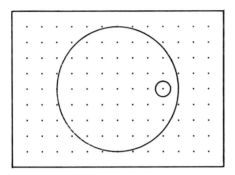 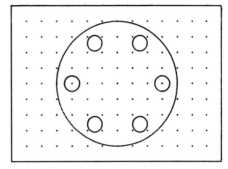

10. With the drawing from Activity 9 on screen, rotate the entire part 30 degrees as shown here. Save the drawing as C6A10.

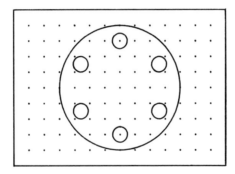

11-16. For each activity, complete the part shown on the left. Use Grid, Snap, and other drawing aids to your advantage. Then, make a copy. Use editing commands to change the copy so that it looks like the drawing on the right. Do not draw any new objects. Save each drawing as C6A?, replacing the question mark with the activity number. Write a brief summary explaining how you constructed and edited each drawing.

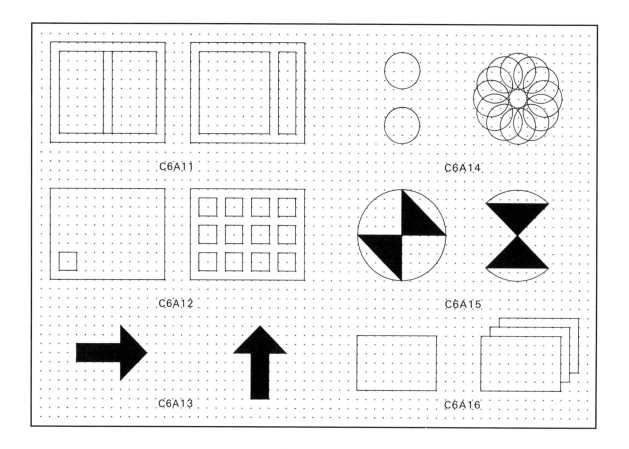

Chapter 7

ADVANCED EDITING AND INQUIRY TECHNIQUES

After studying this chapter, you will be able to:
- Select objects to edit by grouping them together.
- Create a mirror image of a shape.
- Scale a shape to a new size.
- Stretch a shape to shorten, lengthen, or distort it.
- Create multiple copies in a box or ring array.
- Create fillets, rounds, and chamfers.
- Show the properties of an object.
- Change the properties of one or several objects.
- Find the distance between two points.
- Measure the angle formed by three points.
- Measure the area of a closed shape.
- Find the absolute coordinate value of any location on the drawing.
- Determine the bearing between two points.

In Chapter 6, you learned the basic methods to select and edit objects. This chapter covers advanced editing commands that enhance your speed in creating drawings. Remember that most drafters spend more time editing drawings than they do creating them. Having a variety of editing commands is an advantage. In addition, this chapter introduces ways AutoSketch lets you ask questions about your drawing.

SELECTING OBJECTS WITH GROUPS

When editing, you often select objects with the Crosses/window box. All objects that lie within or crossing the box are chosen. Grouping is another method to select more than one object at a time. A *group* is a collection of objects that is treated as one item, not as individual objects. Thus, if you copy the group, all objects that belong to the group are copied. The objects remain together as a group until you order AutoSketch to ungroup them.

Why Use Groups?

You might wonder why a drafter would take the time to group objects rather than use the Crosses/window box. Refer to Fig. 7-1 for an example of when you might choose to use groups. Suppose you want to make a copy of the OUTPUT SHAFT. (It is shaded in gray to help you see the part better.) It would be impossible to enclose the objects that make up the OUTPUT SHAFT inside a Crosses/window box without also selecting parts of the KEY and SPRING. In this situation, you can use the **Group** command to select, one by one, only those objects that make up the shaft. Then you can move, copy, or perform some other command on the group.

You can move, copy, rotate, erase, mirror, and scale groups just as you do single objects. However, the **Break** command cannot be used to break an object that belongs to a group. This is because objects that belong to a group lose their identity as single objects. Beginning with Version 3.0, the **Stretch** command and Attach modes work on groups.

Building a Group

Selecting objects to form a group is referred to as *building*. To group objects, select the **Change** menu and the **Group** command. You can also hold down [Alt] and press function key [F9]. The following prompt appears:

Group Select object:

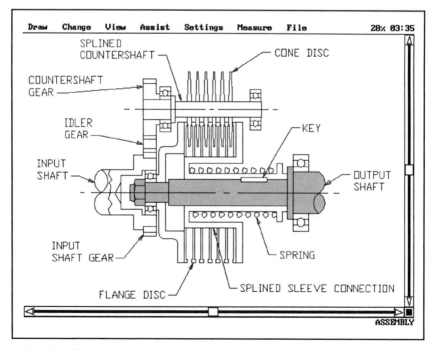

Fig. 7-1. To copy the tinted area, it would be nearly impossible to select the objects with the Crosses/window box. Instead, group the objects and then copy the group.

Begin picking objects that make up the group. You can pick them one at a time or select several with the Crosses/window box. Any object chosen to be in the group becomes dotted on screen, Fig. 7-2. When you are finished picking objects, choose another command. The grouped items then return to their original linetype. But, from now on, the group acts as a single object.

A group may contain up to 1000 objects (Version 3.0), or 100 objects (Version 2.0). Each of these items can be an individual drawing object, such as a line, or another group that itself contains up to 100 objects. Placing groups in other groups is called *nesting*. It allows you to create larger and more complex groups.

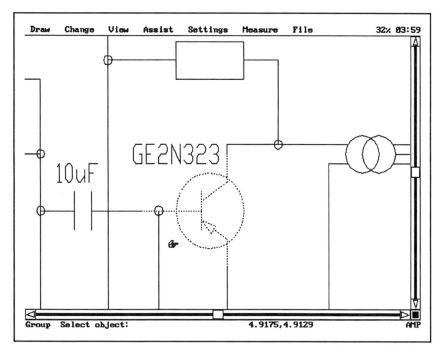

Fig. 7-2. As you build a group, objects chosen to be in the group become dotted on screen. In this electronics schematic, the objects that make up a transistor were grouped.

Nesting Groups

A *nested group* is a group that is chosen to be a part of another group. You can use nested groups to create more complex shapes and layouts. For example, look at the office plan drawing in Fig. 7-3. There are similar items found in each room. In addition, two rooms contain identical desk layouts. Groups were used to help create this drawing quickly. Here are the steps:

1. The floor plan–walls, doors, and windows–can be drawn from scratch or possibly copied from the architect's working drawings. Then it is loaded into AutoSketch.
2. Draw the simple shapes–plant, telephone, chairs, and computer. Then, group each simple shape individually.
3. Next, draw an executive desk and copy a telephone on it. Also, copy the chairs next to the desk. Because these shapes are already grouped, you can pick any part of the group to select the entire shape.

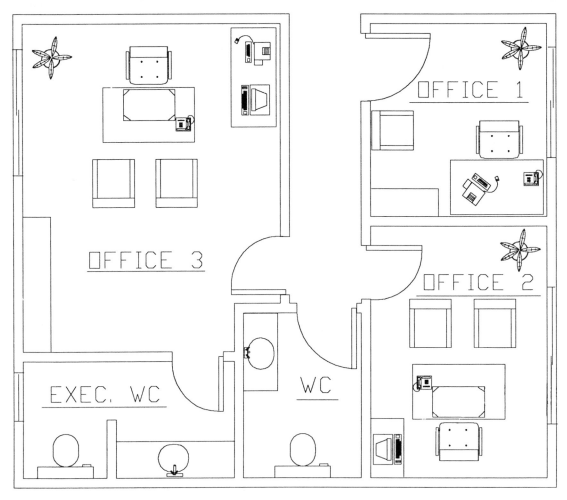

Fig. 7-3. This office plan shows how groups were used to complete a complex layout quickly.

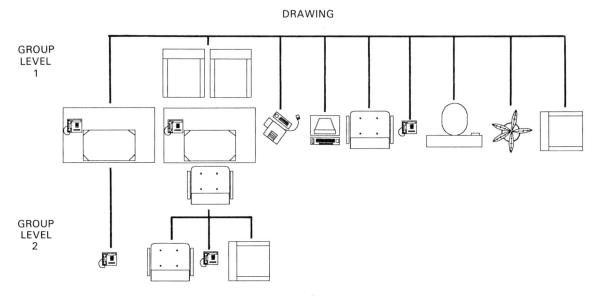

Fig. 7-4. A group chosen to be part of another group is called a nested group. You can nest groups to a depth of seven, meaning seven levels.

4. Then, group together the entire executive desk layout–complete with telephone and chairs.
5. Once the groups are made, layout is easy. Copy the executive desk group to OFFICE 2 and OFFICE 3.
6. In this situation, you would need to draw the desk for OFFICE 1 separately because the room is too small for an executive desk and chairs. However, the computer, telephone, plant, and two chairs are easily copied because each is grouped.
7. Finally, copy the plant into the offices and add the utilities in the two restrooms.

You can see how groups made this layout quite easy. Also, the executive desk group itself contained nested groups because it included the telephone and chairs, which themselves were groups. You can nest groups to a maximum depth of eight. For example, Fig. 7-4 shows that the office layout had a nesting depth of two.

Ungrouping Objects

At some point, the group may no longer be useful. For example, you may want to move an object within a group. You cannot work on individual objects until you ungroup them. If you try to select the object, the entire group is chosen instead. The **Ungroup** command splits a group into its original objects or component groups. Select the **Ungroup** command, found in the **Change** menu. You can also hold down [Alt] and press function key [F10]. The following prompt appears:

Ungroup Select object:

Pick any object in the group. The entire group is then split into its component shapes. Suppose you want to change the size of the executive desk shown in the previous example. You cannot select just the desk because it was grouped with the telephone and chairs. You must first use the **Ungroup** command. Pick any part of the executive desk layout to ungroup it. Suppose you then want to change the shape of the telephone. Because it too was grouped separately, you must **Ungroup** it to make any changes. The **Ungroup** command ungroups only one nesting level at a time, from the top down.

MIRRORING OBJECTS

The **Mirror** command makes a mirror image copy of objects. The image is made on the opposite side of a *mirror line*. The **Mirror** command is often used for designs that are symmetrical, meaning one half is a reflection of the other half, Fig. 7-5. To mirror objects, Fig. 7-6, select the **Change** menu and **Mirror** command. You can also hold down [Ctrl] and press function key [F10]. The following prompt appears:

Mirror Select object:

Select the object, group, or use the Crosses/window box to select objects to mirror. The next prompt to appear is:

Mirror Base point:

This base point is the first end of the mirror line. You can use an Attach mode to place the base point at a precise location. The next prompt that appears is:

Mirror Second point:

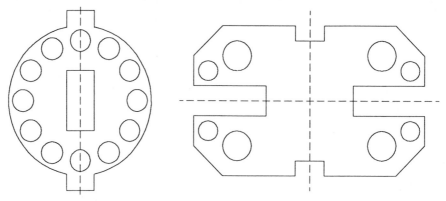

Fig. 7-5. In symmetrical designs, one half is a reflection of the other half.

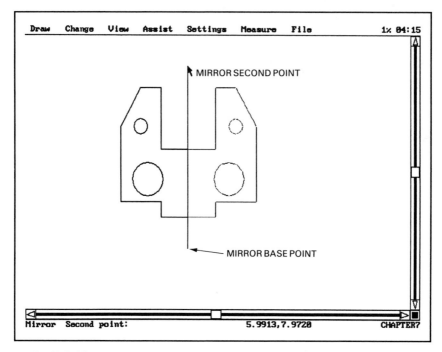

Fig. 7-6. Mirroring objects. After selecting the objects, pick two points that make up the mirror line. The objects are reflected about the mirror line.

This second point is the other end of the mirror line. As you move the pointer, a ghost image of the mirrored objects drags and rotates with it. The ghost image helps you position the mirror image. You might use Snap or an Attach mode to position the mirror line precisely. You can also enter coordinates for the base and second points of the mirror line. Once you select the second point, the mirrored objects are placed.

SCALING OBJECTS

The **Scale** command lets you enlarge or reduce the size of existing objects. Select the **Change** menu and **Scale** command. You can also hold down [Ctrl] and press function key [F6]. The following prompt appears:

Scale Select object:

Select an object, group, or use the Crosses/window box to select several objects to scale. The next prompt that appears is:

Scale Base point:

Select a base point. The *base point* remains fixed while the objects are enlarged or reduced around it, Fig. 7-7. Select your base point carefully. Usually, there is one point on the shape that should remain in the same location. The next prompt that appears is:

Scale Second point:

The second point you pick determines the scale factor. Move your pointer in or out to increase or decrease the size. As you do this, a ghost image of the objects expands and reduces in size. Also, the scale factor appears on the prompt line. Refer to Fig. 7-7. It displays the factor in steps of 0.1. Press the pick button on your pointing device when you reach the desired scale factor, or when the objects appear to be the proper size.

You might think that entering relative or polar coordinates would give an exact scale factor. Unfortunately, this does not happen. It is best to move your pointer slowly and watch the scale factor on the prompt line.

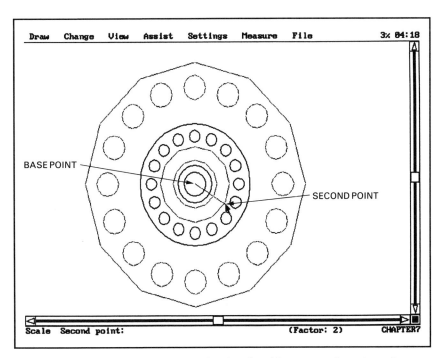

Fig. 7-7. Scaling objects. After selecting the objects to scale, select a base point. Then, move your pointer in or out to change the size. The base point remains fixed. The scale factor appears on the prompt line.

STRETCHING OBJECTS

The **Stretch** command is a combination of the **Move** and **Scale** commands. It allows you to stretch a shape as if it were made of rubber. This leaves all connections between objects intact. Select the **Change** menu and **Stretch** command. You can also press function key [F7]. The following prompt appears:

Stretch First corner:

Notice that this is not the familiar "Select objects:" prompt. This is because the **Stretch** command looks for endpoints and connections rather than whole objects. You must select these using a Crosses box, Fig. 7-8. Pick the first corner of the box. The next prompt to appear is:

Stretch Crosses/window corner:

Pick the second corner of a Crosses box around the objects to stretch. Enclose only those objects you wish to move. The next prompt is:

Stretch Stretch base:

The *stretch base point* is the place the pointer will hold to "pull" the shape. Refer to Fig. 7-8. You can use an Attach mode to place the base point at a precise place, such as the end of a line. The next prompt that appears is:

Stretch Stretch to:

At this prompt, move your pointer to stretch the shape to its new length or shape. The pointer holds on to the stretch base point. A ghost image of the objects appears as you move the pointer. You can also type in coordinates or use the running polar coordinate to stretch the object. In many cases, you will stretch the shape to meet another object.

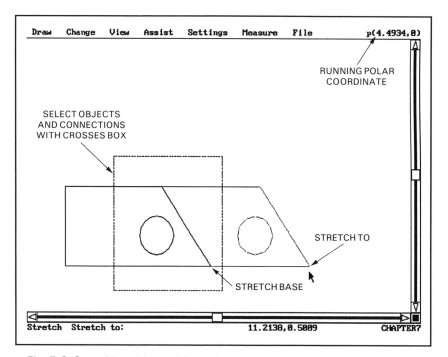

Fig. 7-8. Stretching objects. After selecting objects to stretch, pick a stretch base point. Then, ''pull'' the base point to stretch the objects.

Objects Oddly Affected by Stretch

The **Stretch** command affects objects different ways. If the center point of a circle is within the Crosses box, the entire circle moves. It does not stretch to become oval. Stretching a box will make it nonrectangular.

The **Stretch** command can be used to stretch objects within a group using Version 3.0. If grouped objects are within the selection box, the objects stretch only if they could have been stretched anyway. Otherwise, the group is unaffected.

A curve can be stretched only if its frame is displayed. This occurs if you select the **Frame** option, found in the **Assist** menu.

Text and dimensions are also oddly affected by **Stretch**. If you stretch one end of a text string, the text will compress or expand horizontally, and also rotate. If you stretch a dimension along with objects, its dimension text changes to show the new distance, Fig. 7-9. These topics are further covered in Chapters 9 and 13.

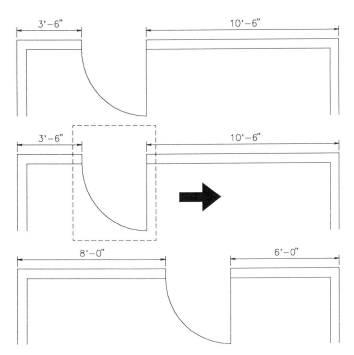

Fig. 7-9. You can stretch a door symbol to a new location. Note how the dimensions also change to reflect the new position.

BOX ARRAY

The **Box Array** command makes multiple copies of an object or group in a rectangular pattern. You can enter the distance between copies, or pick the distance with your pointer. You can also have the array of copies placed at an angle.

Box Array Settings

To make a box array, you must first set the array values. This is done by picking the **Settings** menu and **Box Array** command. The **Box Array Settings** dialogue box will appear, Fig. 7-10. The settings for a simple box array are shown.

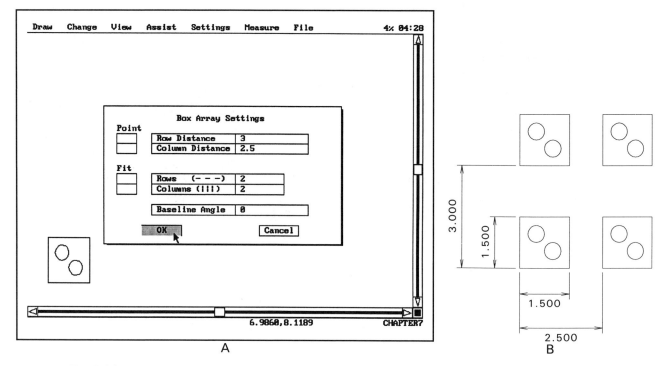

Fig. 7-10. A–The Box Array Settings dialogue box. Here you enter the distance between copies and the number of copies in each direction. B–The resulting array.

Enter the distance between copies vertically opposite the *Row distance* box. Enter the distance between copies horizontally opposite the *Column distance* box. Next, enter the number of copies you want vertically opposite the *Rows* box, and the copies horizontally opposite the *Columns* box. The *Point, Fit,* and *Baseline angle* boxes allow you to create special types of arrays.

Creating a Box Array

Once the settings are made, and one object has been drawn, select *OK* to close the dialogue box. Then, select the **Change** menu and **Box Array** command. You can also hold down [Ctrl] and press function key [F2]. The following prompt will appear:

Box Array Select object:

Select the objects you want to be part of the array. Once you do, the copies are drawn at the proper distance. The illustration in Fig. 7-10B shows the results of the settings in Fig. 7-10A. If for some reason your settings were not correct, AutoSketch allows you to make changes. After each **Box Array** command, the dialogue box in Fig. 7-11 appears. You can either accept the results of your array, or select *Modify*. If you pick *Modify*, the **Box Array Settings** dialogue box reappears for you to enter new values and try again. Once *OK* is picked in the dialogue box, the array is recreated automatically.

Advanced Box Arrays

The *Point* box, when checked in the **Box Array Settings** dialogue box, disregards any settings opposite *Row Distance* and *Column distance*. AutoSketch prompts you for two

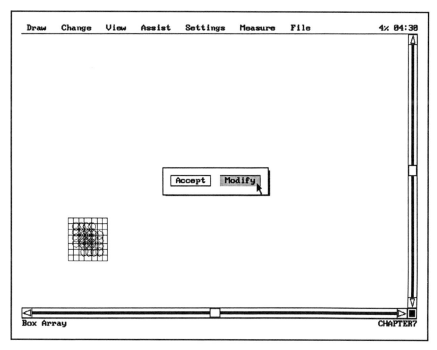

Fig. 7-11. After creating an array, AutoSketch asks whether you want to accept or modify it. In this case, the array did not turn out as expected and you would select Modify.

points for each direction. These two points define the distance between copies. The points, as illustrated in Fig. 7-12, are prompted as follows:

Box Array Select object:

Box Array Column spacing First point:

Box Array To point:

Box Array Row spacing First point:

Box Array To point:

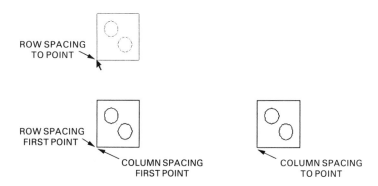

Fig. 7-12. When Point is checked in the Box Array Settings dialogue box, you must manually define the distance between copies.

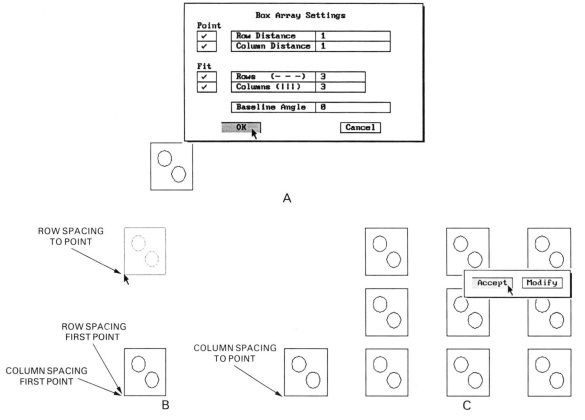

Fig. 7-13. Fitting a box array. A–Check Fit in the Box Array Settings dialogue box. B–Since Point was also checked, pick the total distance of the array. C–Accept or Modify the resulting array.

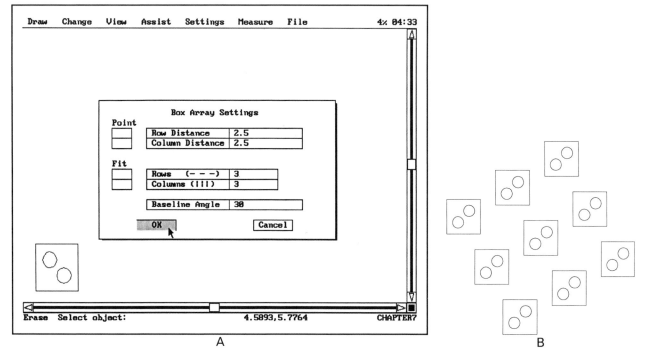

Fig. 7-14. A–To place a box array at an angle, enter an angle value opposite the Baseline Angle box. B–The resulting array.

The *Fit* box, when checked, changes the meanings of *Row distance* and *Column distance* settings. Instead of distance between copies, they now mean the total distance between furthest copies, Fig. 7-13. This command works well if you know the number of objects that must fill an area.

The one last option for **Box Array** is the *Baseline angle* setting in the **Box Array Settings** dialogue box. With the baseline setting you can set the angle at which the copies are placed. See Fig. 7-14 for an example.

RING ARRAY

The **Ring Array** command is much like **Box Array** except that the copies are placed in a circular fashion around a center point. To make a ring array, you must first set the values. This is done by picking the **Settings** menu and **Ring Array** command. The **Ring Array Settings** dialogue box will appear, Fig. 7-15. There are quite a few options for creating ring arrays.

Once the values are set, select the **Change** menu and **Ring Array** command. You can also hold down [Ctrl] and press function key [F4]. Like the **Box Array** command, the prompts that appear when you make a ring array depend on which values are set. However, for most arrays, they are:

Ring Array Select object:

Ring Array Center point of array:

Our example here shows a bicycle pedal assembly design. Fig. 7-15 shows that eight copies were made to reflect the position of the pedal around the crankshaft. This array was made using the settings shown on the left.

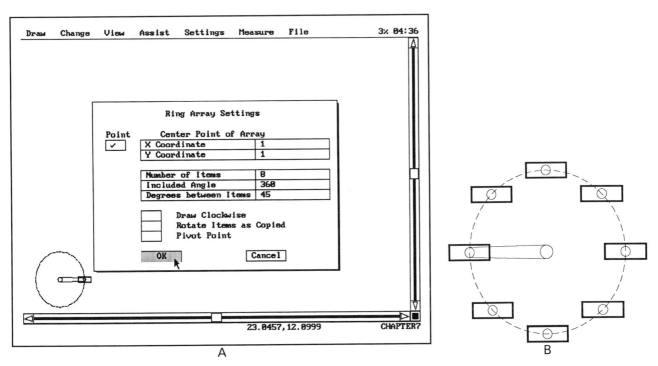

A   B

Fig. 7-15. A–The Ring Array Settings dialogue box. B–This is the array of a bicycle pedal using the values on the left.

To describe the items in the **Ring Array Settings** dialogue box, look at Figs. 7-16 through 7-19 as you read these definitions. *Number of Items* is the total number of copies you want. The *Included Angle* is the angular distance of the entire array. It may be a full circle (360 degrees), or only part. See Figs. 7-17 and 7-18. The *Degrees between Items* always evenly

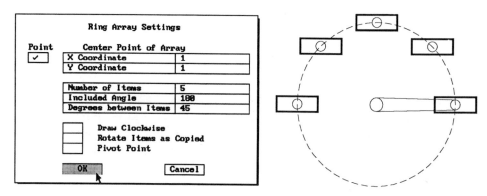

Fig. 7-16. This ring array has five copies that extend 180 degrees (half circle).

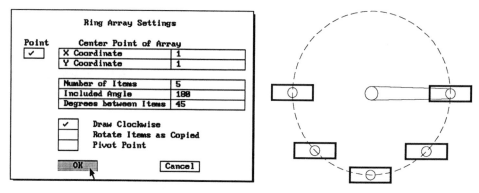

Fig. 7-17. This ring array has five copies that extend 180 degrees (half circle). However, the Draw Clockwise box was checked.

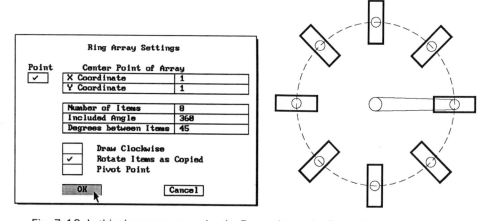

Fig. 7-18. In this ring array example, the Rotate Items As Copied box was checked.

divides the copies within the *Included Angle*. The *Point* option disregards any settings for the *Center Point of Array* you may have typed in previously. Also, copies are made counterclockwise unless the box opposite *Draw Clockwise* is checked. The items are not individually rotated unless *Rotate Items as Copied* is checked, Fig. 7-18. The final item, *Pivot Point,* allows you to pick a new pivot point other than the default center of the object being copied. In Fig. 7-19, a different part of the pedal was chosen as a pivot point. Having this item checked makes one other prompt appear:

Ring Array Pivot point:

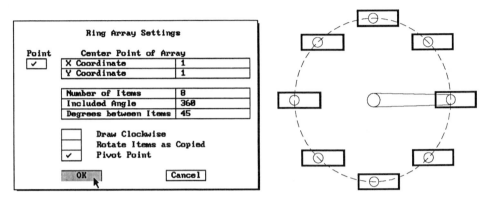

Fig. 7-19. In this ring array example, the Pivot Point box was checked, and the user picked a different pivot spot on the pedal. Notice how the pedal is offset.

DRAWING FILLETS, ROUNDS, AND CHAMFERS

Fillets, rounds, and chamfers refer to inside and outside corner treatments on machined and welded products. The rounding or chamfering (beveling) of an outside corner relieves stress of machined products. A fillet is a rounding of an inside corner for the same purpose. This is usually done by welding. Although the **Fillet** and **Chamfer** commands are named for mechanical drafting applications, they have many uses in all fields of drafting.

Drawing Fillets
The **Fillet** command trims or extends two nonparallel objects and connects their ends with a smoothly fitted arc of a specified radius. To set the fillet radius, pick the **Settings** menu and **Fillet** command. The **Fillet** dialogue box will appear, Fig. 7-20. Enter the radius of fillet you want to create. Then, select the **Change** menu and **Fillet** command. The following prompt appears:

Fillet Select object(s):

Once you pick the objects, the fillet is drawn. You can select both objects at the same time with a Crosses/window box. If you pick only one object, a second prompt "Fillet Select second object:" will appear. If you pick a polygon in Version 2.0, AutoSketch will ask if you want to convert the polygon to line segments. If the lines are parallel, AutoSketch will display a message to this effect.

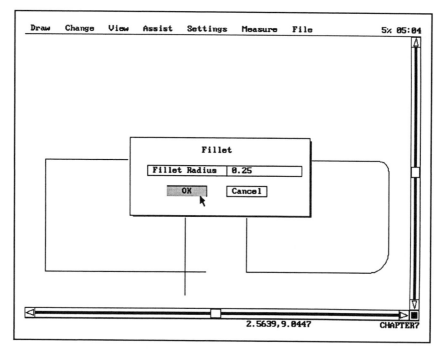

Fig. 7-20. To draw a fillet, set the Fillet Radius in the Fillet dialogue box. Then use the Fillet command in the Change menu and pick the objects to fillet.

Fillets can be performed on the following combination of entities: an arc to an arc, an arc to a circle, an arc to a line, a circle to a circle, and a circle to a line. See Fig. 7-21. Fillets cannot be performed on curves, ellipses, text, or from a polyline to a polyline.

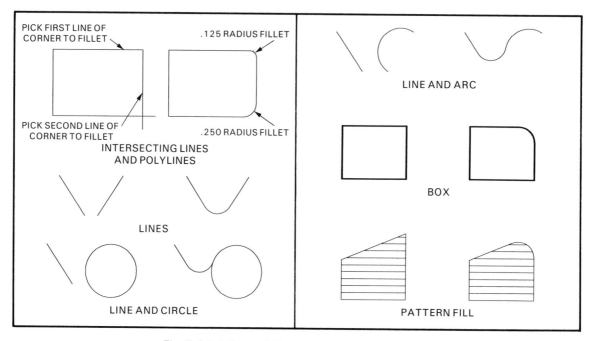

Fig. 7-21. Effects of filleting objects in Version 3.0.

Drawing Chamfers

The **Chamfer** command trims or extends two lines the same or different distance, and connects the ends with a line. To set the chamfer distances, pick the **Settings** menu and **Chamfer** command. The **Chamfer** dialogue box will appear, Fig. 7-22. Enter distances you want each line trimmed or extended. Once you set these values, select the **Change** menu and **Chamfer** command. The following prompt appears:

Chamfer Select object(s):

Once you pick the lines, they are trimmed and the chamfer is drawn. As with drawing fillets, you can select both lines at the same time with a Crosses/window box. If you pick only one line, a second prompt "Chamfer Select second line:" will appear. Be careful when selecting two objects to chamfer with the Crosses/window box. If there are more than two objects selected, AutoSketch picks the last two objects that were drawn to create the chamfer.

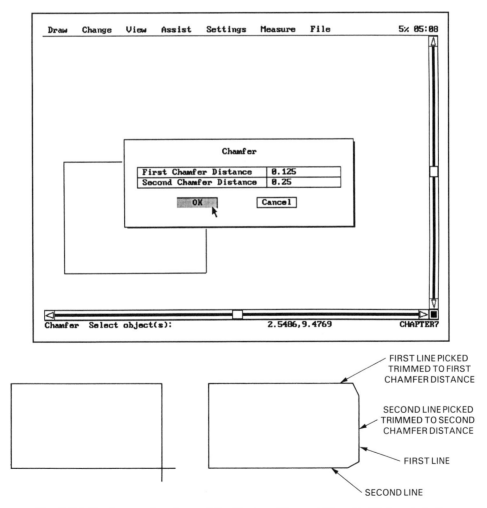

Fig. 7-22. To draw a chamfer, set the First and Second Chamfer Distances in the Chamfer dialogue box. Then use the Chamfer command in the Change menu and pick the lines. The order in which you pick the lines determines their chamfer distance.

Also like the **Fillet** command in Version 2.0 , if you pick a polygon, AutoSketch will ask if you want to convert the polygon to line segments. If you pick an arc, circle, or pattern fill, AutoSketch will not complete the command. A message dialogue box will appear reminding you that you must select two lines. If the lines are parallel, AutoSketch will display a message to this effect.

In Version 3.0, you can chamfer lines, boxes, and consecutive segments of polylines and pattern fills. Arcs and polyarcs cannot be chamfered. Boxes are converted to zero width polylines when they are chamfered. The **Show Properties** command in the **Measure** menu will indicate that the box is now a polyline. The polyline width will be changed to the polyline width setting if you then change properties on the chamfered box.

A useful application for the **Chamfer** command is to extend two nonparallel lines until they intersect. To do so, set both chamfer distances at 0. Thus, when you select the lines, they will extend to meet precisely.

MODIFYING OBJECT PROPERTIES

There are times when you need to change an object's color, linetype, or layer. (Layers are discussed in Chapter 10.) For example, you might draw several shapes in black using a solid linetype. However, later you may want the shapes in red with a hidden linetype. This is easy to do with AutoSketch.

Showing Object Properties

The **Show Properties** command lists an object's color, linetype, and layer, as well as the type of object you have chosen. This command is helpful for several purposes.

- If you have a monochrome monitor, you cannot see different colors. Remember from Chapter 5 that to plot drawings with different pens, you must draw objects different colors. Select the object with **Show Properties** if you question an object's color.
- A rectangle on screen could be a box, polygon, or four lines. The difference can be important if you plan to edit the shape. The **Show Properties** command lists the type of object you have chosen.
- Chapter 10 will discuss how to place objects on different levels, called layers. The layer of an object is not visible, even with a color monitor. However, you can check the layer with the **Show Properties** command.

To view object properties, select the **Measure** menu, and then the **Show Properties** command. The following prompt will appear:

Show Properties Select object:

After you pick an object, a dialogue box appears listing various values, depending on the object that was selected. The values for a polyline are shown in Fig. 7-23. Pick *OK* to continue with your drawing session.

If you pick a text object, more information on text features will appear, Fig. 7-24. The linetype is not given since text always has a solid linetype.

Changing Object Properties

The **Change Property** command allows you to change the properties of objects to the current values. The properties that are changed depend on which are marked in the **Change**

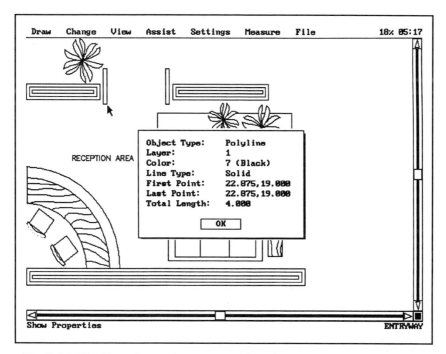

Fig. 7-23. The Show Properties command lists the values associated with any object.

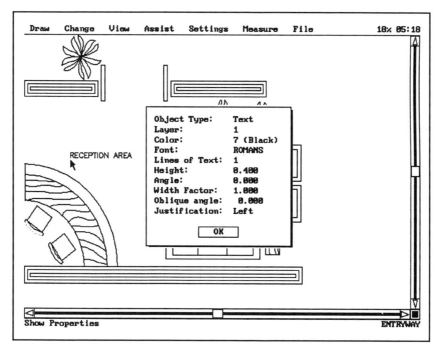

Fig. 7-24. When a text feature is picked, the dialogue box displays the object type, layer, color, font, height, angle, width factor, and obliquing angle.

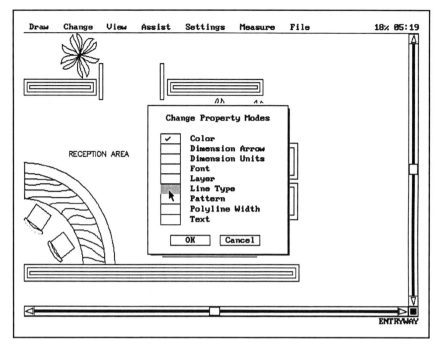

RECEPTION AREA

Change Property Modes

✓   Color
     Dimension Arrow
     Dimension Units
     Font
     Layer
     Line Type
     Pattern
     Polyline Width
     Text

     [OK]   [Cancel]

ENTRYWAY

Fig. 7-25. The properties that are changed by the Change Property command
depends on which are marked in the Change Property Modes dialogue box.

Property Modes dialogue box, Fig. 7-25. To select which properties you want changed, select
Settings menu and **Property** command. Pick those modes you wish to have changed. A check
mark appears in the box opposite the particular mode.

Next, select the **Change** menu and the **Property** command. The following prompt appears:

Change property Select object:

Select the object, group, or use the Crosses/window box to select several objects. The
objects immediately assume the current values for color, linetype, and layer. Remember to
first check which values are current in the **Settings** menu.

INQUIRY COMMANDS

Inquiry commands let you ask questions about your drawing. You might want to know
the distance, area, perimeter, or other data about the design. In manual drafting, distance is

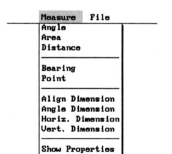

Measure   File
Angle
Area
Distance

Bearing
Point

Align Dimension
Angle Dimension
Horiz. Dimension
Vert. Dimension

Show Properties

Fig. 7-26. Inquiry commands are
found in the Measure menu.

measured with a ruler and angles are measured with a protractor. Area and volume are calculated by multiplying measurements. Inquiry commands are found in the **Measure** menu, Fig. 7-26.

Inquiry commands are transparent. This means that you can use them while in the middle of using another command. Also, inquiry commands do not repeat. They return you to the prompt displayed before you chose the inquiry command.

Measuring Distance

Distance is measured between two points you pick on the drawing. For example, you may want to know the distance between the endpoint of a line and the center of a circle. Select the **Measure** menu, and then the **Distance** command. The following prompts appear:

Distance From point:

Distance To point:

Use drawing aids to precisely pick the locations you want to measure. After you pick the points, a dialogue box appears telling the distance, Fig. 7-27.

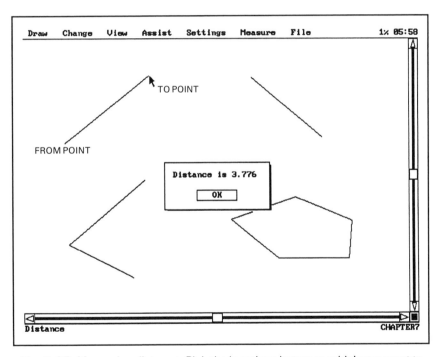

Fig. 7-27. Measuring distance. Pick the locations between which you want to measure. A dialogue box appears telling the distance.

Measuring an Angle

AutoSketch lets you measure the angle formed by three points, Fig. 7-28. Select the **Measure** menu and the **Angle** command. The following prompt appears:

Angle Base point:

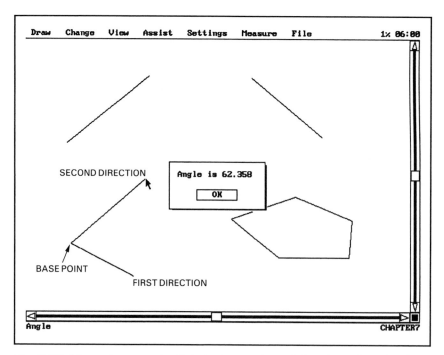

Fig. 7-28. Measuring an angle. Pick the base point and direction points that form the angle. A dialogue box appears giving the angle.

This first point to pick is the base point, or vertex of the angle. Use drawing aids to precisely pick the location. If you are measuring the angle formed between two lines, carefully pick where the lines intersect. The next two prompts that appear are:

Angle First direction:

Angle Second direction:

These two points are the "legs" of the angle. As you pick a point in each direction, a rubberband line extends from the base point. Once you pick the second direction, a dialogue box appears telling the angle.

Measuring Area

Area is the surface enclosed by a shape. The measurement is expressed in square units. An architect might measure the square feet enclosed by a house. To measure an area, you must pick the corners of the shape, Fig. 7-29. Select the **Measure** menu and the **Area** command. The first prompt to appear is:

Area First perimeter point:

Select the first point of the shape. An "X" will appear to mark the location. You do not have to pick on an object. You can measure the invisible area of an empty section of the drawing.

Area Next point:

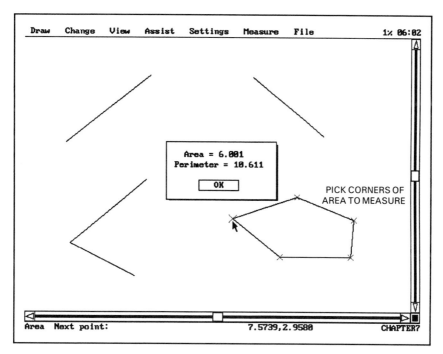

Fig. 7-29. Measuring area. Pick the corners that form the shape. A dialogue box appears giving the angle.

Pick the second, third, and other corners of the shape. As you do, "X"s appear to mark each location. Continue picking corners until you pick the first point again to define a closed shape. A dialogue box then appears to display the area and perimeter.

Displaying Point Coordinates

The **Point** command lets you find the exact Cartesian coordinate values of any location on screen. Select the **Measure** menu, and then the **Point** command. As you move the pointer, its location on the Cartesian coordinate system appears on the prompt line:

Point coordinates: 0.00000,0.00000

When you pick a location, a dialogue box appears giving the exact coordinate values. See Fig. 7-30.

Measure Bearing

The **Bearing** command lets you measure a direction from a base point. The angle measurement is given in degrees measured counterclockwise from due east (right). See Fig. 7-31 as you select the **Measure** menu and the **Bearing** command. The first prompt is:

Bearing Base point:

Pick the base point. Consider using a drawing aid like Attach mode to place the base point at a precise place. For example, to measure the bearing of a line, pick its endpoint. The next prompt is:

Bearing Enter point:

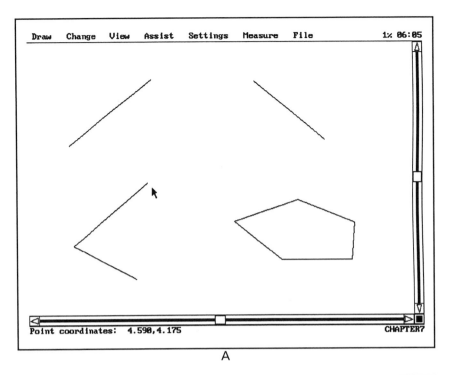

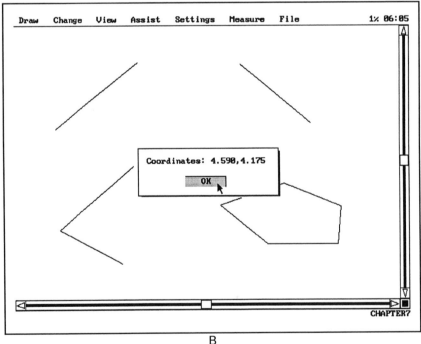

Fig. 7-30. Displaying point coordinates. A–Pick the point on screen you want to identify. B–A dialogue box appears giving the absolute coordinates of that point.

As you move the pointer, the bearing angle appears on the prompt line. If you were measuring the bearing of a line, pick the line's other endpoint. Once you press the pick button of your pointing device, a dialogue box appears giving the exact angle.

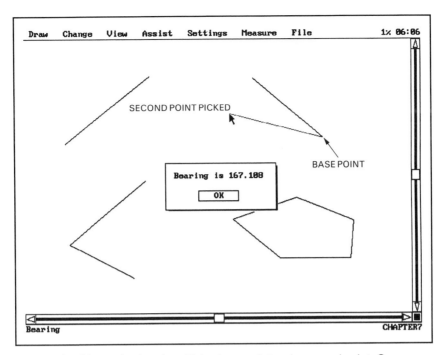

Fig. 7-31. Measuring bearing. Pick a base point and a second point. Once you pick the second point, a dialogue box appears giving the exact angle.

SETTING THE PICK DISTANCE

In selecting items to edit, you may have noticed that you must pick very close to select an object. The pick interval determines how close you must pick to select an object, and how far AutoSketch will look for an Attach point. To set the pick interval, select the **Settings** menu and the **Pick** command. The **Pick Interval** dialogue box appears, Fig. 7-32. The pick interval is expressed in percentage of screen height. For example, if your screen has 480 pixels vertically, you must pick within 4.8 pixels of the object. Setting the pick distance best for you is a matter of trial and error. If necessary, reset it and then use Attach to pick an object. Do this until you find the right value.

SUMMARY

This chapter has covered more advanced methods to select and edit objects. In addition to selecting objects individually and with the Crosses/window box, you can also group them. Grouped objects act like a a single item, and can be copied, moved, or otherwise edited with one pick. A group can contain single objects or other groups, called nested groups.

Many designs you create will be symmetrical, meaning one half is a reflection of the other half. You do not have to draw the entire drawing. Instead, create one-half or one-fourth of the drawing and mirror the rest. All you need to do is select the objects and the endpoints of a mirror line.

There are times when you need to enlarge or reduce the size of a shape by a certain factor. You can do this with the **Scale** command. Simply select the objects scale, pick a base point,

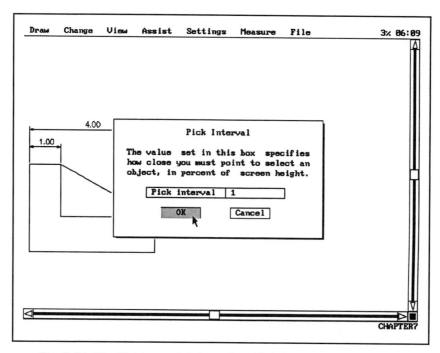

Fig. 7-32. The Pick Interval dialogue box. Pick distance is measured in percentage of screen height.

and pick a another point to set the scale factor. The scale factor appears on the prompt line as you move your pointer to select the second point.

The **Stretch** command allows you to stretch a shape as if it were made of rubber. You select the objects to stretch using only the Crosses box. Once you select the objects, pick a base point and stretch the objects to size with your pointer. Remember that some objects are oddly affected by stretching.

The **Box Array** command makes multiple copies of an object or group in a rectangular pattern. You can enter the distance between copies, or pick the distance with your pointer. You can also have the copies fit within boundaries you pick. When needed, you can place the box array at an angle.

The **Ring Array** command is much like the **Box Array** command except that the copies are placed in a circular fashion around a center point. The copies can be placed in a full circle, or only partial circle. In addition, the individual copies can each be rotated as they are arrayed, if desired.

Rounds, chamfers, and fillets refer to inside and outside corner treatments on machined and welded products. Although the **Fillet** and **Chamfer** commands are named for mechanical drafting applications, they have many uses in all fields of drafting. The **Fillet** command trims or extends two nonparallel objects and connects their ends with a smoothly fitted arc of a specified radius. The **Chamfer** command trims or extends two lines the same or different distance, and connects the ends with a line. The command will also extend two nonparallel lines until they meet.

When you need to change an objects properties (color, linetype, or layer), select the **Change property** command. The selected object(s) properties are changed to the current values. Which properties are change depends on the options marked in the **Change Property**

Modes dialogue box. If you aren't sure of the objects, color, linetype, or layer, use the **Show Property** command to list these items.

Inquiry commands let you ask questions about your drawing. Inquiry commands are found in the **Measure** menu. They let you measure distance, angle, area, bearing, and coordinate location. Because inquiry commands are transparent, you can use them while in the middle of using another command.

NEW TERMS

Group, **Group** command, building, nested group, **Ungroup** command, **Mirror** command, mirror line, **Scale** command, scale base point, **Stretch** command, stretch base point, **Box Array** command, row distance, column distance, baseline angle, **Ring Array** command, included angle, pivot point, **Fillet** command, fillet, round, **Chamfer** command, chamfer, properties, **Show Property** command, **Settings** menu, **Change Properties** command, **Measure** menu, inquiry commands, **Distance** command, **Angle** command, **Area** command, **Point** command, **Bearing** command, **Pick** command, pick interval.

REVIEW QUESTIONS

Write your answers on a separate sheet of paper. Do not write in this book.
1. An object that is part of a group can be edited individually. True or false?
2. Grouped objects remain as a group until you select another drawing command. True or false?
3. List methods you can use to build a group.
4. A group that is chosen to be a part of another group is called a _____.
5. Describe how you might place more than 1000 objects in a group.
6. The _____ command splits a group into its original objects.
7. Explain the steps you would take to ungroup a nested group.
8. Drawings where one half of an object is a reflection of the other half are called _____.
9. After selecting objects to mirror, you must pick endpoints of a _____.
10. You cannot type in relative or polar coordinates to enter an exact scale factor for scaling objects. True or false?
11. Usually, when scaling a shape, there is one point that should remain fixed in its location. Select this point as the _____.
12. When you stretch a shape, which objects of the shape are actually stretched?
13. Explain how the **Stretch** command affects circles, boxes, curves, text, and dimensions.
14. The *Column distance* in a box array refers to the horizontal distance between copies unless _____.
15. The *Row distance* in a box array refers to the vertical distance between copies unless _____.
16. The number of copies you want vertically in a box array is set opposite the _____ box.
17. The number of copies you want horizontally in a box array is set opposite the _____ box.
18. In what two ways can you set the distance between copies in a box array?

19. Suppose you want to make a ring array that has 9 copies and spans three-quarters of a full circle. What would be the settings for *Included angle* and *Degrees between items?*
20. Parallel lines can be chamfered. True or false?
21. List three situations when you might use the **Show Properties** command.
22. What four values appear after select the **Show Properties** command?
23. The **Change Property** command allows you to change the properties of objects to the _____ values.
24. The properties that are changed by the **Change Property** command depend on _____.
25. When measuring distance, it is wise to use _____ to precisely pick the locations you want to measure.
26. To measure an angle, simply pick the two lines that form the angle. True or false?
27. AutoSketch allows to measure an empty area in a drawing that has no objects in it. True or false?
28. To measure bearing, you must pick _____ points.
29. When measuring a bearing, the angle measurement is given in degrees measured counterclockwise from _____.
30. The setting that determines how close you must pick to select an object, and how far AutoSketch will look for an Attach point, is the _____.

ACTIVITIES

Here is a mixture of drawing activities to develop your skills with advanced editing and inquiry commands. Use drawing aids to your advantage, unless the directions tell otherwise. Save your AutoSketch drawings on your file disk, not on the program disk. Clear the previous drawing from screen and memory using **New** before completing each activity. Refer to the illustrations they are provided.

1. Draw a series of lines and circles jumbled together. Group the circles. Move the circles away from the lines. **Do not move the circles one by one.** Then, change the linetype of the group to a hidden linetype. Save the drawing as C7A1.

2-10. Complete the drawing shown on the left. Use Grid, Snap, and other drawing aids to your advantage. Then, use editing commands to change the copied drawing so that it looks like the drawing on the right. Use only editing commands. Do not draw any new objects. Save each drawing as C7A?, but replace the question mark with the activity number. Write a brief report of how you constructed and edited each drawing.

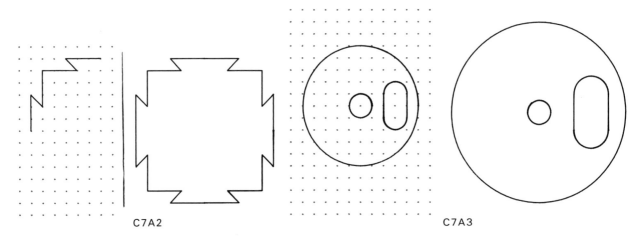

C7A2   C7A3

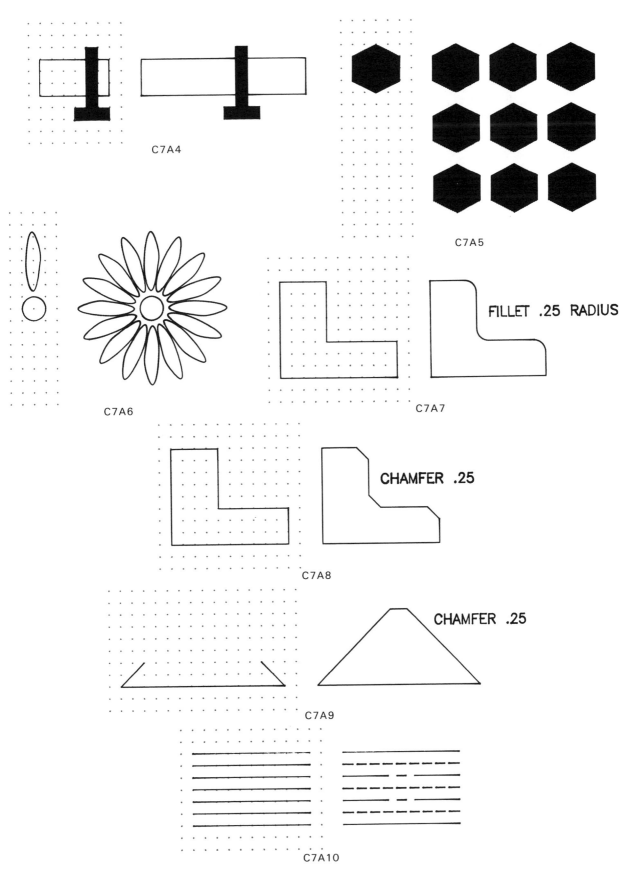

C7A4

C7A5

C7A6

FILLET .25 RADIUS

C7A7

CHAMFER .25

C7A8

CHAMFER .25

C7A9

C7A10

11. Draw one of each object type offered by AutoSketch–line, circle, ellipse, arc, polyline/polygon, box, text, and curve. Use the **Show Property** command to list data about each object.

12. Draw an arc and a circle. Measure the distance between their centers. Hint: Make sure the Attach mode Center is on and Quadrant is off. Do not save the drawing.

13. Draw three single lines that form a triangle. Use the Attach mode Endpoint to make sure the lines connect precisely. Label the lines A, B, and C. Measure the angle between each pair of lines.

    Angle between lines A and B: _____

    Angle between lines B and C: _____

    Angle between lines C and A: _____

14. Draw a closed polyline/polygon consisting of several lines. Measure the perimeter and the area.

15. Draw a series of connected lines that do not form a closed polyline/polygon. Measure the area inside the lines.

16. Draw a series of five connected lines using the **Line** command and Attach mode Endpoint. Label the lines A, B, C, D, and E. Measure the bearing of each line.

    Bearing of line A: _____

    Bearing of line B: _____

    Bearing of line C: _____

    Bearing of line D: _____

    Bearing of line E: _____

17-21. For each activity, draw the design or object shown using drawing aids. Grid and Snap are especially useful. Draw the dimensioned drawings using exact measurements, either by typing coordinates or using your pointer with drawing aids. Save the drawings using the activity file names given underneath.

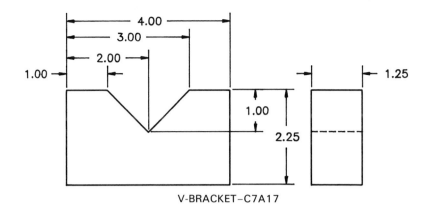

V-BRACKET–C7A17

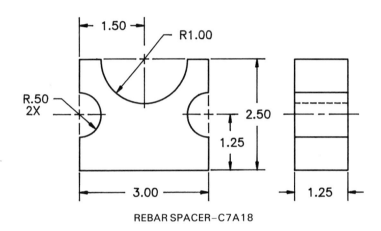

REBAR SPACER–C7A18

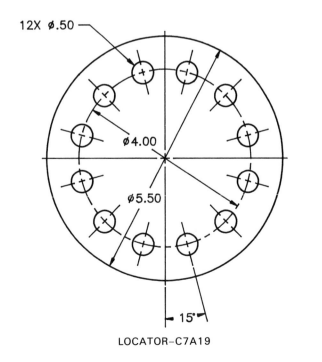

LOCATOR–C7A19

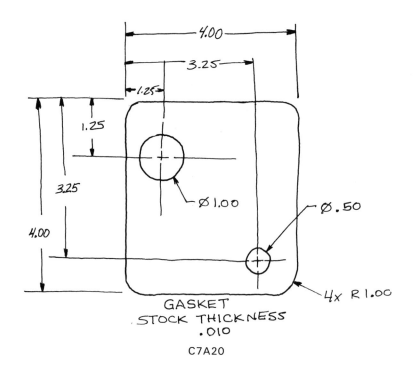

GASKET
STOCK THICKNESS
.010

C7A20

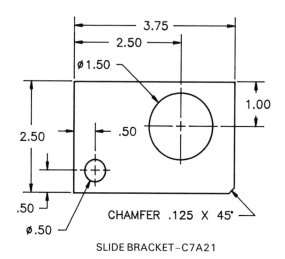

SLIDE BRACKET–C7A21

Chapter 8

VIEW OPTIONS

After studying this chapter, you will be able to:
- Enlarge the view by picking a box around the objects to see.
- Enlarge or reduce the current view by a magnification factor.
- Change the view so that the entire drawing fits on the screen.
- Show the portion of the drawing within the drawing limits.
- Show the portion of the drawing within the last plot box.
- Move across an enlarged view of the drawing.
- Recall the previous displayed view.
- Redraw the screen to clean it of unwanted clutter.

Your display screen is the "window" in which you see and work on your drawing. *View options* are commands that determine how much and what parts of your drawing appear on screen. Because your drawing is held as data in computer memory, AutoSketch can show you as much or as little as you want. With view options, you might enlarge a complicated part of your drawing to do detail work. Then, you could move across the enlarged view. Finally, you might view the entire drawing again. View options are found in the **View** menu, Fig. 8-1, and as icons along the sides of the drawing area.

ZOOM BOX

The **Zoom box** command shows the portion of the drawing within a box you pick. The view inside the box expands to fill the screen. This command is probably the most used view option.

To change the view, Fig. 8-2, select the **View** menu and the **Zoom Box** command. You can also press function key [F10]. The prompts that appear are:

Zoom Box First corner:

Zoom Box Second corner:

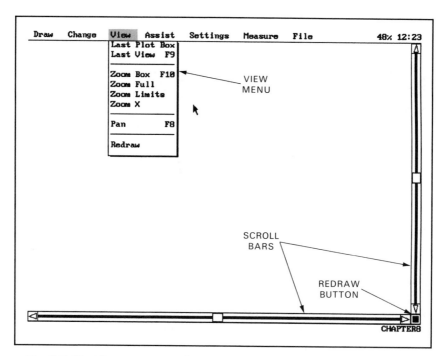

Fig. 8-1. The View menu contains commands that determine how much and what parts of your drawing appear on screen.

Pick opposite corners of a box around the portion of the drawing to view. As you locate the second corner, your pointer pulls a box. It shows you what portion you are about to view. Once you pick the second corner, the view on screen changes accordingly.

ZOOM X

The **Zoom X** command lets you enlarge or reduce the current view by a specific magnification factor. It gives you less control over what is shown. However, when the view expands or reduces in size, the same point remains centered on screen. This can be helpful when the shape you are working on needs to remain centered on screen.

To change the view, Fig. 8-3, select the **View** menu and the **Zoom X** command. The **Zoom Factor** dialogue box appears. Point to the box opposite *Magnification Factor* and type in a value. A factor less than 1 reduces the size of the view. A factor more than 1 enlarges the view. For example, a zoom factor of 2 would make the drawing look twice as big. A zoom factor of .5 would reduce your view of the drawing by one half. After entering a value, pick *OK* and the view changes.

ZOOM FULL

The **Zoom Full** command changes the view so that your entire drawing fits on the screen. Select this command to see the entire drawing, and whenever you "get lost" using other zoom commands. You always return to a "birds-eye" view of the drawing, Fig. 8-4. It does not matter how large or small your drawing is. Also, **Zoom full** will return a view of the entire

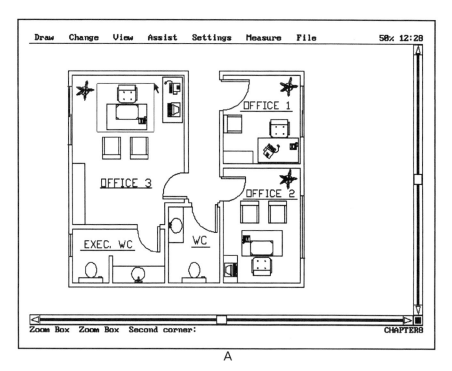

A

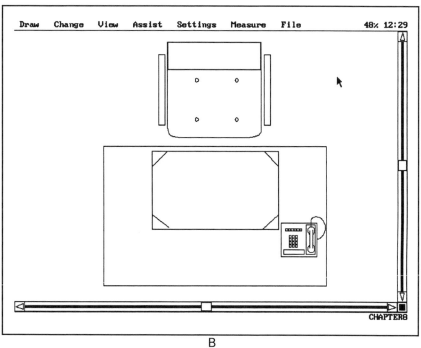

B

Fig. 8-2. Using Zoom Box. A—Pick opposite corners around the portion of the drawing to view. B—That portion expands to fill the screen.

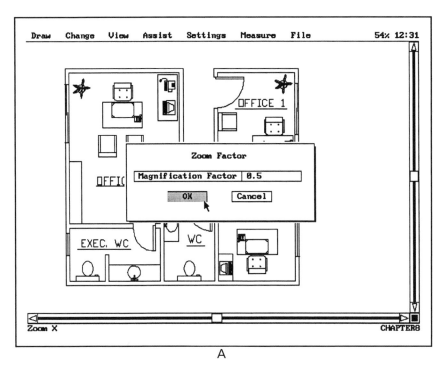

A

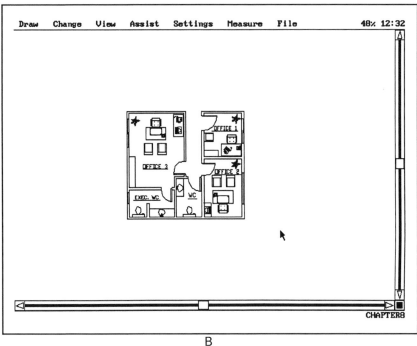

B

Fig. 8-3. Using Zoom X. A—Enter the magnification factor. B—The view reduces (or enlarges) in size, but remains centered on screen.

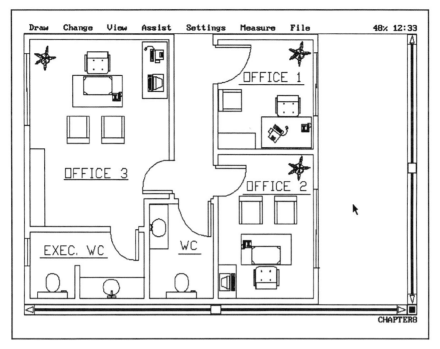

Fig. 8-4. The Zoom Full command always returns the view so that the entire drawing fills the screen.

drawing regardless of how many times you have used other view options. There are no prompts since this command is instant.

ZOOM LIMITS

The **Zoom Limits** command returns the displayed view to the drawing limits. As you will learn in Chapter 10, the limits define the "edges" of your drawing area. **Zoom Limits** will return the view to the limits regardless of how many times you have used other view options. Also, there are no prompts since the command is instant.

LAST PLOT BOX

The **Last Plot Box** command displays the portion of the drawing enclosed in the last plot box. As you will learn in Chapter 14, the plot box is a rectangle you place around the portion of the drawing to plot. This command displays the plot box view regardless of how many times you have used other view options.

PANNING

After using zoom commands to enlarge a view, you cannot see the outer edges of the drawing. Sometimes it is necessary to see an object that is "just off" the screen. *Panning* allows you to move around the magnified view. It lets you slide your viewing window over the drawing, Fig. 8-5. Panning is done by using the **Pan** command or by picking the *pan bars*.

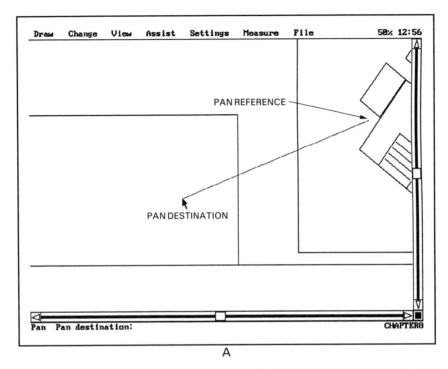

A

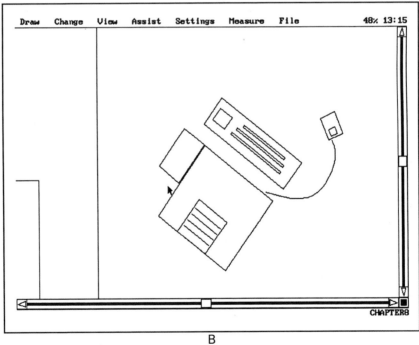

B

Fig. 8-5. Using Pan. A–Pick pan reference and pan destination points.
B–The view moves that distance in the direction of the pan destination point.

Panning Using the Pan Command

To shift your view, select the **View** menu and **Pan** command. You can also press function key [F8]. Panning is done by picking two points or entering coordinates, Fig. 8-5. The following prompts appear:

Pan Pan reference:

Pan Pan destination:

The *Pan reference* point marks a handle you hold to pull the drawing into your viewing window. The *Pan destination* point shows the distance and direction you want to move the view. The current view then moves across the drawing that distance. You can select these points several ways.

The easiest way to pan is to pick the two locations with your pointer. As you locate the destination point, a rubberband line connects your pointer to the pan reference point. The rubberband shows the amount you want to shift the view.

The second way to pan is by entering one or two coordinates. For example, pick the pan reference point with your pointer. However, at the "Pan Pan destination:" prompt, you can enter a relative coordinate.

Pan Pan destination: **R(3,3)**

This entry tells AutoSketch to shift the view 3 units to the right and 3 units up. Pan can also be used even when the entire drawing is shown. You may want to draw beyond the current extents of the screen.

Panning Using Scroll Bars

Scroll bars are icons along the bottom and right edges of the drawing area. You can pick the scroll bars to pan across the drawing. Each scroll bar has arrows at the end, plus an elevator box that shows the position of the current view on the drawing, Fig. 8-6. The scroll bars allow you to pan across the drawing three ways:

- Pick an arrow to pan across the drawing one-quarter screen in that direction.
- Pick the rectangular region between the arrow and elevator box to pan across the drawing one-half screen.
- Pick the elevator box, move it the relative distance you want to pan, and pick again.

When you pick the elevator box and move the pointer, a ghost image of the view you will see appears. After picking the elevator box the first time, you can move the pointer to the drawing area for precise alignment of the view. Pick a location on the drawing area, or pick the elevator box to complete the pan.

LAST VIEW

The **Last View** command returns the previous view. You can pick the command from the **View** menu, or press function key [F9]. **Last View** is used after you have chosen another view option. For example, suppose you enlarged a portion of a drawing to do detail work. When you are finished, select **Last View** to return to the previous view.

The **Last View** command is also often used when you make a mistake using one of the other view commands. Suppose you have zoomed in on a portion of the drawing. However, you

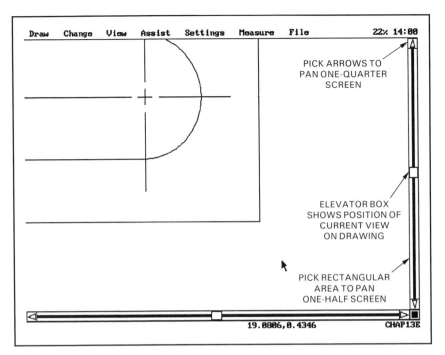

Fig. 8-6. The scroll bars allow you to pan across a drawing

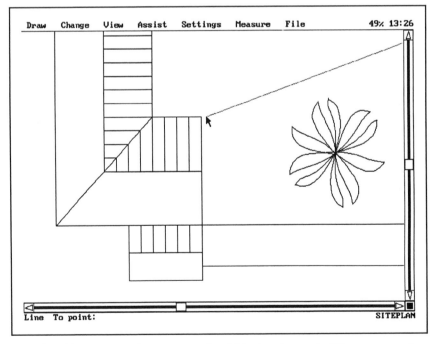

Fig. 8-7. You can use view commands within drawing and editing commands. Here, a water line was started at another location. Then, the drafter zoomed in on the house before picking the second endpoint.

realize you need to look at a different portion. Select **Last View** to return to the previous view to redo your view command. There are no prompts since the **Last View** is instant.

REDRAW

Selecting the **Redraw** command or picking the *Redraw Button* cleans off the drawing and redraws the same view. This process removes marks and holes left by some drawing and editing commands. It renews the view of the drawing by clearing the current display and then redrawing the same view. There are no prompts since the **Redraw** is instant. The location of the Redraw Button is shown in Fig. 8-1.

USING VIEW OPTIONS WITHIN OTHER COMMANDS

You can select a view option at any time, even during a drawing or editing operation. Once you change the view, the drawing or editing command resumes. For example, suppose you need to draw a long line between two small objects that are far apart. See Fig. 8-7. You can zoom in on one object and place the first endpoint. Next, move across to the other object using **Pan** or another view option. Finally, place the second endpoint of the line.

SUMMARY

View options are commands that determine how much and what parts of your drawing appear on screen. AutoSketch can show you as much or as little of the drawing as you want to see. There are six view options offered by AutoSketch. All can be used from within another drawing or editing task.

The **Zoom Box** command enlarges the portion of the drawing within a box you pick. The **Zoom X** command lets you enlarge or reduce the current view by a specific magnification factor. The **Zoom Full** command changes the view so that your entire drawing fits on the screen. The **Zoom Limits** command returns the displayed view to the drawing limits. The **Last Plot Box** command displays the portion of the drawing enclosed in the last plot box. The **Pan** command allows you to move around the magnified view. The **Last View** command returns the previous view. The **Redraw** command cleans off the drawing, removing marks and holes left by drawing and editing objects.

NEW TERMS

View options, **View** menu, **Zoom Box** command, **Zoom X** command, magnification factor, **Zoom Full** command, **Zoom Limits** command, **Last Plot Box** command, **Pan** command, pan reference, pan destination, **Last View** command, **Redraw** command.

REVIEW QUESTIONS

Write your answers on a separate sheet of paper. Do not write in this book.
  1. Commands that determine how much and what part of your drawing appears on screen are found in the _____ menu.

2. After choosing the **Zoom box** command, you must pick opposite corners of a _____ around the portion of the drawing to display.

3. To enlarge the view of the drawing two times, you would select the _____ command.

4. The center of the drawing always remains centered after what view command?

5. The view command that will always display your entire drawing is _____.

6. To see an object that is only partly shown on screen, you usually select the _____ command.

7. When panning across the drawing, the view moves the distance between two picked points. They are the _____ point and _____ point.

8. For what view command can you also enter coordinates? _____ Explain how.

9. In what two situations is the **Last view** command often used?

10. The _____ command renews the current view of the drawing to remove marks and holes left by some drawing and editing commands.

ACTIVITIES

Here is a mixture of drawing activities to develop your skills with view options. Save your AutoSketch drawings on your file disk, not on the program disk. Clear the previous drawing from screen and memory using **New** before completing each activity.

1. Complete the tasks labeled A through G. Refer to the illustration as you go.
   A. Draw a very small circle and box.
   B. Enlarge the view using **Zoom Box** so that both the circle and box fill the screen.
   C. Pan across the drawing so that the circle is centered on screen.
   D. Reduce the size of the view using **Zoom X** so the view is only half as big.
   E. Return to the previous view using **Last View.**
   F. Use **Zoom Full** to make the drawing fill the extents of the screen.
   G. Quit the drawing without saving it.

A B C

D E F

2-9. Complete each of the drawings. Use view options when appropriate to help you see details. Use drawing aids to your advantage. Use editing commands when needed, especially when they help you construct the drawing quicker. Save each drawing as C8A?, but replace the question mark with the activity number. Write a brief report of how you constructed each drawing.

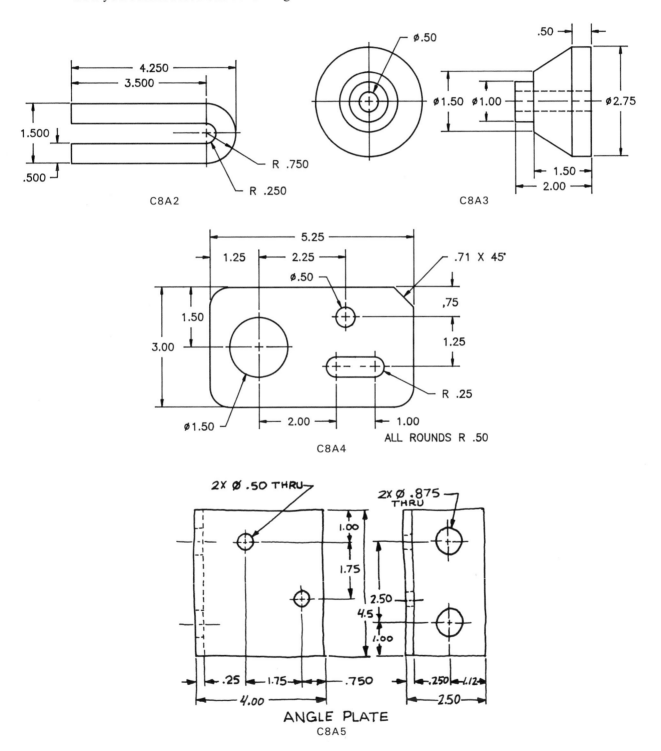

C8A2

C8A3

C8A4

ALL ROUNDS R .50

ANGLE PLATE
C8A5

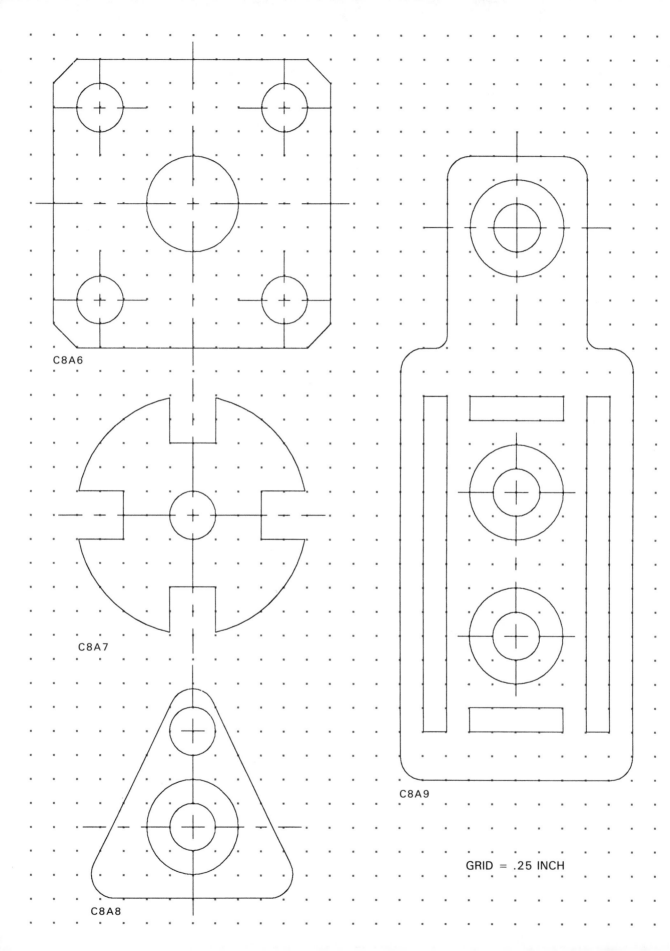

C8A6

C8A7

C8A8

C8A9

GRID = .25 INCH

Chapter 9

ADDING TEXT

After studying this chapter, you will be able to:
- Select features that determine the appearance of text.
- Pick a starting position for a text string.
- Enter text to be placed on the drawing.
- Place multiple lines of text on a drawing.
- Draw special characters.

Almost all technical drawings, graphs, and illustrations contain information given as text. *Text* refers to letters, numbers, words, and sentences which are added to explain features that cannot be described with graphics, Fig. 9-1. Text is needed because a drawing, by itself, often cannot convey all the features of a design idea. Text can specify:
- Material used to make the product.
- Special instructions for manufacturing or constructing the product.
- Drawing name, part name, revision number, and other necessary information to document the project.
- Dimensions and tolerances.

BENEFITS OF CAD TEXT

There are many benefits to adding text with a computer-aided drafting program compared to lettering in manual drafting. First, text is easy to place on the drawing. There are only three steps:
1. Select text features. Features refer to the font, height, width, and angle of the text.
2. Pick a location for the text on the drawing.
3. Type in the text using the keyboard.

A second benefit is neatness. Because a technical drawing must inform the reader, text should be legible. Some drafters have sloppy lettering habits. However, text drawn with AutoSketch and plotted on a hardcopy device is clear and precise.

A third and very important benefit of CAD text is standardization. Companies and schools can specify standard text features that should be used for all drawings. The text font, height, width, and angle are set as company policy. Any drawing created adheres to that standard, no

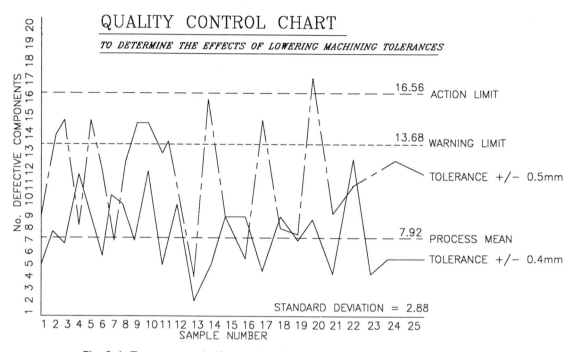

Fig. 9-1. Text was needed here to label important parts of the chart. (Autodesk)

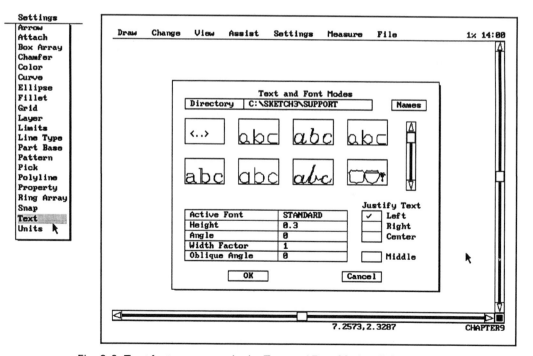

Fig. 9-2. Text features are set in the Text and Font Modes dialogue box.

matter who the drafter is. All lettering will look alike. Also, if more than one person works on a drawing, the text style remains the same. This makes drawings look neater.

SELECTING TEXT FEATURES

Text features must be set before placing text on a drawing. *Text features* determine the appearance of the text. Features include font, height, width, obliquing angle, and angle. To set the features, select the **Settings** menu, and the **Text** command. The **Text and Font Modes** dialogue box appears, Fig. 9-2.

Font

The *text font* refers to the style of the lettering. Text characters may be made of simple lines, complex shapes, or even symbols. Fonts that are bold and easily seen are used for titles and labels. All of the characters in a font follow the same general style. AutoSketch Version 3.0 includes six basic text fonts, Fig. 9-3. AutoSketch Version 2.0 includes five basic fonts. The fancier ones are included to be used by graphic artists or for business graphics and presentations. In addition, AutoSketch includes three symbol fonts, Fig. 9-4. When you type in a character, a symbol appears instead.

To choose a font in Version 3.0, pick the font icon. The font name appears opposite the *Active Font* box, Fig. 9-5. You can view font names only by picking the *Names* button.

In Version 2.0, you must do two things to use a different font: load the font and select the font. To load the font, pick the box opposite the font name on the left. The font name will appear opposite the *File* box. Then, pick the *Load Font* box to load the font into AutoSketch.

STANDARD	ABC123	The quick brown fox jumps over the lazy dog.
ITALICC	*ABC123*	*The quick brown fox jumps over the lazy dog.*
MONOTXT	ABC123	The quick brown fox jumps over the lazy dog.
ROMANC	ABC123	The quick brown fox jumps over the lazy dog.
ROMANS	ABC123	The quick brown fox jumps over the lazy dog.
SCRIPTC	*ABC123*	*The quick brown fox jumps over the lazy dog.*

Fig. 9-3. The six basic fonts from which to choose in Version 3.0. The ROMANS font is used most often.

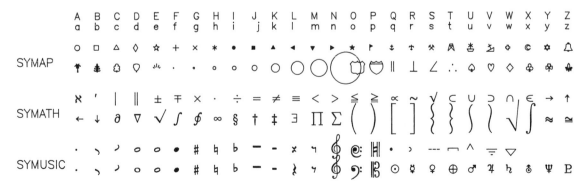

Fig. 9-4. AutoSketch includes three symbol fonts. The capital and lower case characters create different symbols.

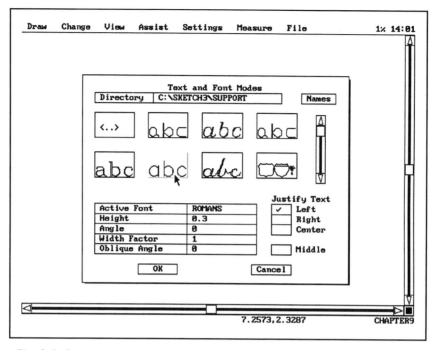

Fig. 9-5. Pick the font icon to choose a text font. The font name appears in the Active Font box.

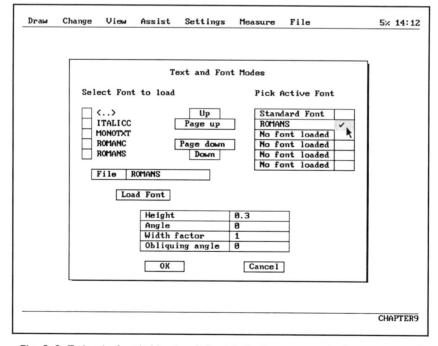

Fig. 9-6. To load a font in Version 2.0, pick the box next to the font name, and then pick the Load Font box. Once a font has been loaded, its name appears under the Pick Active Font list.

The next step is to select the font. Notice in Fig. 9-6 that after loading, the font name appears under the *Pick Active Font* heading. Select your newly loaded font by picking the box next to it. A check mark will appear.

Height

Text height determines how tall the text is going to appear. The height is based on the height of capital letters, Fig. 9-7. Lower case letters will obviously be smaller. Most text you add to a technical drawing should be capital letters. Occasionally, capital and lower case letters will be used for notes. The height you set will also be used for all dimension text.

To change the height, pick the **Settings** menu and **Text** command to access the **Text and Font Modes** dialogue box. Then, place the pointer opposite the *Height* box. Enter the new text height. A standard height for technical drafting is .125, Fig. 9-8. Text that is too small cannot be seen clearly. Changing the height also proportionally changes the width.

All new text entered will assume the current height setting. All text previously entered will remain at the height at which it was entered.

Text Height = .125

Text Height = .18

Text Height = .25

Fig. 9-7. On most drawings, the text height looks best between .125 and .25. Titles and labels may be larger.

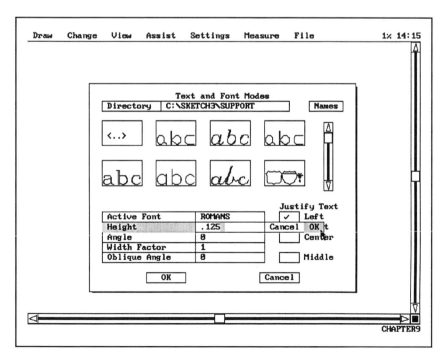

Fig. 9-8. To set the height (and other text features), point to the box, type in a value, and then pick the extended OK box.

Width

Text width is the width of each character. AutoSketch uses a *width factor* to determine the width of text. Changing the width squeezes and expands the text string, Fig. 9-9. It does not change the height. The default factor is 1, which is normal text. Entering a factor greater than 1 expands the text. Entering a factor less than 1 compresses the text.

To change the width, place the pointer opposite the *Width Factor* box. Enter any positive value. For most technical drawings, use the default factor. Entering another factor might cause the text to look awkward and not conform to standards.

Width Factor = .5

Width Factor = .75

Width Factor = 1

Width Factor = 1.5

Fig. 9-9. A width factor less than one squeezes text. A factor greater than one expands text. The height does not change.

Obliquing Angle

Obliquing angle is the slant, or angle, of each individual character in the text string. This option allows you to make the text look italic. A 15 degree slant is frequently used on technical drawings. See Fig. 9-10.

The obliquing angle is measured clockwise from vertical. When the slant is 0 degrees (the default value), text is upright. A positive value slants the text clockwise (forward). A negative value slants the text counterclockwise (backwards).

All new text entered will be at the new obliquing angle. Previously drawn text will not be affected. The recommended range of angle values is between -30 and +30 degrees.

Text at 10° Obliquing Angle

Text at 15° Obliquing Angle

Text at 30° Obliquing Angle

Fig. 9-10. The obliquing angle is the slant of text characters. You can also have negative obliquing angles for text that slants to the left.

Angle

The *angle* determines the rotation for an entire line of text, called a text string. Rotation is measured from horizontal in a counterclockwise direction, Fig. 9-11. The default rotation is 0 degrees (horizontal). If you enter a negative rotation angle, the text string is rotated clockwise. An angle of 90 degrees would make the text vertical (read bottom to top). All text is placed at the current rotation until the angle value is reset.

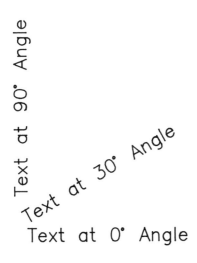

Fig. 9-11. The angle of a text string is measured counterclockwise from horizontal.

Justification

Justification determines the alignment of the text in relation to the point you pick to place the text, Fig. 9-12. AutoSketch offers three types of justification–*Left, Right,* and *Center.* These are set in the **Text and Font Modes** dialogue box. You can also select *Middle* with any justification. This setting adjusts the text string so that the middle of it is aligned with the point you pick. Justification is only available in Version 3.0.

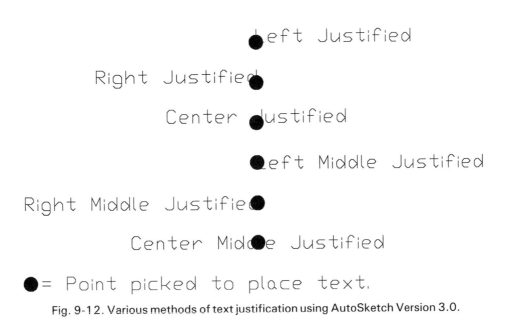

Fig. 9-12. Various methods of text justification using AutoSketch Version 3.0.

Color

A setting for text color is not found in the dialogue box. However, because each text string is an object, you can set the color with the **Color** command, found in the **Settings** menu.

There are two reasons to make text a different color. First, special notes and specifications should stand out from shapes and dimensions. Second, AutoSketch uses the color to determine which pen to pick when plotting. Choosing a unique color allows you place a different color or width pen in pen plotters.

PLACING TEXT ON THE DRAWING

Once you have set the text features, you are ready to add text to the drawing. AutoSketch Version 3.0 allows you to place text using two methods–**Quick Text** and **Text Editor.** Auto-Sketch Version 2.0 has one method, the **Text** command, which works just like Version 3.0 **Quick Text** command.

Placing Text Using Quick Text
Quick Text is a fast way to add single lines of text to your drawing. Select the **Draw** menu, and the **Quick Text** command. The first prompt that appears is:

Text Enter point:

Pick the start point of the text string. The *start point* gives the placement of the text on the drawing. AutoSketch Version 2.0 always places text left justified, meaning the left side of the text string will be placed at the start point. Version 3.0 places text according to the justification you set. Once you pick a start point, a small underline appears on the drawing. The next prompt then appears:

Text Enter text:

Type in the required text at this prompt. Use the keyboard to enter characters, letters, numbers, words, and sentences. The text appears on the drawing as well as on the prompt line, Fig. 9-13. If you make a mistake, press the [Backspace] key to back up. When you finish typing in the line of text, press [Enter] or [Return]. The "Text Enter point:" prompt reappears to let you pick another place on the drawing to enter text.

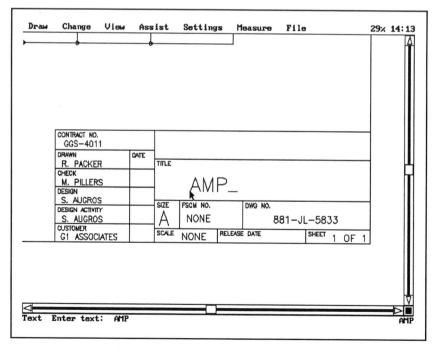

Fig. 9-13. After picking the Text command and a start point, type in the text. It appears both on the drawing and on the prompt line as you type.

Multiline Text. You may want to type in more than one line of text at a time. In this case, do not press [Enter] or [Return] after typing in the text string. Instead, press the pick button of your pointing device. This causes the cursor to jump down to the next line on screen. Continue to enter a new line of text. When finished, press [Enter] or [Return] to enter text elsewhere, or pick another command. (Hint: A better way to enter paragraphs in Version 3.0 is with the Text Editor.)

Placing Text Using the Text Editor

Version 3.0 introduces a powerful way to enter text, the Text Editor. This method allows you to add entire blocks (paragraphs) of text to the drawing. The block of text is treated as a single object. Select the **Draw** menu, and the **Text Editor** command. The first prompt that appears is:

Text Enter point:

Pick the start point of the text string. Once you pick the start point, the **Text Editor** dialogue box appears, Fig. 9-14. The major parts of the **Text Editor** dialogue box are:

- The *editing box* is where you type in text. You must position the pointer within the box to enter text. The box is limited to 2000 characters, with each line no longer than 256 characters.
- *Scroll bars* along the top and side allow you to pan left, right, up, and down across large amounts of text.
- The *status line* shows the line and column where the cursor is positioned. It also shows whether text you type in inserts or types over text already typed in.
- *OK* accepts the text and places it on the drawing.
- *Cancel* closes the dialogue box without placing text on the drawing.

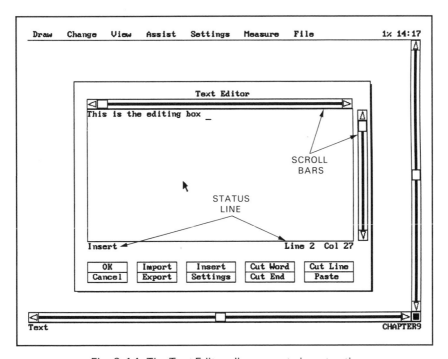

Fig. 9-14. The Text Editor allows you to insert entire blocks of text.

- *Import* brings in an ASCII text file that you created outside of AutoSketch. Files are discussed in more detail in Chapter 16.
- *Export* saves the text in the editing box to an ASCII file.
- *Insert* determines whether text you type in inserts or types over existing text in the editing box. The status line shows either *Insert* or *Typeover*. The cursor is either an underline (Insert mode) or a box (Typeover mode).
- *Settings* brings up the **Text and Font Modes** dialogue box so that you can reset text features.
- *Cut Word* deletes the word at the cursor. The cursor should be located under the first letter of the word to delete the entire word.
- *Cut End* deletes text from your cursor to the end of the line.
- *Cut Line* deletes an entire line of text.
- *Paste* types in the text that you last cut. The text is placed at your cursor position.

You can move and copy words and lines of text in the editing box by cutting and pasting text. To move text, simply cut it and paste it where you want it. To copy text, cut the text and immediately repaste it without moving your cursor. Then, paste the text again where you want the copy.

When you pick *OK* in the **Text Editor** dialogue box, the block of text appears on the drawing. Note that the entire block of text, not just each line, is justified according to your *Justify Text* setting.

Drawing Special Characters

AutoSketch allows you to draw several special characters without having to use a symbol font. This is done by typing a control code as you type in text. A *control code* is two percent signs (%%) followed by a letter. Using a code, you can overscore or underscore text, or place degrees, plus/minus, and diameter symbols. Fig. 9-15 shows how to type in control codes to receive these characters. You will not see the overscore, underscore, or special character in the drawing until you press the [Enter] or [Return] key.

EDITING TEXT

You can edit text just as you can edit other AutoSketch objects. Text can be changed, moved, scaled, or rotated in a similar manner to boxes, arcs, and other objects.

TYPED	ENTERED ON SCREEN
%%oToggle Overscore%%o	Toggle Overscore
%%uToggle Underscore%%u	Toggle Underscore
%%uUnder %%oand%%u Overscored%%o	Under and Overscored
%%dDraw Degrees Symbol	°Draw Degrees Symbol
%%pDraw Plus/Minus Symbol	±Draw Plus/Minus Symbol
%%cDraw Diameter Symbol	⌀Draw Diameter Symbol
%%%Draw Percent Sign	%Draw Percent Sign

Fig. 9-15. Using a control code, you can enter commonly used symbols and effects.

Changing Words and Letters

You can edit the characters of a text string or text block using AutoSketch Version 3.0. Select the **Change** menu and **Text Editor** command. The following prompt appears:

Text edit Select object:

Select the baseline of the text string or text block you would like to edit. It does not matter whether the text was created with the **Quick Text** or **Text Editor** commands. Once you pick the text, it appears in the **Text Editor** dialogue box. Make any changes and then pick *OK*. If you pick the *Settings* button while in the Text Editor, those settings will take effect on the changed text.

AutoSketch Version 2.0 does not have a method to edit existing text. You must erase the entire text string and then re-enter it using the **Text** command to change a letter or word.

Changing Text with Other Editing Commands

You can use standard editing commands, such as **Move, Copy,** and **Rotate** to change the location or orientation of text. These commands consider text like any other object. When you edit text, the pointer drags a box that represents the text, rather than the text itself.

Some commands have rather special effects on text, Fig. 9-16. If you **Stretch** one end of a text string, the text will compress or expand horizontally, and also rotate. If you **Mirror** text,

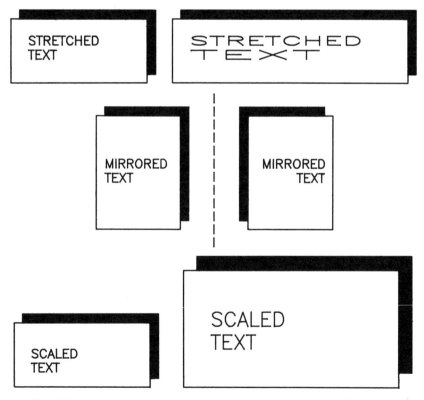

Fig. 9-16. Some editing commands affect text strangely. Top–Stretched text changes in width factor. If stretched diagonally, the obliquing angle will also change. Middle–Individual characters of mirrored text are not reflected, but the position of the text string is. Bottom–Scaled text changes in height and width.

the text occupies the mirror, but does not mirror itself; it continues to read from left to right. The **Scale** command enlarges and reduces the size of text as it does other objects. You cannot **Break** a text string.

You can change the properties of text two ways. Notice in the **Change Property Modes** dialogue box (select **Settings** and **Property**) that there are items for both font and text, Fig. 9-17. When *Font* is checked, the **Change Property** command will change the font of selected text. When *Text* is checked, the **Change Property** command will affect the other text features–height, width, obliquing angle, angle, and justification.

You can connect to text using **Attach** in a manner similar to other objects. Text has two points that define a baseline. You can use the **Attach** option *Node Point* to grab these points if necessary, Fig. 9-18.

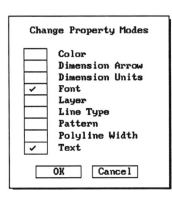

Fig. 9-17. To change the font or features of text, make sure the appropriate box is checked in the Change Property Modes dialogue box.

Fig. 9-18. Two points define the baseline of text. Use the Attach mode Node to connect to these points.

SUMMARY

Technical drawings contain text to convey information that cannot be described with graphics. Text can take on many appearances, depending on which text features are selected. The font refers to the style of the text. The height determines how tall the text will be shown. AutoSketch uses a width factor to determine the width of text in relation to the height. The obliquing angle is the slant, or angle, of each individual character in the text string. The angle determines the rotation for an entire line of text, called a text string. Justification determines the alignment of the text in relation to the point you pick to place the text.

To place text on a drawing, you pick the **Draw** menu and **Quick Text** (**Text** in Version 2.0) or **Text Editor** command. Quick Text is a fast way to add single lines of text to your drawing. The Text Editor allows you to add entire blocks (paragraphs) of text to the drawing. You must pick a start point for the text after picking the command. Finally, you simply type in the text. Special characters can be used, but you must type in a control code.

NEW TERMS

Text, text features, **Text** command, **Text and Font Modes** dialogue box, text font, text height, text width, width factor, obliquing angle, angle, justification, text string, **Quick Text** command, **Text Editor** command, start point, editing box, scroll bars, status line, Cancel, Import, Export, Insert, Typeover, Settings, Cut Word, Cut End, Cut Line, Paste, special characters, control code.

REVIEW QUESTIONS

Write your answers on a separate sheet of paper. Do not write in this book.
1. List five times when you might place text on a drawing.
2. Text _____ refer(s) to the font, height, width, and angle of text.
3. List three benefits of CAD text over traditional lettering.
4. Which font do you believe is most appropriate for a technical drawing?
5. In symbol fonts, capital letters mean the same symbol as lower case letters. True or false?
6. The *Width* value you set in AutoSketch refers to the actual width of individual characters. True or false?
7. Explain how *Obliquing angle* and *Angle* values are different.
8. The _____ gives the placement of the text on the drawing.
9. What makes up a control code?
10. Text is considered an object, just like a line, circle, or arc. True or false?

ACTIVITIES

Here is a mixture of drawing activities to develop your skills with adding text. Save your AutoSketch drawings on your file disk, not on the program disk. Clear the previous drawing from screen and memory using **New** before completing each activity.
1. Using the default text features, place your name, course, and date on separate lines. Determine the default values AutoSketch assigns for:
   Font:
   Height:
   Width:
   Obliquing angle:
   Angle:

2. Draw a 3 unit square box. Inside the box, enter the paragraph shown in the following illustration. Use both the **Text Editor** command and multiline feature of **Quick Text** to place the text. Which one is easier to use? Save the drawing as C9A2.

```
This is .125 high text
in the ROMANS font.
To end each line, press
the pick button on your
mouse or digitizer.
This jumps the cursor to
the next evenly spaced
line. When you are
finished entering text,
press the [Return] key.
```

3. Enter the sentence given below. Use the proper control codes to enter each of the special characters. Save the drawing as C9A3.

The temperature can vary ±5° in a ø5.25 inch can.

4. Draw text inside a box for each example shown in Fig. 9-16. Make a copy of the text, and perform the three example editing commands on the text, **Stretch, Mirror,** and **Scale.** Save the drawing as C9A4.

5. Using the STANDARD font, enter your name and class on screen. Then, select the ROMANS font and enter your address on the drawing. Now, enter the proper settings and use the **Change Property** command to change all of the text to the ROMANS font. Save the drawing as C9A5.

6. With the drawing from Activity 5 on screen, use the **Change Property** command to change the text features to the values below. Save the drawing as C9A6.
   Height: .18
   Width: .75
   Obliquing angle: 10
   Justification: Right

7. Draw a four-sided irregular polygon. Find the bearing of two sides, and place text at the proper angle along the two sides. See the illustration below. Save the drawing as C9A7.

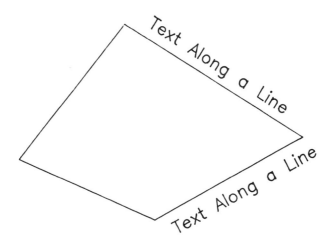

8-10. Complete each of these drawings using various text features. For each activity, record the font and text features you set to draw the text. The grid for Activity C9A9 is .29 horizontally and .23 vertically. The grid for Activity C9A10 is .25 horizontally and vertically. Save each drawing as C9A?, replacing the question mark with the activity number.

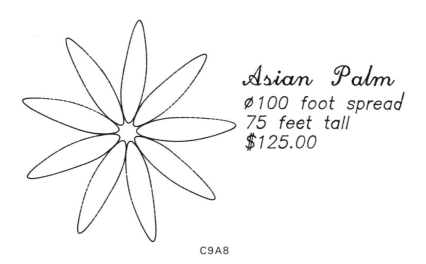

C9A8

CRITICAL PATH

DURATION (DAYS)

ACTIVITY		
1-2	⊠	BASIC RESEARCH
1-3	☐	BRIEF
1-4	▭	MARKET RESEARCH
2-3	⊠	SPECIFICATION
2-4	▭	APPLIED RESEARCH & PROTOTYPE
3-4	⊠	DEVELOPMENT
4-5	☐	DESIGN
4-6	⊠	PLANNING & COSTING
6-7	⊠	MARKETING
6-8	☐	DESIGN APPROVAL
7-9	⊠	PRODUCTION

Scale: 5, 10, 15, 20, 25, 30, 35, 40, 45, 50, 55, 60, 65, 70, 75, 80, 85, 90, 95, 100, 105

⊠ = CRITICAL PATH

C9A9

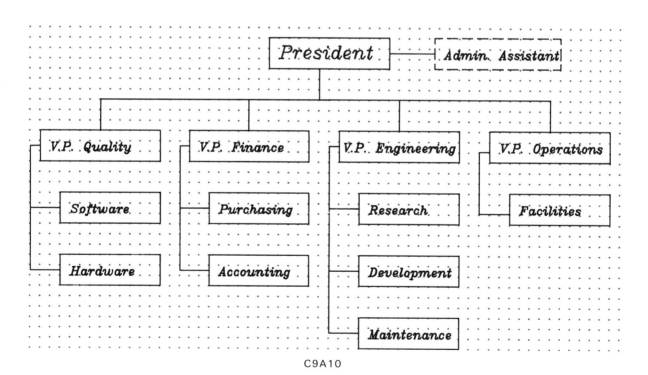

C9A10

Chapter 10

DEVELOPING DRAWINGS

After studying this chapter, you will be able to:
- Identify steps of the design process.
- List values set during drawing setup.
- Set the size of your drawing area.
- Organize objects on separate layers.
- Develop prototype drawings.
- Draw a standard title block.
- Recognize techniques that let you construct drawings quicker.

The chapters up to now have focused mainly on drawing and editing single objects and basic shapes. This chapter pulls together your skills and shows you how to set up a simple drawing. You will first learn some guidelines that affect how you approach a design problem. Then, the chapter lists steps taken to set up and construct a drawing complete with a border and title block. Finally, the chapter offers tips and techniques to help you construct drawings quickly.

THE DESIGN PROCESS

Technical drawings are made to document a design idea. Designs do not pop out of midair. Rather, they evolve over time. There are six distinct steps that lead to solving a design problem. These steps are known as the *design process:*
1. Identify the problem or need.
2. Set guidelines.
3. Gather information.
4. Develop possible solutions.
5. Select the final solution.
6. Evaluate the solution.

This chapter applies the design process to solving needs for products. For example, a design sketch might describe the size and shape of a computer table. A drafter then develops the working drawings for that design using AutoSketch, or another CAD program.

Identify the Problem or Need

New designs are the result of a problem or need. For example, a situation might be that birds are nesting in your fireplace chimney, Fig. 10-1. This causes a health hazard because smoke backs up into your house.

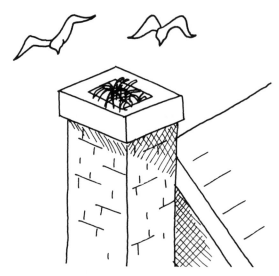

Fig. 10-1. Designs usually result from a problem or need. Here, the problem is that birds are nesting in a chimney.

When you recognize a problem, also recognize what is needed and what is not. For example, solving the chimney problem does not mean moving to another neighborhood. Focus your efforts on solving the problem at hand. It helps to write out a description. For example, the statement for the chimney problem might be:

> "Birds are nesting in the fireplace chimney, causing a heath hazard. A device or method is needed to prevent birds from nesting in or blocking the normal operation of the chimney."

Write a clear statement that does not imply any one solution. For example, you would not say "A screen is needed to prevent birds from nesting in the chimney." This is too specific. It limits the possible solutions. A well-written statement gives the other design steps direction.

Set Guidelines

Guidelines provide a focus to your problem solving. Also called *design criteria,* they set the limits within which you must work. For example, guidelines for the solving the "birds in the chimney" problem might be:

1. The shape of the chimney is _____ (round/square).
2. The opening of the chimney is _____ inches.
3. Must be simple to install.

4. Fastens securely and will withstand wind gusts.
5. Made of safe, noncombustible material.
6. Does not harm birds.
7. Must be affordable.

These are just a few items. You might think of other criteria, depending on the problem or need. They set limits, such as:

1. Who will use the product?
2. When will they use it?
3. Where will they use it?
4. Must the product follow a particular style?
5. What is the maximum or minimum size?
6. What is the maximum or minimum weight?
7. What is the maximum or minimum strength?
8. What is the cost range?

Make sure that you do not strictly limit the number of potential solutions with your guidelines. For example, suppose you are still setting guidelines for a method to keep birds out of the chimney. By writing "Must fit in chimney," you exclude any ideas for devices that fit over or around the chimney. Thus, be careful when setting guidelines.

Gather Information

The research stage of the design process is often the most neglected step. Be informed. Gather all the information needed to develop potential solutions to the problem or need. The ideas you can generate are only limited by your knowledge on the subject. Examples of information include:

1. Recent technical information from trade publications.
2. Similar products and competing products.
3. Feedback received on similar products.
4. Market research.
5. Customer opinion.
6. Available materials to make the product.
7. Existing parts and supplies that could reduce cost and labor.
8. Supplier catalogs.

Check every detail, even one that may seem trivial or unimportant at first. You could find an item, perhaps buried deep in some magazine, that helps solve your problem. For example, you might find an article on an electronic device that keeps birds away. You might also see an ad for a screen that fits over round metal chimneys.

Develop Possible Solutions

After identifying the problem and gathering information, begin to think of possible solutions. Write down all ideas that are related to the design. Do not dismiss any idea at first. Record any thought that comes to your mind or is offered by others in your group. This process is called *brainstorming*. Look for quantity of ideas, not quality.

Once you have exhausted ideas, begin to review them. Look for good and bad points in each. See which begin to solve the problem. Sketch those ideas on paper. These first drawings are only rough sketches because the solutions are not yet well thought out. Many times, you will combine good points from two or more ideas. This is all part of refining your design. At this stage, do not ignore even far-out ideas.

Sometimes, you can build on previous designs. By making small changes to an existing product, you may answer the design problem. The data you gather may identify a device similar to that you need. For example, remember the electronic device that keeps birds away. The current model may not be heat-resistant for use in the chimney. One of your possible solutions might be a heat-shielded device. Recall the screen that fits over round metal chimneys. You might modify that screen to fit inside your square brick chimney. See Fig. 10-2.

As you refine possible solutions, prepare detail sketches, models, or renderings. When possible, test models using actual conditions the product must endure. Look for function, safety, appearance, and durability as they relate to your design. Your tests may lead to changes.

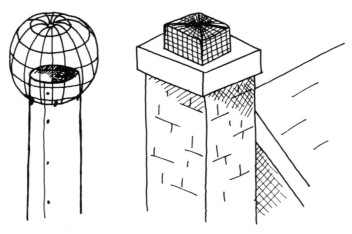

Fig. 10-2. Often, a design you make will be a variation of a previous product. Herc, a square screen (right), is a modification of a previous design (left).

Select the Final Solution

The final design comes after you refine the best ideas to form one effective solution. Weed out weak ideas and combine the good points of all practical options.

Sometimes the best solution is not acceptable. It may not meet the guidelines you set earlier in the design process. For example, you might develop an bird vacuum that sucks birds out of the chimney, but costs $100,000. Of course, you probably could not afford it, and no one else would buy it. One of your guidelines should read, "Must be affordable to the average consumer." Always check the solutions to see that they fall within the guidelines.

Often, the final solution is a compromise between the most ideal and the most practical ideas. Take into account any factor that relates to your design. This might include: cost to build, purchase price, service, repair, market, environment, social aspects, looks, and durability. There will also many factors unique to your design that you must consider.

In most companies, the final design is presented to management before it is manufactured or built. This involves presentation drawings, written reports, cost estimates, and market analysis. Many times, you must "prove" that the design will be a profitable venture.

Once the final design has been selected, the work of the drafter begins. The design ideas, sketches, and specifications must be converted into working drawings. This includes detail drawings, assembly drawings, bills of materials, parts lists, and other data. Making working drawings often requires cooperation among many people and departments.

Evaluate the Solution

The design process does not end with the final solution. Next comes evaluation, or *feedback*. Check to see whether the designed product or method has fulfilled its purpose. Talk with users of the product. A customer might have found a flaw that you did not foresee. Sometimes, the compromises you make when choosing a final solution affect the quality of the product.

Feedback is important because the design process is not a one-time routine. It cycles so that feedback helps refine the product, Fig. 10-3. The feedback you receive on one product is also important data for future products.

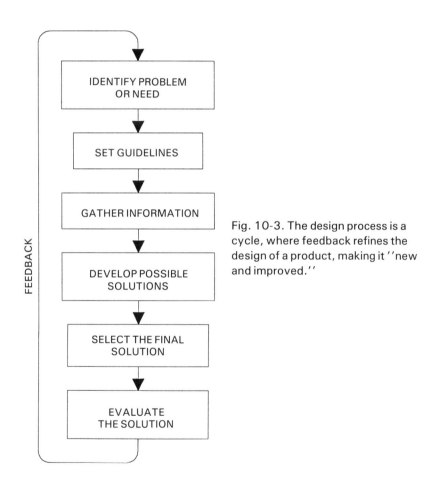

Fig. 10-3. The design process is a cycle, where feedback refines the design of a product, making it ''new and improved.''

SKETCHING

Throughout the design process you will need to make notes of your ideas. Many popular products begin as a pencil sketch on the back of a napkin or envelope. During the initial stages, sketch your rough ideas since a sketch often communicates better than words.

Documenting an idea, using manual drafting tools or CAD, can take time. Yet, with a sketch you can quickly jot down dozens of ideas. The design evolves as sketched concepts are reviewed. When the best ideas are combined, refined sketches can be drawn. Engineering sketches are very refined sketches that are given to a drafter to convert into manual or computer drawings.

When you sketch ideas before using AutoSketch, there are three suggestions to remember.

1. Proportion is important. A circle twice the size of another circle should look that way. Two lines at a 30 degree angle should appear to be at that angle, Fig. 10-4.

2. Add dimensions. Show the size and location of features so that your sketches are not misunderstood, Fig. 10-5. Do not worry about proper dimensioning methods at this time. You will learn them in Chapter 13.

3. Use graph paper (also called grid paper) when available. It helps you draw more accurately, Fig. 10-6.

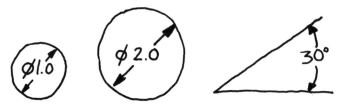

Fig. 10-4. Your sketches should be proportional. Shapes should appear to be the proper size, location, angle, and shape.

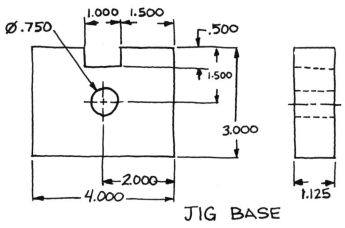

Fig. 10-5. Add dimensions to sketches. You might draw well, but your drawing most likely is not perfectly accurate.

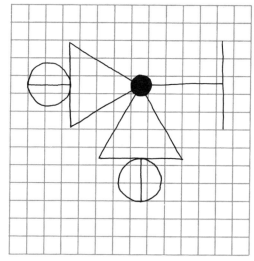

Fig. 10-6. Use graph paper to help your sketches be more accurate. Assign each square of the grid some measurement, such as .25 inch, or 10 millimeters.

DRAWING PLAN SHEET

When you are about to create a CAD drawing, it is a good idea to have a plan on paper. This can be done on a standard form, often called a *drawing plan sheet,* Fig. 10-7. Transfer or tape your sketch onto the plan sheet. Also list the steps you expect to follow to complete the drawing. Some companies have formal documents that track the progress of a project. The plan sheet shown in Fig. 10-7 is one that you might use in the classroom. The main parts are the sketch and procedure.

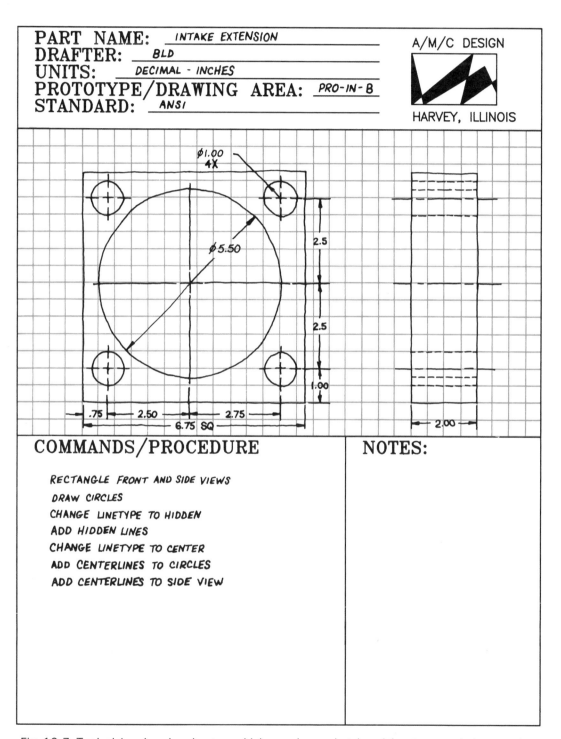

Fig. 10-7. Typical drawing plan sheet on which you place a sketch and the steps needed to complete the drawing.

DRAWING SETUP

With a sketch and/or plan sheet in hand, it is time to start up AutoSketch. Your first steps after starting the program are known as *drawing setup*. Drawing setup involves the actions you take to prepare the drawing file before adding objects. Mostly, this includes entering values for drawing aids, linetype, and color. In addition, you might draw a border and title block. Usually, you will take 5 to 10 minutes to set the following values:

- Drawing color.
- Drawing linetype.
- Limits.
- Layers.
- Grid spacing.
- Snap spacing.
- Active Attach modes.
- Pick spacing.
- Text font and features.
- Properties changed in the **Change Properties Modes** dialogue box.

Most of these settings have been covered in previous chapters. Two have not: limits and layers. Limits set the size of your drawing area. Layers help you organize details.

SETTING DRAWING LIMITS

When drafting on paper, your drawing area is limited to the sheet size of the paper. Standard sheet sizes are given in Fig. 10-8. To create a large design, a house for example, you

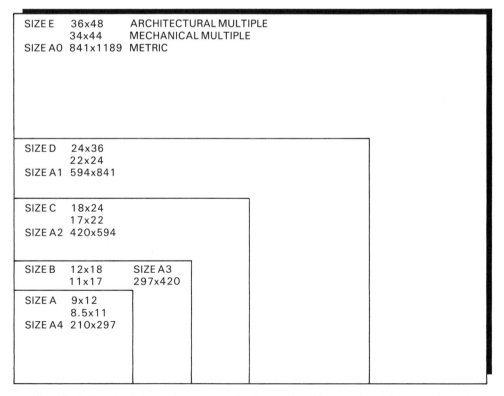

SIZE E	36x48	ARCHITECTURAL MULTIPLE
	34x44	MECHANICAL MULTIPLE
SIZE A0	841x1189	METRIC

SIZE D	24x36
	22x24
SIZE A1	594x841

SIZE C	18x24
	17x22
SIZE A2	420x594

SIZE B	12x18	SIZE A3
	11x17	297x420

SIZE A	9x12
	8.5x11
SIZE A4	210x297

Fig. 10-8. Standard sheet sizes for mechanical and architectural multiples, and metric sheet sizes.

cannot make the drawing full size. Instead, you need to scale the drawing. By drawing every 1 foot of the house only 1/4 inch long (a scale of 1/4″ = 1'-0″) you can easily fit a house plan on a C-size sheet of paper.

Although AutoSketch is a drafting program, it does not restrict you to a fixed sheet size. In fact, AutoSketch lets you set any size drawing area by entering limits. *Limits* define the left, right, bottom, and top edges of your drawing area, or "sheet," Fig. 10-9. By setting a large drawing area, you can draw using full-size measurements. You do not have to scale the drawing as you would on a sheet of paper. For example, suppose you are drawing a bridge design that is 500 feet long and 60 feet high. Set your limits at least that big and draw shapes full size.

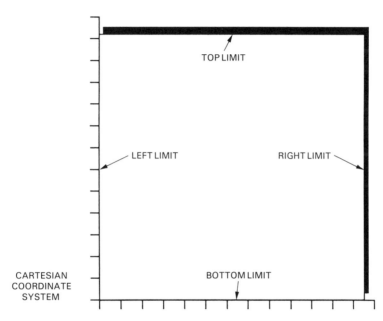

Fig. 10-9. Limits in AutoSketch define the left, right, bottom, and top edges of your drawing area, or "sheet," as measured by the Cartesian coordinate system. Create your drawing within the limits.

Obviously, a full-size bridge drawing is much larger than the computer's display screen. AutoSketch can hold full-size designs in memory. However, to see the drawing on screen, you can use the view option **Zoom Limits.** AutoSketch reduces the size of the drawing within the limits to fit on screen. Of course, the drawing shown on screen is not real size. That does not matter. At least you can see all of it. When you condense such a large drawing into a small space, not much detail is shown. When you need to draw fine detail, use **Zoom Box** to get a closer look.

Setting Limits

To set limits, select the **Settings** menu and **Limits** command. AutoSketch displays the **Drawing Limits** dialogue box. Move your pointer into each box and enter the left, bottom, right, and top borders of your "sheet," Fig. 10-10. Pick the *OK* box at the bottom when finished entering limits.

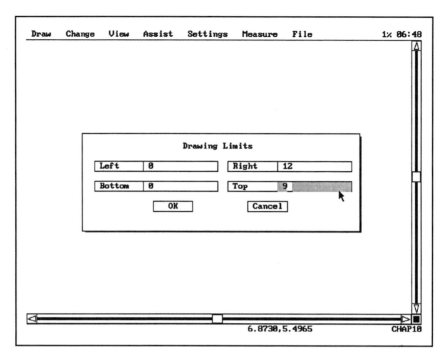

Fig. 10-10. The Drawing Limits dialogue box.

Rules for Setting Limits. You can make the limits as large or small as you wish. However, there are three general rules.

1. Set the left and bottom limits to 0. This places the lower-left corner of your drawing area at the 0,0 coordinate (origin) of the coordinate system. This way, you can always measure coordinate positions from the lower-left corner of your "sheet."

2. Set the right and top limits large enough to contain the entire drawing. Look at the limits for the bridge drawing in Fig. 10-11. Remember, you will be drawing in full-size units. This is where a sketch is important. Know beforehand the amount of space you will need to construct the drawing.

3. After setting limits, draw a border line .5 units in from the extents of the drawing area. This lets you see the size of your "sheet."

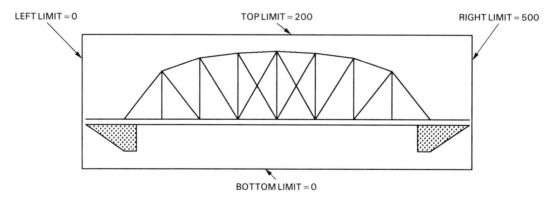

Fig. 10-11. Anticipate how large your design will be. Then set the right and top limits large enough. Here, a bridge design requires a right limit in excess of 500 feet.

Sometimes, you may not know the maximum drawing area you will need. In these situations, first estimate the size and set the limits. If you need more space, simply reset the limits. Always select the **Zoom Limits** command after resetting the limits to display the new drawing area. AutoSketch will give you a "birds-eye" view and show you how much room you have.

Setting Limits for Scaled Plots

When it is time to plot the drawing, AutoSketch has a plot scale command to make the drawing fit on standard paper sheet sizes. In Chapter 14, you will learn how to select a specific scale at plot time. However, there are certain limit values that let you plot the drawing at an exact scale to fit the various sheet sizes. If you plan to plot a hardcopy, set the limits proportional to the paper size. For example, suppose you set limits for a drawing area 80 units wide and 60 high. Choosing a plot scale of .25 will fit the drawing on a C-size sheet of paper. By setting the limits properly, you can choose a specific scale to fit the drawing on a standard sheet size. The procedure is:

- First determine the final scale of the drawing you want. For example, architectural drawings are often .25 = 1. Mechanical drawings are often .5 = 1.
- Divide the paper width by the scale to find the right limit.
- Divide the paper height by the scale to find the top limit.
  Here are the maximum limits for plotting a drawing .25 scale on a D-size sheet of paper.
    Paper size: C (34 x 22)
    Final scale: .25
    Right limit: 34 divided by .25 = 136
    Top limit: 22 divided by .25 = 88

If you later find that the limits are not large enough to contain your drawing, reset them based on a new scale. Several combinations of limits and plot scale values to fit certain sheet sizes are shown in Fig. 10-12.

	SELECTED SHEET SIZE	USABLE AREA ON SHEET	DESIRED PLOT SCALE PLOT UNIT = DRAWING UNITS	RIGHT, TOP LIMITS
Mechanical	11 x 8 1/2 A	9 x 7	2' = 1'' 3/4'' = 1'' 1/2'' = 1'' 1/4'' = 1''	4.5,3.5 12,9.33 18,14 36,28
	17 x 11 B	15 x 10	2' = 1'' 3/4'' = 1'' 1/2'' = 1'' 1/4'' = 1''	7.5,5 20,13.33 30,20 60,40
	22 x 17 C	20 x 15	2' = 1'' 3/4'' = 1'' 1/2'' = 1'' 1/4'' = 1''	10,7.5 26.67,20 40,30 80,60
	34 x 22 D	32 x 20	2' = 1'' 3/4'' = 1'' 1/2'' = 1'' 1/4'' = 1''	16,10 42.67,26.67 64,40 128,80
	44 x 34 E	42 x 32	2' = 1'' 3/4'' = 1'' 1/2'' = 1'' 1/4'' = 1''	21,16 56,42.67 84,64 168,128

Fig. 10-12. The limits you set are closely related to the paper size and scale you choose to plot the drawing.

	SELECTED SHEET SIZE	USABLE AREA ON SHEET	DESIRED PLOT SCALE PLOT UNIT = DRAWING UNITS	RIGHT, TOP LIMITS
Architectural	12 x 9 A	10 x 8	1″ = 1′-0″ 1/2″ = 1′-0″ 1/4″ = 1′-0″ 1/8″ = 1′-0″	10,8 20,16 40,32 80,64
	18 x 12 B	16 x 11	1″ = 1′-0″ 1/2″ = 1′-0″ 1/4″ = 1′-0″ 1/8″ = 1′-0″	16,11 32,22 64,44 128,88
	24 x 18 C	26 x 16	1″ = 1′-0″ 1/2″ = 1′-0″ 1/4″ = 1′-0″ 1/8″ = 1′-0″	26,16 52,32 104,64 208,128
	36 x 24 D	34 x 22	1″ = 1′-0″ 1/2″ = 1′-0″ 1/4″ = 1′-0″ 1/8″ = 1′-0″	34,22 68,44 136,88 272,176
	48 x 36 E	46 x 34	1″ = 1′-0″ 1/2″ = 1′-0″ 1/4″ = 1′-0″ 1/8″ = 1′-0″	46,34 92,68 184,136 368,272
Metric	279 mm x 216 mm A	229 mm x 178 mm	1 mm = 5 mm 1 mm = 10 mm 1 mm = 20 mm 10 mm = 1 mm	1145,890 2290,1780 4580,3560 22.917.8
	432 mm x 279 mm B	381 mm x 254 mm	1 mm = 5 mm 1 mm = 10 mm 1 mm = 20 mm 10 mm = 1 mm	1905,1270 3810,2540 7620,5080 38.125.4
	559 mm x 432 mm C	508 mm x 381 mm	1 mm = 5 mm 1 mm = 10 mm 1 mm = 20 mm 10 mm = 1 mm	2540,1905 5080,3810 10160,7620 50.8,38.1
	864 mm x 559 mm D	813 mm x 508 mm	1 mm = 5 mm 1 mm = 10 mm 1 mm = 20 mm 10 mm = 1 mm	4065,2540 8130,5080 16260,10160 81.3,50.8
	1118 mm x 864 mm E	1067 mm x 813 mm	1 mm = 5 mm 1 mm = 10 mm 1 mm = 20 mm 10 mm = 1 mm	5335,4065 10670,8130 21340,16260 106.781.3

Fig. 10-12. Continued

NOTE: On most plotters, the usable area on which you can plot is somewhat less than the sheet size, typically 90 percent. This is because the plotter cannot reach all the way to the edge. Substitute the usable area when figuring your limits. This information is usually found in the operator's manual of your hardcopy device. Typical usable area is given in Fig. 10-12. You can also find the area by trial and error.

SORTING INFORMATION WITH LAYERS

In manual drafting, different parts of a design are often drawn on separate sheets of vellum or film. For example, suppose you were drawing a house plan. The floor plan might be drawn on one sheet, the foundation plan on another, and the electrical plan on still another. You could stack any or all of the sheets together to see the needed information. Placing similar details on the same layer helps organize your drawing.

AutoSketch has 10 layers that work much the same way. Each *layer* is like a clear sheet of plastic on which you can draw, Fig. 10-13. Objects you add to the drawing are assigned to the *current layer*. You can draw on only one layer at a time, and there is no limit to the number of entities that can be included on any one layer.

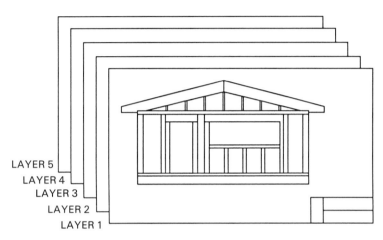

Fig. 10-13. Each of 10 layers is like a clear sheet of plastic on which you draw. The layers are always in perfect alignment.

You can display any one or all of the layers at the same time. Turn off layers that contain unneeded information. For example, suppose you were drawing a house plan. The floor plan might be drawn on one layer, the foundation plan on another, and the electrical plan on another. You might turn off the layer having the foundation plan to see only the floor and electrical plans.

Setting and Displaying Layers

To set the current and visible layers, select the **Settings** menu and **Layer** command. The **Layer Status** dialogue box appears, Fig. 10-14. When you begin a drawing, the default current layer is 1. When you wish to draw on a different layer, pick the box opposite the layer number you want to draw on.

Even though you draw on only one layer at a time, any one or all of the layers may be displayed. Objects on a layer not displayed are still there, just hidden. They are not affected by editing commands, nor are they plotted. To make layers visible or invisible, pick the box under *Visible* next to the layer you want displayed.

Moving Objects to a New Layer

Objects drawn on one layer can be moved to another layer. For example, suppose you are making an architectural drawing and have added a sink to the floor plan layer. However, you should have placed the sink on the plumbing plan layer. Instead of erasing the sink from one layer and drawing it on another, set the current layer to the layer with the plumbing plan. Then, select the **Change Property** command and pick the sink to assign it the new layer.

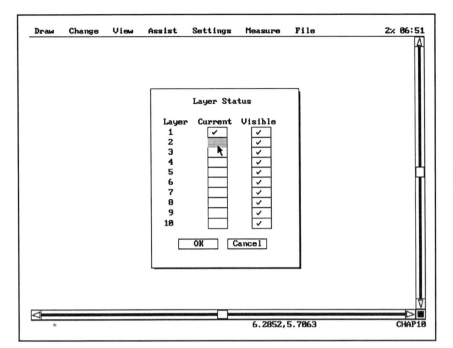

Fig. 10-14. The Layer Status dialogue box.

Layering Schemes

It is wise to establish standards for using layers. Some companies specify a *layering scheme* that determines what details are to be placed on which layer. A layering scheme helps you keep track of where different information resides, Fig. 10-15. Dimensions, object lines, title block and border, hidden and center lines, and specifications typically have their own layer. Other designers then know which layer to select to review or edit those details.

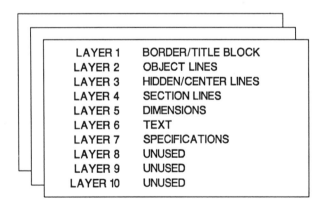

Fig. 10-15. A layering scheme dictates where information is placed.

TITLE BLOCKS

The *title block* is an area on the drawing that gives important information about the product and progress of the project. A typical title block is shown in Fig. 10-16. Any title block might include:

1. Part name.
2. Drawing number.

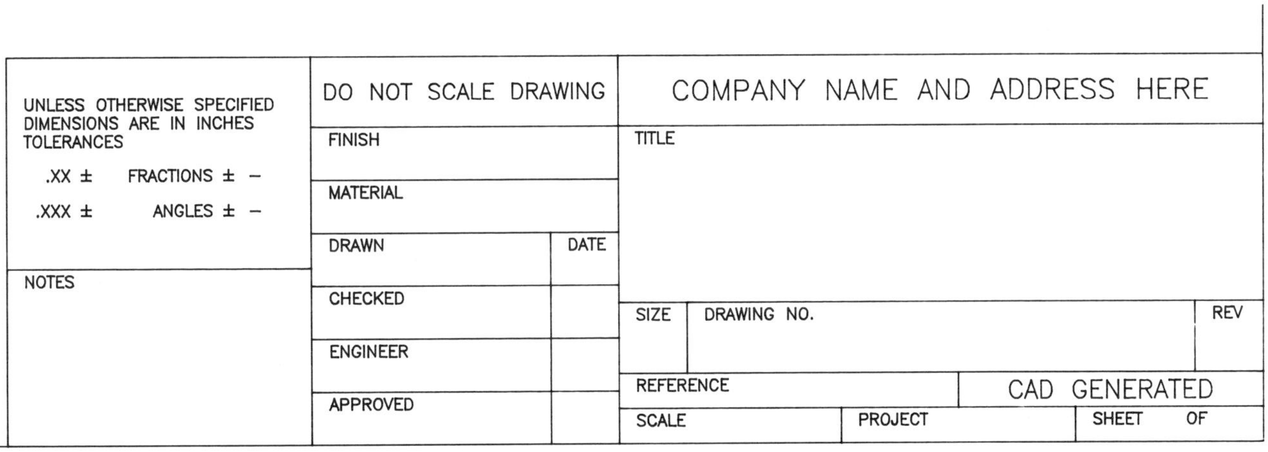

UNLESS OTHERWISE SPECIFIED DIMENSIONS ARE IN INCHES TOLERANCES	DO NOT SCALE DRAWING		COMPANY NAME AND ADDRESS HERE		
.XX ± FRACTIONS ± —	FINISH		TITLE		
.XXX ± ANGLES ± —	MATERIAL				
	DRAWN	DATE			
NOTES	CHECKED		SIZE	DRAWING NO.	REV
	ENGINEER				
	APPROVED		REFERENCE	CAD GENERATED	
			SCALE	PROJECT	SHEET OF

Fig. 10-16. Typical industry title block.

3. Scale of the drawing.
4. Material specifications and special treatment.
5. Company name and address.
6. Date of completion.
7. Revision dates.
8. General tolerances.
9. Names of the drafter, checker, and persons responsible for engineering, materials, and production approvals.

Every drawing, from your first AutoSketch problem to a complex industrial print, should have a title block. The style of the title block varies between companies. Generally, it is found in the lower-right corner or along the bottom of the print. A standard style and size of title block is shown in Fig. 10-17.

Companies using CAD systems frequently have a standard title block saved as a drawing by itself, or as part of a prototype drawing. It contains the labels like "Drafter:" and "Part name:" but leaves spaces to add the information. You use this "model" drawing to begin a new drawing. After adding graphics, text, and other information, save the drawing under a new name. Most often, drawings are saved with names that follow the drawing or product number.

DEVELOPING PROTOTYPE DRAWINGS

A manual drafter begins a drawing with a sheet of paper, vellum, or film. The media is typically preprinted with a border line, title block, and may be labeled with the company

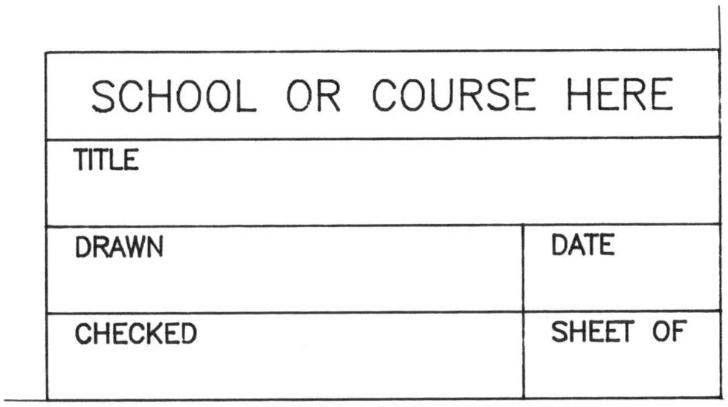

SCHOOL OR COURSE HERE	
TITLE	
DRAWN	DATE
CHECKED	SHEET OF

Fig. 10-17. Standard size and format title block you might choose. (It is printed here full size for you to measure.)

name, address, and other headings. The drafter lays down the sheet, fills in the title block, and begins the drawing. The printed sheet of paper is really a starting point, or prototype, to which the drafter adds the drawing.

Prototypes can also be developed in computer-aided drafting. A *prototype drawing* is a drawing file with setup steps already performed. The drawing might also contain a border and title block. The drafter calls up the prototype drawing file, adds some information, and saves the drawing under a new name using the **Save as** command. The original prototype drawing file is left unchanged. See Fig. 10-18.

Prototype drawings save much time since the drafter does not have to proceed through drawing setup. A number of prototypes can be set up for each drafting situation and every paper size. Also, having all drafters use the same prototypes assures that drawings conform to specific standards.

Name prototype drawings according to the parameters. For example, a B-size mechanical prototype might be named MPROTOB, where "M" stands for mechanical. A C-size architectural prototype might be named APROTOC.

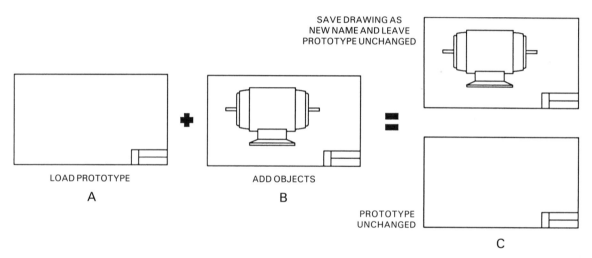

Fig. 10-18. Using a prototype. A–Call up the prototype drawing file on screen. B–Add your information. C–Save the modified drawing file under a new name, leaving the prototype unchanged.

DRAWING SHAPES EFFICIENTLY

Over time, you will become skilled with the drawing and editing functions of AutoSketch. You will learn that there are often several ways to draw a complex shape. When starting a new drawing, do not jump right into it. Instead, plan a strategy to construct the drawing efficiently. Although each design will present different problems, consider these important topics before drawing the first line.

Begin at Reference Points

It is best to begin a drawing at one key reference point. On your sketch, look for points from which other objects are measured or located. Usually, these points are the corners of rectangular objects and the centers of circular objects, Fig. 10-19. On mechanical drawings,

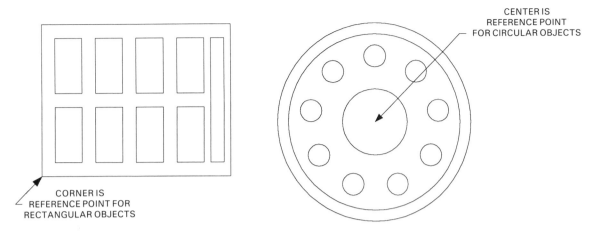

CENTER IS
REFERENCE POINT
FOR CIRCULAR OBJECTS

CORNER IS
REFERENCE POINT FOR
RECTANGULAR OBJECTS

Fig. 10-19. In most cases, start your drawing at a reference point, usually a corner or center.

the reference might be a machined surface or corner. On architectural drawings, features (doors, windows, etc.) are located from exterior walls.

Construct the Minimum Number of Objects

Rarely do you need to construct every object in the drawing. Many drawings have similar features that can be copied. Symmetrical designs can be mirrored. A design with circular patterns can be made using **Box Array** and **Ring Array** commands. Thus, you need only construct a few basic shapes. Then use editing techniques as the primary method to complete the drawing.

Plan Your Commands

You are not limited to using just a few commands. A drawing might require that you copy, mirror, *and* rotate one or several shapes to form a complex object. Before you begin, look at the design sketches. Determine which commands will work best to complete the drawing. Some CAD systems have more features than others. If you later work on a system other than AutoSketch, be aware that it may have more or less functions. This can affect how you approach a drawing.

Avoid Switching Properties Often

A drawing may contain many different linetypes and colors. Avoid constantly switching values for these properties as you develop the drawing. This consumes precious time. It is better to construct all shapes with the same color or linetype at the same time. You can also construct all shapes with solid, black lines. Then, use the **Change Properties** command to change the objects to the needed style.

SUMMARY

Most technical drawings are made to record a design. You might create drawings for products you invent. The final drawing is done after the designer works through a series of steps, called the design process. These steps include identifying the need, setting guidelines, gathering information, developing possible solutions, selecting a solution, and evaluating the solution. Whether you realize it or not, these steps are done each time you make a decision.

With a design in mind, you will probably sketch it first. Sketching is the quickest and easiest way to jot down your ideas. As you prepare to use AutoSketch, transfer you sketch to a plan sheet. Consider how you will construct the drawing with AutoSketch.

Once you have a refined sketch, start AutoSketch and proceed to set up the drawing file. This includes setting the color, linetype, limits, layers, grid spacing, snap spacing, attach modes, and text features. Of these options, the limits and layers were first introduced in this chapter. The limits define the edges of your drawing area. Layers allow you to separate objects on different "levels" to help organize your drawing. All setup settings could already be stored in a prototype drawing. If so, simply call up the prototype and begin.

As you draw, remember the tips to help you create drawings quickly. Remember, with a computer you should never have to draw the same shape twice. Also, add a title block to the drawing to give important information about you and the design. The title block could already have been placed in the prototype drawing. This saves you time.

NEW TERMS

Design process, brainstorming, feedback, drawing plan sheet, drawing setup, limits, **Limits** command, layer, **Layer** command, current layer, layering scheme, prototype drawing, title block.

REVIEW QUESTIONS

Write your answers on a separate sheet of paper. Do not write in this book.
1. List the six steps of the design process.
2. The design process begins when you realize that you have a _____ or _____.
3. Also called design criteria, _____ set the limits within which you develop solutions.
4. To develop possible solutions, what should you do to increase your knowledge on the subject?
5. List four sources other than those given in the text that you might reference for design information.
6. A group that is thinking of many ideas, without throwing out any unusual ideas, is doing what?
7. At what stage of the design process do you usually begin making sketches?
8. Many times, making minor changes to a(n) _____ will solve your design problem.
9. Why might the best solution to your design problem not be acceptable?
10. Often, the final solution is a _____ between the most ideal and the most practical ideas.
11. The design process cycles so that _____ helps refine the product.
12. List three suggestions that will help you sketch ideas better.
13. The two main parts of a drawing plan sheet are the _____ and _____.
14. Your first steps after loading AutoSketch, known as _____, involve preparing the drawing file before adding objects.
15. List the values you would enter during drawing setup.
16. _____ define the left, right, bottom, and top edges of your drawing area.

17. Set your limits large enough so that you can draw using _____ measurements.
18. To fit a very large drawing on screen, use the _____ command. It reduces the size of the drawing within the limits to fit on screen.
19. You can place a ruler against your display screen and accurately trace the size of objects. True or false?
20. It is best to set your left and bottom limits at _____. This makes the lower-left corner of your drawing area align with the origin or the Cartesian coordinate system.
21. What limits would you need to set to fit a drawing at half scale (.5 = 1) on a B-size mechanical sheet? Use the chart in the text.
22. Suppose you have a boat design that is 80 feet wide and 60 feet tall. You have made each unit of your drawing equal to 1 foot. What scale would allow this design to fit on a C-size mechanical sheet?
23. Objects you add to the drawing are assigned to the _____ layer.
24. Only the current layer can be visible. True or false?
25. The command used to set the current and visible layers is _____, found in the _____ menu.
26. A _____ is a drawing file with drawing setup steps already performed. It may even have a border and title block.
27. The _____ is a chart on the drawing that gives important information about the product and project.
28. Explain how AutoSketch can save you much time when constructing drawings.
29. What factor most influences how large you set the drawing area with the **Limits** command?
30. Avoid constantly switching values for _____ as you develop the drawing.

ACTIVITIES

1-10. Practice your sketching skills by reproducing each of these images. Sketch them about the same size, and make sure that you keep the shapes proportional.

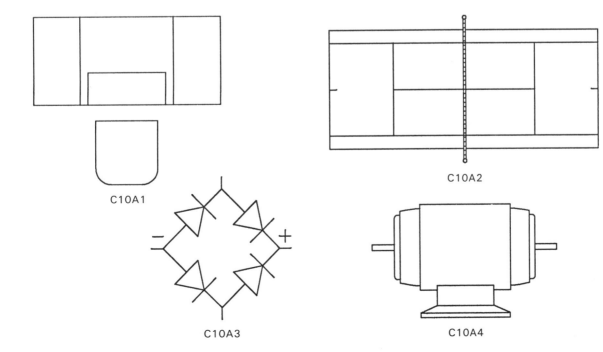

C10A1

C10A2

C10A3

C10A4

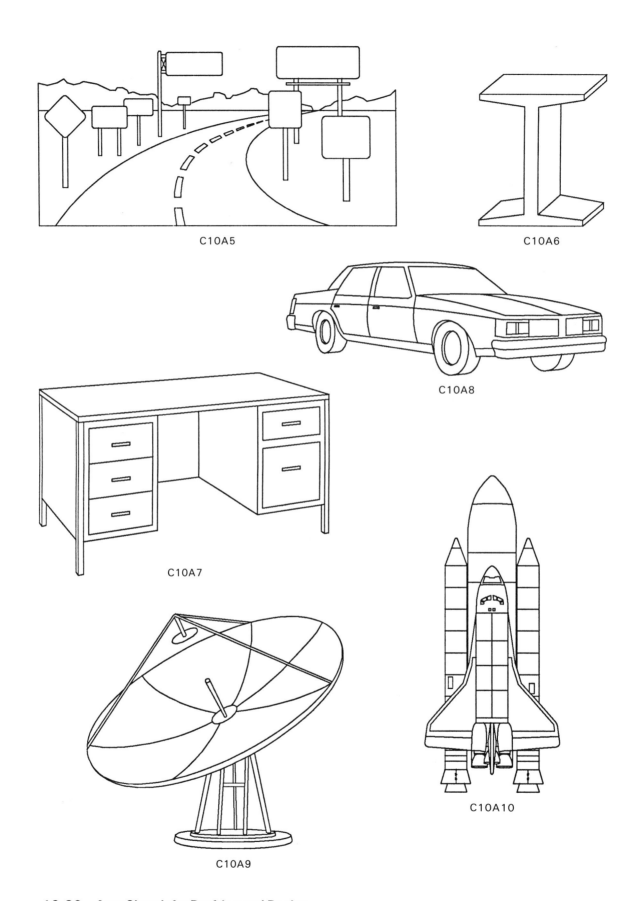

C10A5

C10A6

C10A8

C10A7

C10A9

C10A10

11-12. Practice your sketching skills by reproducing each of these drawings. Use graph paper and make each square equal to .25 units. Sketch dimensions, following the same style shown, on a sheet of tracing paper placed over the drawing. Label the tracing paper as "Layer 2."

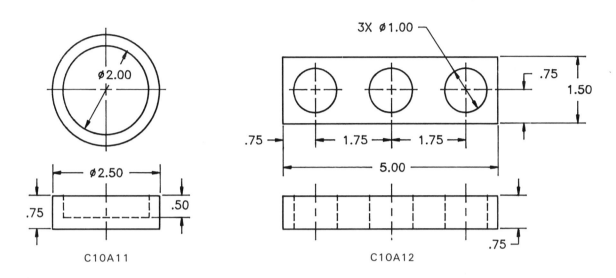

13. Develop a drawing plan sheet like that shown in the text. It should fit an 8 1/2 x 11 inch sheet of paper. Have your instructor plot it or read Chapter 14 to make a plot yourself. Make 10 photocopies of the plot to have handy when you need them. Save your planning sheet as C10A13, and as PLANSHET.

14. Set up a drawing with the following values. Save the completed drawing as C10A14.
    Drawing color: Black
    Drawing linetype: Solid
    Limits (A-size sheet)
      Left: 0
      Bottom: 0
      Right: 9
      Top: 7
    Layers
      Current: 1
      Visible: 1,2,3,4,5
    Grid spacing: .25
    Snap spacing: .125
    Attach modes: Endpoint, Midpoint, Center
    Pick spacing: 2
    Text features
      Font: ROMANS
      Height: .18
      Width: 1
      Obliquing angle: 0
      Angle: 0
      Justification: Left

15. Develop eight prototype drawings for A-, B-, C-, and D-size drawing areas (sheets) in both mechanical and architectural formats. Plan for the drawing to be plotted full size based on the usable area given in the chart in this chapter. Draw a border line .5 units in from the limits of the drawing area. Set the values (other than limits) using those given in Activity 14. Place a title block the same as Fig. 10-17 in the lower-right corner of each prototype. Save the mechanical prototypes as MPROTOA, MPROTOB, MPROTOC, and MPROTOD. Save the architectural prototypes as APROTOA, APROTOB, APROTOC, and APROTOD.

16-17. Complete drawing plan sheets for Activities 11 and 12 of this chapter. Then, for each activity recall the prototype drawing MPROTOB from Activity 15 and create the drawing using the procedure you recorded on the plan sheet. Do not add dimensions. Save the drawings as C10A16 and C10A17. Make sure you use the **Save As** command to save the drawings so that the prototype drawing is left unchanged.

18-20. Gather pictures (magazine clippings, photographs, etc.) of products designed in industry. For three of the products, write down the problem or need you think the product solved. Also, write a brief list of information you feel may have been needed to develop the design.

Chapter 11

DRAFTING WITH AUTOSKETCH

After studying this chapter, you will be able to:
- Explain how multiview drawings are used to document an idea in mechanical drafting.
- Describe the meaning of "orthographic projection."
- Describe how a "glass box" is used to help develop a multiview drawing.
- Diagram the relationship of views for third-angle projection.
- Show how different linetypes and widths are used to indicate features in a view.
- Develop a simple multiview drawing.

Nearly ever industry creates drawings to explain and document ideas. In fact, can you think of an industry that does not use drawings? This chapter covers making drawings that help describe products to be manufactured, otherwise known as *mechanical drafting*. The drawings you develop will convey the size, shape, material, and other features of a design idea. When complete, mechanical drawings are plotted on paper, and may later be reproduced for distribution to people who will manufacture the product.

The graphics used to describe an object with CAD are no different than those developed with manual drafting tools. You must follow accepted drafting practices no matter which tools you choose. However, as you learned in Chapter 10, the *method* of creating the drawing can be different with CAD. With AutoSketch, you rely on editing commands and special techniques that help simplify the drawing process.

MULTIVIEW DRAWINGS

Every field of drafting has its own method to describe the product to be manufactured or constructed. In electronics drafting, a schematic is used to diagram circuit layouts. In architectural drafting, floor plans and exterior elevations show the design of a house, office, or other structure. In mechanical drafting, the main presentation style used to convey the design idea is called a multiview drawing.

When sketching an idea, you usually make it look three dimensional. This type of drawing is called a pictorial drawing, because it looks like a picture, Fig. 11-1. Unfortunately, pictorial drawings do not show the true size, shape, and relationship of features. Holes and curves appear oval, and edges may not be drawn true size. Although the drawing looks nice, it rarely gives enough information to manufacture the product.

A *multiview drawing* gives true shape and size by showing the object as viewed straight on from two to six different positions, Fig. 11-2. In these views, each face of the object appears

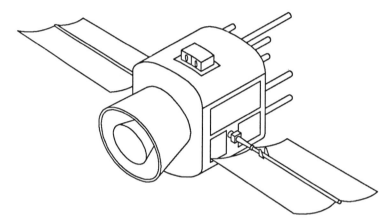

Fig. 11-1. A pictorial drawing gives a three-dimensional view of an object. However, the drawing does not provide true size and shape of the features.

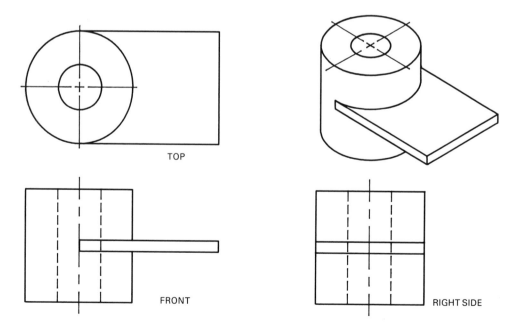

Fig. 11-2. This multiview drawing gives the three views needed to describe the object.

true size and shape. The views are developed through a process known as *orthographic projection*. Orthographic refers to right (90 degree) angles. Projection means to project images outward. Thus, orthographic projection means to project views of an object onto planes placed at 90 degree angles.

This may all sound somewhat confusing. There is an easier way to learn orthographic projection. It begins by imagining the object as if it were inside a glass box.

The Glass Box

The *glass box* is a technique many drafters use to develop multiview drawings. Imagine the object to design as if it were placed inside a glass box, Fig. 11-3. When you look directly through the front of the box, you see the front view of the object. Looking through the side of the box, you see the object's side. In the same manner, by looking through the top of the box, you see the top of the object. You might also look through the back, bottom, and other side to see these views.

Fig. 11-3. To help visualize the views of a multiview drawing, imagine that the object is placed inside a glass box.

Now, imagine that you projected, or painted, each of the views seen onto the surface of the glass, Fig. 11-4. Each side of the box becomes a *projection plane*, because you are projecting images on it. Looking at the six planes, you see views showing the front, top, sides, bottom, and back of the object. By unfolding the glass box (the projection planes), the views fold out next to each other in an orderly manner, Fig. 11-5. You have just created a multiview drawing.

Most often, two or three views are sufficient to describe an object. These views are the front, top, and side. However, more views are needed if you find that three views fail to totally describe the object.

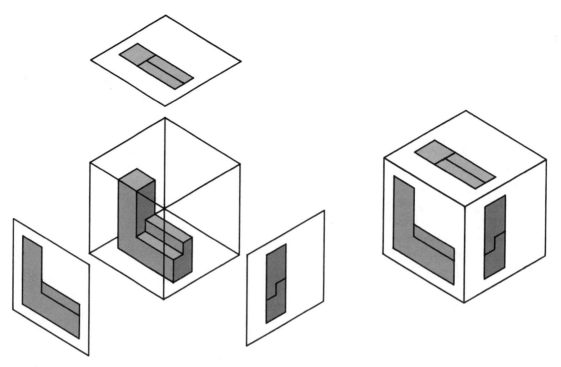

Fig. 11-4. By painting the image seen on each face of the glass box, you ''project'' the views—front, sides, top, bottom, and back.

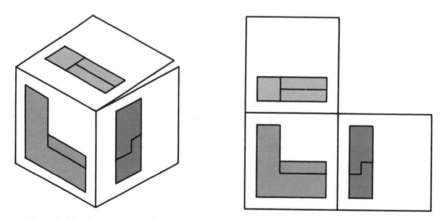

Fig. 11-5. After you project the views, ''unfold'' the glass box to position the views into a multiview drawing.

Sketching Your Ideas

Obviously, you cannot place a glass box around a product idea you might have. Thus, it may be difficult to think of each of the views. To help you, prepare a sketch of your idea. Sketch the approximate size and shape of the object to be drawn. Show the outlines and estimated dimensions of the object. If you are a drafter, this sketch may have been handed to you by an engineer. You can then sketch a multiview drawing of the design.

Some drafters are able to visualize (picture) an object and do not use a sketch. However, a sketch is a wise choice in both manual and computer-aided drafting. It becomes a useful document for showing your idea to other designers for review. Then use the sketch to select how you lay out the multiview drawing. Sketching was discussed in Chapter 10.

Relationship of Views

The purpose of a drawing is to communicate information. To do so, you must place the views in an orderly fashion. Each view should align with adjacent views. This makes it easier to look from one view to the next and visualize the shape. Also, the relationship of views is very important. Each view must be in a position that can be understood by another person "reading" the drawing. The relationship of the views is different between the United States and Europe.

Third-angle projection. United States drafting practices advise *third-angle projection*. The relationship of the views is shown in Fig. 11-6. The front view is the central view. The left side view is on the left of the front view, and the right side view is on the right. The top view is above and the bottom view is below the front view. The rear view, if needed, is shown beside the left side view. Third-angle projection is preferred for purposes of this text. The International Standards Organization (ISO) symbol that appears in the title block of drawings using third-angle projection is shown in Fig. 11-6.

First-angle projection. European standards advise *first-angle projection*. The relationship of the views is shown in Fig. 11-7. The front view is once again the central view. However, the projection technique for the remaining views creates "shadow" images. The left side view is on the right. The right side view is on the left. In a similar manner, the top view is below and the bottom view is above the front. The rear view is shown beside the right side view. The ISO symbol that appears in the title block of drawings using first-angle projection is shown in Fig. 11-7.

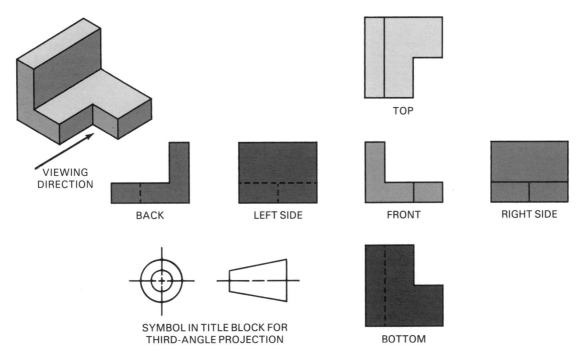

Fig. 11-6. Location of views for third-angle projection. Note the symbol that often appears in the title block to indicate that this projection technique was used.

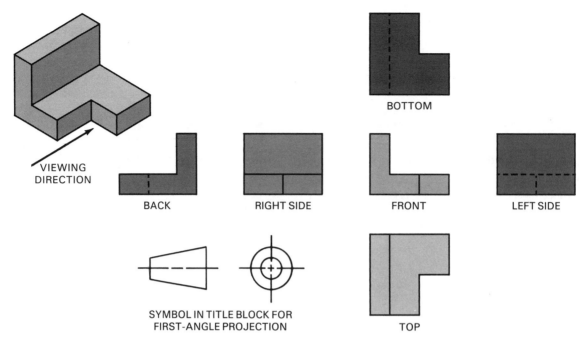

Fig. 11-7. Location of views for first-angle projection. Also note the symbol that often appears in the title block.

VIEWING DIRECTION

BACK

RIGHT SIDE

FRONT

LEFT SIDE

BOTTOM

SYMBOL IN TITLE BLOCK FOR FIRST-ANGLE PROJECTION

TOP

Selecting Views to Draw

In all cases, you should choose the fewest number of views that will still fully describe the object. For many parts, you will need three views. They describe the part's shape, features, and also provide the width, height, and depth. Too many views are unnecessary and can clutter the drawing.

Use your pictorial sketch to decide which side of your object should be the front view. There are several key rules to consider. The front view normally should be one or more of the following:

1. The side which best shows the overall shape of the object.
2. The side of the object with the most detail.
3. The part's normal position in use.
4. The position of the object you are most likely to see in real life.
5. The view which will have the fewest hidden edges.
6. The view having the longest dimension.
7. The most stable position of the product.
8. Also, when possible, place the object with the most surfaces parallel to the projection planes.

Once you have selected the front view and other views to draw, sketch a multiview drawing before using AutoSketch. Check to see whether one, two, three, or more views are needed to describe the object completely. For most products you design at home or in school, three views are required.

Two-view drawings. Simple parts, such as basic cylindrical objects, can be drawn with just two views. Notice the diameter dimension given to show the size of the cylinder, Fig. 11-8. The diameter symbol appears before diameter dimensions. A top view for this item would only repeat what was drawn in the front view.

One-view drawings. At times, an object can be fully described using one view. A product with little depth, such as a gasket or flat sheet metal design, requires only one view. The thickness is given as a note, Fig. 11-9. This is called a one-view drawing, rather than a multiview.

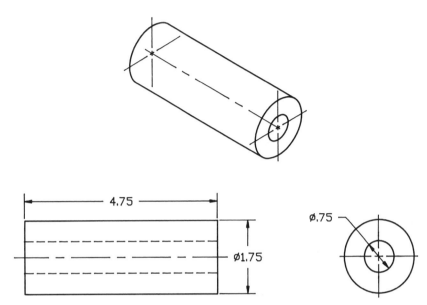

Fig. 11-8. Simple parts can often be described with just two views. Here, a cylinder needs only two views. A top view would merely repeat the front view.

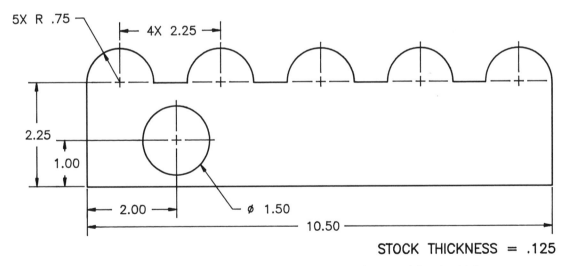

Fig. 11-9. This gasket can be described with one view, and a note giving the thickness.

SHOWING FEATURES IN MECHANICAL DRAWINGS

In any view, there can be both visible and hidden edges of the object. A complex object may have many hidden edges. For example, Fig. 11-10 shows an object with several holes. In

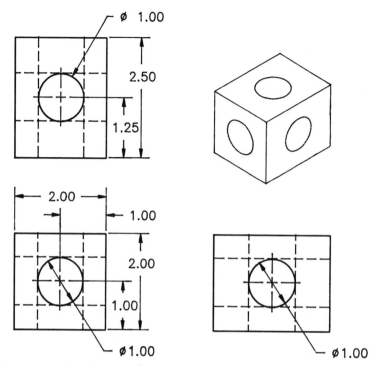

Fig. 11-10. This multiview drawing describes an object with three holes. In each of the views, the holes appear in true size and shape. Also, in each view the edges of the holes are shown with hidden lines. Center lines show the centers of the holes.

each view, you can see one hole, but the other two cannot be seen. Thus, hidden lines (dashed lines) are placed in the view to indicate the location of the hidden holes.

A drawing may contain many types of lines to represent centers, breaks, cutaways, and other details. To help show features, each line on a technical drawing has a certain meaning. A thick, solid line typically defines the visible edge of a shape. A thin, dashed line generally depicts a hidden edge of an object. A pattern of short and long dashes indicates the center of a hole. The American National Standards Institute (ANSI) has set guidelines, call the *alphabet of lines,* that assign meanings to various line patterns and widths. See Fig. 11-11. With this standard each drafter can "read," or interpret, the drawing the same way. Thick lines are .030 to .038 in. (0.5 to 0.8 mm) wide. Thin lines are between .015 and .022 in. (0.3 and 0.5 mm) wide.

Showing Visible Features in a View

Object lines show edges and contours of the object that are visible in that view. Object lines are drawn solid and thick so that they stand out. They should clearly contrast with other lines on the drawing.

Make all object lines the same color. You can use the **Polyline** command of Version 3.0 to draw wide lines and arcs. Remember that AutoSketch Version 2.0 does not support multiple line widths. However, because a pen plotter selects the pen based on the object's color, you can use different pen widths in the plotter. This text recommends that you choose black for object lines. When plotting the drawing, select pens that follow the standard line widths prescribed by ANSI, your school, or company.

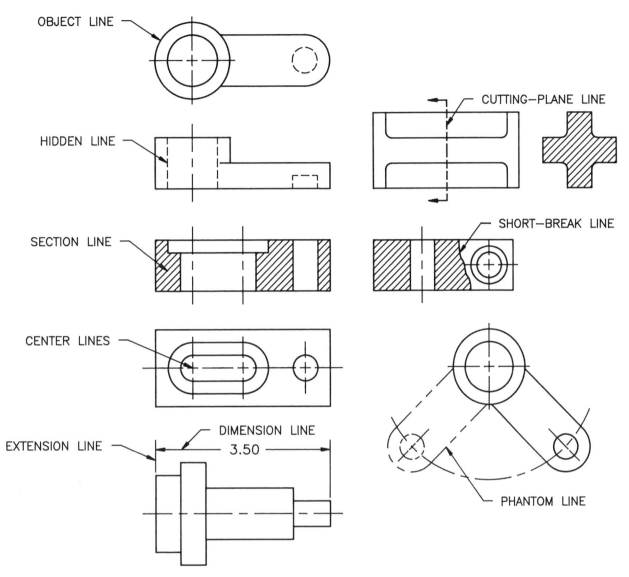

Fig. 11-11. The alphabet of lines gives meaning to various combinations of linetypes and line widths.

Showing Hidden Features in a View

Hidden lines show edges of the object that are not visible in a view. Hidden lines are drawn with a dashed linetype, Fig. 11-12. A hidden edge includes the circumference of a hole that passes through an object.

With AutoSketch, select the *Hidden* linetype in the **Drawing Line Type** dialogue box. You should make hidden lines a different color. This text suggests that you choose yellow for hidden lines.

Showing Centers and Symmetry

Center lines shows the centers of holes, cylindrical objects, and symmetrical objects. Along an object's length, a center line notes the axis extending lengthwise through the object's center. In an end view, center lines cross to show the center, Fig. 11-13.

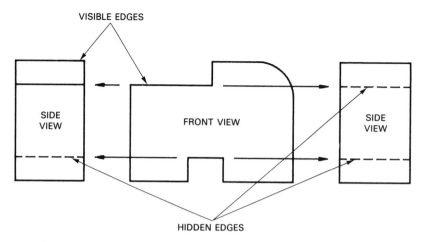

Fig. 11-12. Hidden lines indicate edges that are hidden in the view.

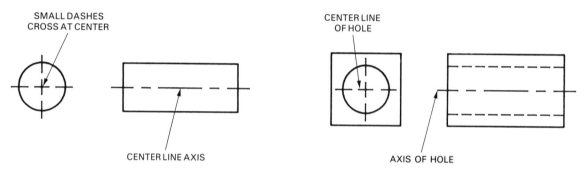

Fig. 11-13. Center lines mark the center of symmetrical objects, and the centers of circles.

Select the *Center* linetype from the **Drawing Line Type** dialogue box. Also select a different color from the **Drawing Color** dialogue box. This text suggests that you choose cyan, or light blue, for center lines.

Precedence of Lines

There are times when two or more linetypes coincide on a drawing. The rule that decides whether to draw an object line, hidden lines, or center line is called the *precedence of lines*. The order is object lines, followed by hidden lines, and then center lines. For example, if a hidden line coincides with an object line, draw the object line. If a center line coincides with a hidden line, draw the hidden line.

Showing other Features

There are more lines to show other features of a part. Many of these are covered in later chapters. A *cutting-plane line* designates where an imaginary cut occurred. *Section lines* indicate surfaces in a section view where material was "cut away" to show interior detail. *Long-break lines* are used to shorten the view of a long part. *Short-break lines* are used in a single view to show where material was "cut away." An assortment of *dimensioning lines* are used to show size and location of features on an object. *Phantom lines* show the alternate positions of moving parts.

DEVELOPING A MULTIVIEW DRAWING

Once you have chosen the views to draw, sketch a multiview drawing before using Auto-Sketch. Check to see whether one, two, three, or more views are needed to describe the object completely. Also, add in hidden and center lines on your sketch. Finally, add dimensions. See Fig. 11-14. This planning step is important when drafting with CAD. The sketch and dimensions help you set up the drawing or select a prototype. Also, your drawing session with CAD is more productive because the sketched views serve as a reference.

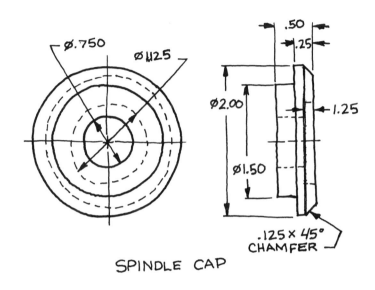

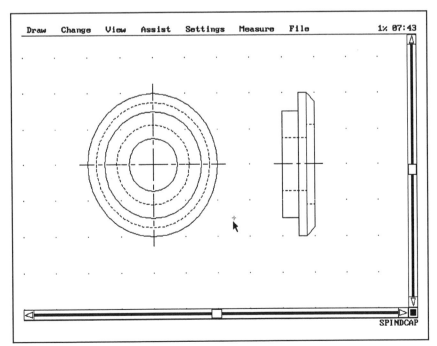

Fig. 11-14. After sketching a multiview drawing, add dimensions. Then create the CAD drawing.

Determining Drawing Area Required

Chapter 10 discussed how to set the size of your drawing area using the **Limits** command. To determine the area you need, calculate the space required by the drawing. Consider the drawing itself plus dimensions, notes, a border, and title block. It is important that you allow ample space for these items. Of course, you can always reset the limits. However, if you start a prototype with a predrawn border and title block, resetting the limits causes problems. It is better to get it right the first time.

The space for the views in a simple three-view drawing is calculated using the height, width, and depth of the object. Also, leave space between and around the views. A general rule for simple drawings is to allow 1 to 2 inches between and around views. However, more complex drawings require space for details, auxiliary views, section views, and specifications. It is better to have too much room rather than not enough.

Fig. 11-15 shows how to calculate the horizontal and vertical drawing area needed for the three-view drawing. The horizontal distance is the sum of the object's width and depth, plus space between views. The vertical distance is the sum of the height and depth, plus space between views. With these measurements, you can select a prototype or proceed with drawing setup. Remember that adding a revisions schedule, bill of materials, dimensioning table, or other information later will further increase the drawing area needed.

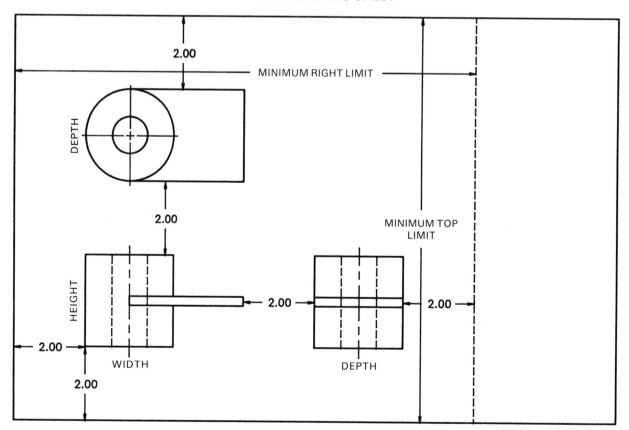

B—SIZE DRAWING SHEET

Fig. 11-15. When calculating the required drawing area, take into account the height, width, and depth of the object, and leave 1 to 2 inches between views.

Drawing Setup or Prototype

Once the planning is complete, proceed with your drawing session by starting AutoSketch. Load the proper size prototype, if one is available, using the **Open** command in the **File** menu. Prototypes should have been developed in activities of Chapter 10. The drawing in Fig. 11-15 would require a B-size prototype.

If no prototype is available, or the design is too large for any prototype, proceed through drawing setup. Enter the limits and text features. Make sure the linetype and color are set. Set your Attach modes and Grid and Snap spacing. Turn on the Ortho mode if it will be needed. Set the layer on which you will draw. Also, draw a title block and fill in the information. You might draw a border .5 in. (13 mm) in from the limits.

Laying Out Views

When finished with drawing setup, you are ready to add objects to the drawing. Because of the planning steps taken thus far, the task of laying out the views should be easy. Use Snap and Attach when possible to locate your objects precisely. In most cases, it is best to draw each linetype and color at one time. This prevents having to switch between linetypes and colors while drawing one view. Another common construction method is to draw the views using one linetype and color. Then, change the colors and linetypes later.

Begin with the front view, about 2 inches to the right and above the lower-left corner of your border. Draw object lines of the front view. Then add the top and side views. You might choose change the color and linetype when adding hidden lines. Finally, in the example of Fig. 11-15, you need to add center lines. These locate the center of the hole in both views.

Spacing and Centering Views

There are two basic ways to space views. You can calculate the exact distance between views based on the number of views and size of the drawing area. The other method is to space the views approximately. This method is preferred by most CAD drafters. First, use a grid to make sure the views align. However, if the drawing looks crowded, space the views further apart using the **Move** command. You might need more space between them for dimensions or other information. Make sure the moved views still align.

Save the Drawing As...

If you have recalled a prototype, your drawing is currently held in memory under the prototype name. You need to select the **Save As** command from the **File** menu to save the drawing under its own name. Do not save the drawing under the prototype name. After saving the drawing, select **New** from the **File** menu to begin a new drawing or **Quit** to end your drawing session.

SUMMARY

Each field of drafting uses slightly different presentation styles for their drawings. Most give views of the building or product showing the different sides. In mechanical drafting, these views form a multiview drawing. Each view shows one face of the object in true size and shape.

A multiview drawing is made by projecting each view onto a projection plane. The planes can be thought of as the sides of a glass box. Once the views are projected, the "glass box" is unfolded to position the views. The arrangement of views follows third-angle projection in this text. Arrange your projection so that the front view meets one or more of the guidelines given in this chapter. Usually, three views are needed to fully describe the object.

When drawing views, use different linetypes and colors for unique features. For example, use thick, solid, black lines to show outlines and visible edges. Use thin, dashed, colored lines to show hidden features. Doing so will help other drafters "read" your drawing.

As you prepare to create a multiview drawing with AutoSketch, make a sketch of the drawing first. It helps you lay out the drawing area needed. It also helps you develop the views. You might choose to do this on a drawing plan sheet like that shown in Chapter 10.

Begin laying out the front view in the lower-left corner. As a general rule, draw the object lines of the views, and then proceed to add hidden, center, and other lines. You can also draw all lines in all views using one linetype and color and then change them to the proper linetype when complete. This prevents having to change linetypes often.Make sure the views align. If the drawing seems crowded, move the views apart. Hopefully, you have selected a prototype or set limits large enough to contain the drawing.

NEW TERMS

Mechanical drafting, multiview drawing, orthographic projection, glass box, projection plane, third-angle projection, first-angle projection, alphabet of lines, object lines, hidden lines, center lines.

REVIEW QUESTIONS

Write your answers on a separate sheet of paper. Do not write in this book.
1. In mechanical drafting, the main presentation style for making drawings is called a _____.
2. The graphics used to describe an object with CAD are different than those developed with manual drafting tools. True or false?
3. A sketch that is three dimensional is called a _____ drawing.
4. A multiview drawing gives true _____ and _____ of the item being designed.
5. How does the "glass box" technique of developing a multiview drawing help you visualize the six possible views?
6. Why is it a good idea to make a sketch before starting a CAD drawing?
7. In which projection method is the left side view on the left of the front view, and the right side view on the right?
8. Sketch the each ISO symbol that appears in the title block of drawings made by each projection method.
9. For most products, the multiview drawing will require at least _____ views, and possibly more auxiliary views.
10. List the factors to consider when choosing which side of the object will be placed as the front view.
11. When might you need only one view to describe a product?
12. The standard that assigns meaning to different styles and thicknesses of lines is called the _____.
13. What linetype and thickness is given to lines that show edges of the object that are not visible in a view?

14. When a center line and object line coincide, a(n) _____ should be drawn.
15. What top and right limits should you set for a three-view drawing of a rectangular object that is 5 inches high, 12 inches wide, and 2 inches deep? Leave 2 inches between and around views. Assume that your left and bottom limits are 0.
16. What size prototype would you choose to draw the object described in Question 15?

ACTIVITIES

Here is a mixture of drawing activities to develop your skills with developing multiview drawings. Save your AutoSketch drawings on your file disk, not on the program disk. Clear the previous drawing from screen and memory using **New** before completing each activity.

1-5. Develop each multiview drawing. Determine the drawing area required, and set limits or select a prototype developed in the activities of Chapter 10. Use the .25 grid spacing for size reference, but do not add dimension to your drawing. Place different linetypes on different layers. Also use the colors recommended in this text for the linetypes. Save the drawings as C11A?, replacing the question mark with the activity number.

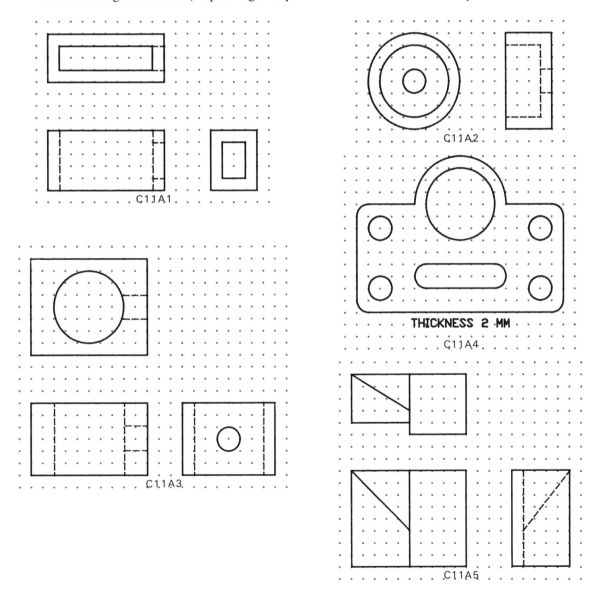

C11A1

C11A2

THICKNESS 2 MM

C11A4

C11A3

C11A5

6-10. Using the pictorial sketch, develop a multiview drawing. Draw only the number of views needed to describe the object. Set the drawing area, layers, and color following the directions given for Activities 1-5. Save the drawings as C11A?, replacing the question mark with the activity number.

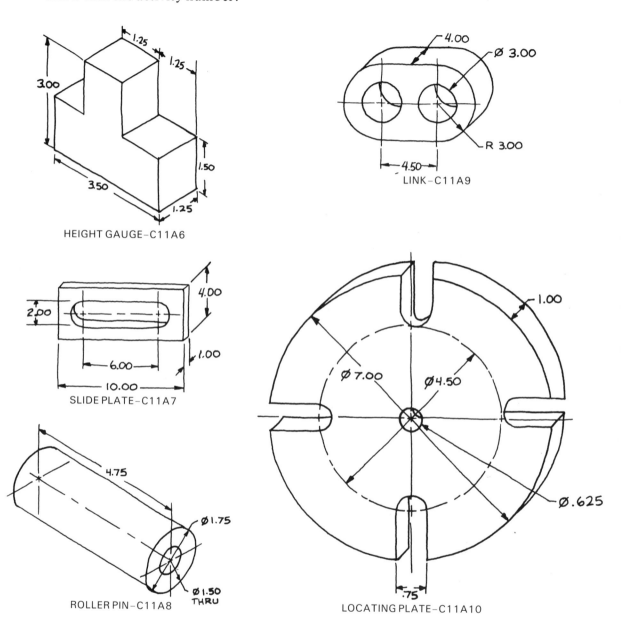

HEIGHT GAUGE–C11A6

LINK–C11A9

SLIDE PLATE–C11A7

ROLLER PIN–C11A8

LOCATING PLATE–C11A10

11-12. Choose two simple objects around you and develop multiview drawings to describe them. Make sure that your AutoSketch drawings conform to good drafting practice. Use the proper layers, colors, and linetypes. Save the drawings as C11A11 and C11A12.

Chapter 12

ADVANCED DRAWING CONSTRUCTIONS

After studying this chapter, you will be able to:
- Draw geometric constructions.
- Control the appearance of curves.
- Explain when section views are used to describe the interior features of a product.
- Describe the various types of section views.
- Create pictorial drawings using special grid settings.
- Draw various types of charts and graphs.

This chapter presents a mixture of drawing techniques you will use in mechanical and architecture drafting as well as technical illustration. It covers more advanced methods of constructing complex shapes, discusses ways to better manipulate curves, and shows methods to create pictorial drawings.

ADVANCED GEOMETRIC CONSTRUCTION

Chapter 1 mentioned that AutoSketch was not the most powerful drafting program. It was not meant to be. Thus, some of the more powerful commands found in high-end CAD systems, like AutoCAD, are not included. Yet, you can create any geometric construction that can be made with traditional drafting tools. You will find that the **Bearing** command and polar coordinates are very important to geometric construction with CAD.

Drawing Parallel Lines
Parallel lines are equal distance from each other along their length. To draw a line parallel to an existing line, Fig. 12-1, simply use the **Copy** command and polar coordinates. First, find the bearing of the existing line. Then, select the **Copy** command and pick any point on the drawing as the base point. When the "Copy To point:" prompt appears, enter a polar

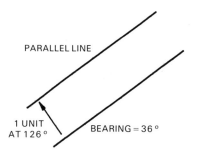

Fig. 12-1. You can use the Copy command to create parallel lines.

coordinate. Enter the distance value as the distance you want between the parallel lines. Enter the angle as the bearing plus 90 degrees.

Drawing Perpendicular Lines

A *perpendicular line* is a line placed at 90 degrees to another object. You can draw lines and polylines perpendicular to other objects, including arcs, circles, ellipses, and polyarcs using the Perpendicular Attach mode in AutoSketch Version 3.0. There are three methods, Fig. 12-2:

- **Drawing a perpendicular line from a point to an object.** Turn on the Attach mode Perpendicular. Pick the first endpoint of the line. Pick the object to which the line should be perpendicular.
- **Drawing a perpendicular line from an object to a point.** Turn on the Attach mode Perpendicular. Pick the object to which the line should be perpendicular. Pick the second endpoint of the line.
- **Drawing a perpendicular line between two objects.** Turn on the Attach mode Perpendicular. Pick the first object to which the line should be perpendicular. Pick the second object to which the line should be perpendicular.

If there is no possible perpendicular between two objects, or between a point and an object, a box appears stating "No perpendicular point found."

You can draw a line perpendicular to an existing line in AutoSketch Version 2.0 using the **Bearing** command and a polar coordinate. First, find the bearing of the existing line. Then,

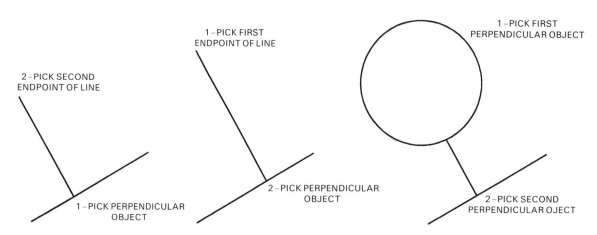

Fig. 12-2. Using the Attach mode Perpendicular to draw perpendicular lines.

start a line with one endpoint where you want the perpendicular line to begin. Next, enter the second endpoint using a polar coordinate. The angle value of the coordinate should be the existing line's bearing plus or minus 90 degrees.

Drawing Lines at an Angle to Existing Lines

Drawing a line at a angle to an existing line requires the **Bearing** command and a polar coordinate. First find the bearing of the existing line. Then, draw a line with the first endpoint where you want the angled line to begin. Enter the second endpoint using a polar coordinate. The distance value should be the length of the line. The angle value should be the existing line's bearing plus the angle value you want between the two lines. See Fig. 12-3.

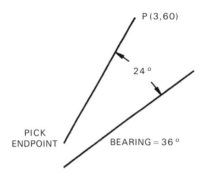

Fig. 12-3. The new line is placed at an angle plus the bearing of the existing line.

Drawing Regular Polygons

Regular polygons include triangles, squares, hexagons, and other closed polygons with equal length sides and internal angles. Drawing regular polygons is done using the **Polyline** or **Polygon** command and polar coordinates. Draw the first side as a horizontal line equal to the length of one polygon side. Then, using the Attach mode Endpoint and a polar coordinate, begin to draw the other sides. Each successive line should start at the endpoint of the previous line. The angle of each successive line should be increased by a value equal to 360 degrees divided by the number of sides. In Fig. 12-4, a hexagon is used as an example.

Sometimes, the first side of the regular polygon already exists. It may be part of another feature of the drawing. To draw a polygon with that line as the first side, measure the length

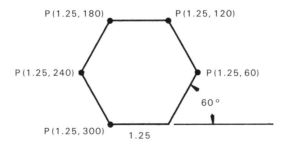

Fig. 12-4. A regular polygon consists of equal length lines placed at equal angles. Increase the angle each time by 360 degrees divided by the number of sides.

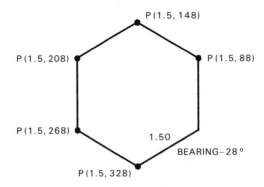

P (1.5, 148)

P (1.5, 208)   P (1.5, 88)

P (1.5, 268)

1.50

BEARING–28°

P (1.5, 328)

Fig. 12-5. If one side of the polygon already exists, and is at an angle, you
must increase the angle of each side 60 degrees plus the initial bearing.

and bearing of that line. Then, draw the other sides using the same side length. Increase the
angle to equal the internal angle value plus the bearing of the previous line. See Fig. 12-5.

Bisecting an Angle

To construct a line to bisect an angle, Fig. 12-6, first measure the bearing of one existing
line and the angle between both lines forming the angle. Then, draw the bisecting line's first
endpoint at the vertex of the angle using the Attach mode Endpoint. Enter the second
endpoint as a polar coordinate whose angle value is the bearing plus one-half the measured
angle.

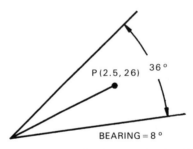

P (2.5, 26)   36°

BEARING = 8°

Fig. 12-6. The bisecting line is half the angle plus the bearing of the
lower line.

Drawing a Circle Between Two Points

To draw a circle that touches two points, Fig. 12-7, you must first draw a line between
those two points. Then select the **Circle** command and place the circle's center at the midpoint
of the new line. Be sure to use the Attach mode Midpoint. Next, place the point on the circle
at the place where it should touch. Your circle will attach to the two original points. Proceed
to erase the temporary line.

Drawing An Arc by Center Point

AutoSketch's arc command only lets you draw arcs using the start point, point on the arc,
and endpoint. To draw an arc using a center point, simply draw a circle rather than an arc.
Then break the unneeded portion out of the circle to make an arc. Remember to pick the
break points in a clockwise order.

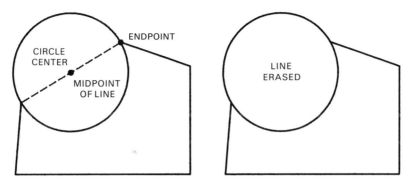

Fig. 12-7. The circle between two points is drawn using the midpoint of a temporary construction line.

Other Geometry for Technical Drawing

When you need to draw a geometric shape with AutoSketch, your best resources are traditional manual techniques. Refer to a traditional drafting textbook for geometric construction methods. Many of the steps can be enhanced using AutoSketch's ability to measure length, bearing, angle, coordinates, and other values.

WORKING WITH POLYLINES

Polylines can be used for a variety of purposes. You can draw wide lines filled with solid color, a pattern, or nothing at all. However, a polyline is not always a straight-line segment. It can be a combination of straight and arced segments. In fact, you can draw a circle using a polyline–called a polycircle.

Drawing a Polycircle

A *polycircle* is a polyline drawn as a circle using Arc mode. See Fig. 12-8 as you read the procedure for drawing a polycircle. Set the width and fill of the polyline in the **Polyline** dialogue box before drawing the polycircle. This is accessed by picking the **Settings** menu and the **Polyline** command. The polyline width must be less than the radius of the polycircle. If the polyline width is greater than the radius, you will receive an error message. Then, select the **Draw** menu and **Polyline** command. The first prompt that appears is:

Polyline First point:

Change to Arc mode by holding down the [Ctrl] key while pressing function key [F1]. The following prompt appears:

Polyline Arc segment start point:

Pick a location on the drawing to start the circle at this prompt. Don't worry about exact location at this time. You can move the polycircle into position later. Next, enter these polar coordinates to draw a 1-inch diameter polycircle:

Polyline Point on arc: **P (.7071,45)**

Polyline Arc segment endpoint: **P (.7071,315)**

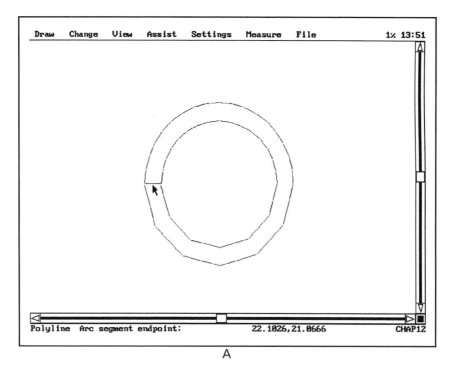

A

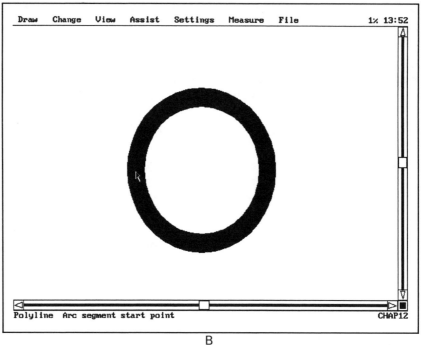

B

Fig. 12-8. Drawing a polycircle. A–Pick the start point again at the second Polyline Arc segment endpoint prompt. B–The completed polycircle.

Polyline Point on arc: **P (.7071,225)**

Polyline Arc segment endpoint: **(pick the start point with pointer)**

The .7071 value is replaced with a larger value when drawing a larger polycircle. Multiply .7071 by the diameter you want to obtain this larger value. For example, to draw a 3-inch diameter polycircle, enter 2.1213 (.7071 x 3 = 2.1213).

Drawing an Exact Diameter Polyarc

Drawing an exact diameter polyarc is similar to drawing a polycircle. However, stop after the first "Arc segment endpoint:" prompt. You can then move and rotate the polyarc into position. Use Attach modes to position the polyarc for greater accuracy.

WORKING WITH CURVES

A curve is a smoothly bending line that you draw by picking a start point, control points, and an endpoint. AutoSketch then uses a mathematical formula to form the curve based on the control points. The closer you place the control points, the closer the curve will be to the frame shape. You can pick up to a maximum of 100 control points.

Curve Frames

The segments that lie between the points you pick to draw the curve make up the *frame*. To edit curves, it helps to have the frame displayed. You may sometimes find it difficult to select a curve without the frame displayed. The **Frame** command in the **Assist** menu reveals control points connected by straight lines. You can select a curve just by picking a point on the frame, or having part of it within a Crosses/window box. With the frame displayed, you can **Stretch** a curve by choosing one of its control points. Most of the other editing commands also work better when curve frames are displayed.

Curve Display

You can control how precisely AutoSketch displays curves using the **Curve** command in the **Settings** menu. The **Curve** dialogue box appears, Fig. 12-9. The number in the *Drawing Segments* box determines how precise curves are displayed. The larger the number, the more precise the curve. The initial setting is 8. Although a high number creates a precise curve, it also takes AutoSketch longer to redraw the curve. Several minutes may be required to draw a curve when a number like 99 is used.

The *Drawing segments* setting also affects the plotted curve. While drawing, use a lower number (1 or 2) for quicker redraw. Reset the drawing segments to a higher value for final output. A value of 9 or 10 is sufficient for plotted drawings. For check plots, set the number low for quick plot time.

SECTIONAL VIEWS AND AREA FILLS

A *section view* reveals interior features by showing the object with a portion cut away. For simple products, the interior features can be represented by hidden (dashed) lines in an exterior view. However, if the product is complex, hidden lines make the drawing look confusing. Sectional views are often used to describe a product with a complex interior.

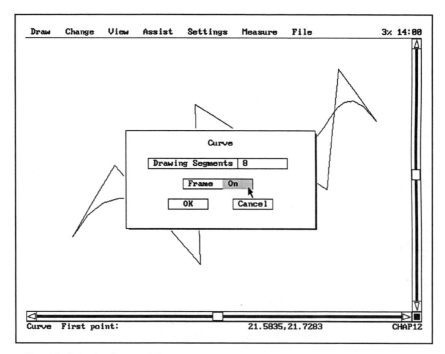

Fig. 12-9. In the Curve dialogue box you set the precision at which curves are displayed and plotted. The default value is 8.

Elements of a Section View

The elements of a section view are shown in Fig. 12-10. The imaginary knife which cuts the object is known as the *cutting plane*. The location of the cutting plane is shown in one view as a *cutting-plane line*. The line is thick with long dashes separated by two smaller dashes, or

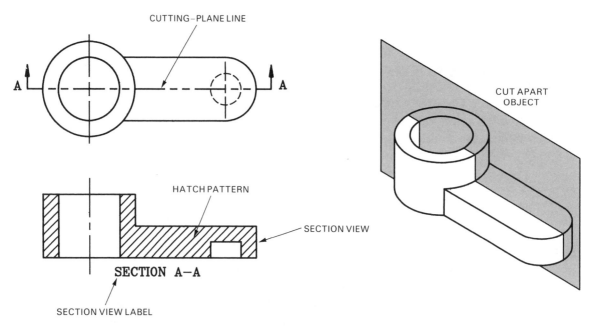

Fig. 12-10. A section view shows the object as if a portion was cut away.

a series of medium-size dashes. Short perpendicular lines with arrows are placed at each end of the cutting-plane line. The arrows indicate the direction in which the section is viewed. Section views are placed on the drawing at a position opposite the direction in which the cutting-plane line arrows point. It is best to project the section view directly behind the cutting-plane line, Fig. 12-11.

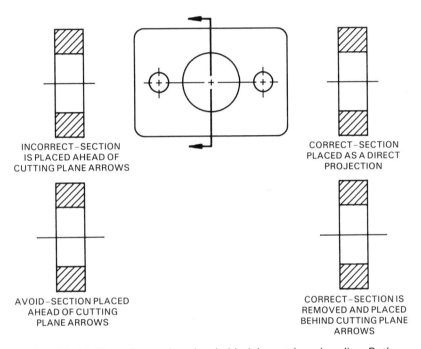

INCORRECT–SECTION
IS PLACED AHEAD OF
CUTTING PLANE ARROWS

CORRECT–SECTION
PLACED AS A DIRECT
PROJECTION

AVOID–SECTION PLACED
AHEAD OF CUTTING
PLANE ARROWS

CORRECT–SECTION IS
REMOVED AND PLACED
BEHIND CUTTING PLANE
ARROWS

Fig. 12-11. Place the section view behind the cutting-plane line. Both proper and improper placement are shown.

In the section view, the surface which is cut is represented with a *hatch pattern*. See Fig. 12-10. The linetype, spacing, and angle of lines in the hatch pattern indicates the material of which the object is made. Patterns recommended by the American National Standards Institute (ANSI) are given in Fig. 12-12. They are provided in AutoSketch Version 3.0.

Since a section view is a cut-away of an object, avoid using hidden lines. They make the view look confusing. Hidden lines may be included *only* if needed for dimensioning. Center lines *are* included on the section view and are typically added after the hatch pattern.

The cutting-plane line should be clearly labeled if more than one section view is included on the working drawing. Place bold, upper-case letters at each corner of the line. The section view is then labeled according to these letters, Fig. 12-10. Place a note below the section view to indicate the cutting-plane line that is referenced. For example, the section view might be labeled as SECTION B-B.

Drawing a Basic Section View with AutoSketch

Most CAD programs let you draw section views quickly because they automatically add the hatch pattern within a specified area. AutoSketch Version 3.0 provides this ability using the **Pattern Fill** command. AutoSketch Version 2.0 does not offer this command; thus, you must create the hatch pattern manually.

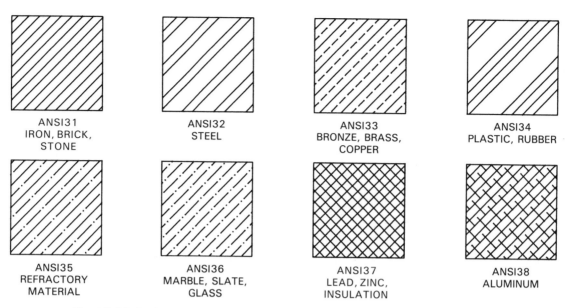

Fig. 12-12. Each hatch pattern indicates the material of which the object is made.

The steps when drawing a section view with AutoSketch Version 3.0 are:

1. Draw the section view outline. The section view may be one view of a multiview drawing or a stand-alone view. There are also several types of section views (discussed in the next section).
2. Select the hatch pattern using the **Pattern** command found in the **Settings** menu. Pick the pattern you need. Also, pick *Boundary* so that it is NOT checked. You do not need a boundary since the section view itself is the boundary.
3. Select the **Pattern Fill** command found in the **Draw** menu.
4. Begin to trace your section view outline. You may want to use some of the Attach modes to exactly align your outline. Switch to Arc mode (press [Ctrl] + [F1]) to trace around circles, arcs, and curves.

Sometimes the section view requires more than one pattern fill. For example, the drawing shown in Fig. 12-13 is difficult to hatch with one pattern fill command because it has islands. *Islands* are areas within a hatch pattern that are to remain open or filled with a different hatch pattern. However, you can perform two or more pattern fill commands to complete the area. The patterns will align perfectly.

The steps when drawing a section view with AutoSketch Version 2.0 are:

1. Draw the section view outline.
2. Draw the hatch pattern in some unused area of the drawing. Use a grid, snap, and possibly a box array to help you create it. Make sure you draw the hatch pattern large enough to fit over your section view.
3. Copy the hatch pattern over your section view.
4. Use the **Break** command to break any lines that extend beyond the section view outline.

Types of Sections

The cutting plane does not have to pass straight through the entire object. An object may be cut in other directions to show special detail. Types of sections include full, half, offset, revolved, broken-out, removed, thin, conventional breaks, and aligned sections.

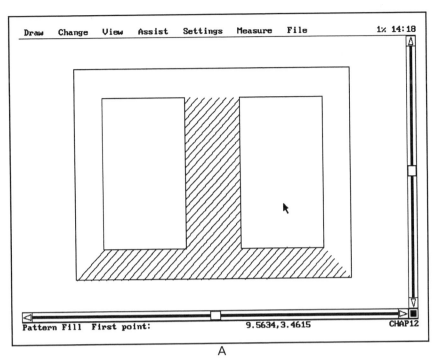

A

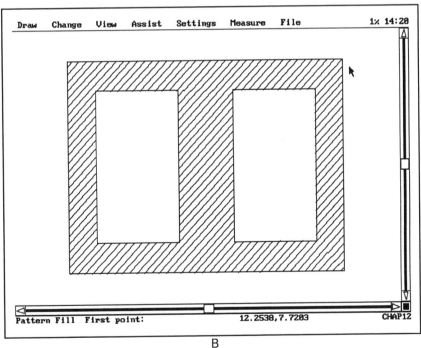

B

Fig. 12-13. Hatching a complex object with islands. A–Pattern fill one section of the object. B–Pattern fill the other section. The hatch patterns will automatically align.

Full Section. In a *full section*, the cutting plane passes straight through the entire object. The section view replaces an exterior view to show some interior feature, Fig. 12-14. The cutting-plane line and section label may be omitted since the section view is one of the multiviews.

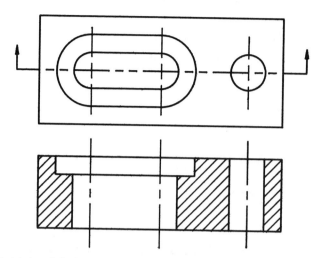

Fig. 12-14. In a full section view, the cutting plane passes straight through the object.

Half Section. In a *half section*, the cutting plane cuts away one-quarter of the object. Two cutting planes intersect at a 90 degree angle. Both internal and external features are shown in the same view, Fig. 12-15. Half sections are used when the object is symmetrical (one half is

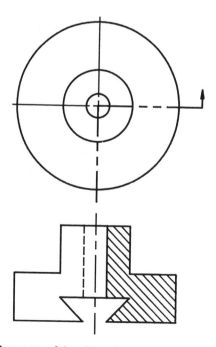

Fig. 12-15. A quarter of the object is cut away in a half section.

the mirror image of the other). Cutting-plane lines and section labels are omitted. Place a center line where the exterior and half section views meet. Only one arrow is given on the cutting-plane line.

Offset Section. In an *offset section*, the cutting plane is not continuous. It is stepped, or offset, at one or more places to show or avoid a certain detail, Fig. 12-16. An offset section is not clearly indicated on the section view. Thus the path of the offset cutting plane is indicated by the cutting-plane line in one of the other views.

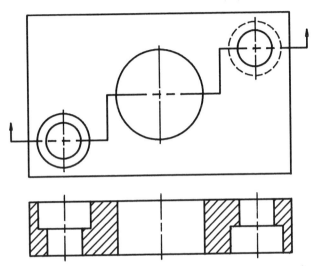

Fig. 12-16. The cutting plane is offset several times to pass through important features.

Broken-Out Section. A *broken-out section* appears as if a portion of the object was broken off to reveal the interior, Fig. 12-17. A broken-out section reveals a small portion of interior detail. No cutting-plane line is indicated. A curved break line is placed between the section and exterior views.

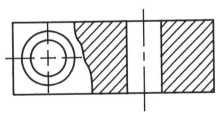

Fig. 12-17. A broken-out section looks as if a portion of the object were broken away.

Revolved Section. A *revolved section* takes a slice of the object, and rotates it 90 degrees to show a cross-section, Fig. 12-18. It is commonly used for shafts, webs, spokes, and flanges.

Conventional Breaks. A *conventional break* is used to shorten extremely long products, such as shafts and tubes, Fig. 12-19. It would be impractical to show the entire length. If

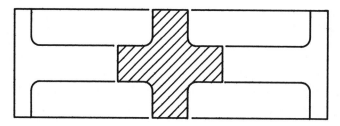

Fig. 12-18. A slice of the object is revolved in place for a revolved section view.

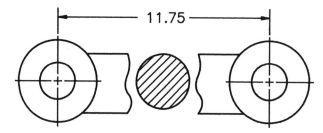

Fig. 12-19. A conventional break line separates a long object that would not fit on the paper. A revolved view may be part of the section view.

scaled to fit, details might be too small. A revolved section may be placed within the break. The overall distance is still given, even through the entire object is not drawn. The measurement should reflect the actual total length of the part.

Removed Section. A *removed section* is formed when a section view is taken from its normal projected place on the drawing and moved elsewhere. The cutting-plane line and section view must be clearly labeled.

Thin Section. Section views of sheet metal, gaskets, or other thin products are often too narrow to add hatching. The hatch pattern would serve no practical purpose. In a *thin section*, the hatch pattern is replaced with a solid color, Fig. 12-20. Use the **Fill Region** command to place this color.

Aligned Section. It is not a good practice to make a full section of a symmetrical object which has an odd number of holes. In an *aligned section*, rotate the cutting plane so that the

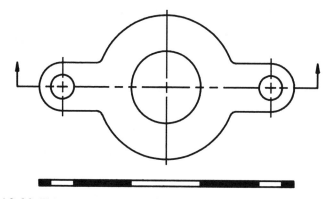

Fig. 12-20. Thin sections, such as this gasket, are given solid color rather than a hatch pattern.

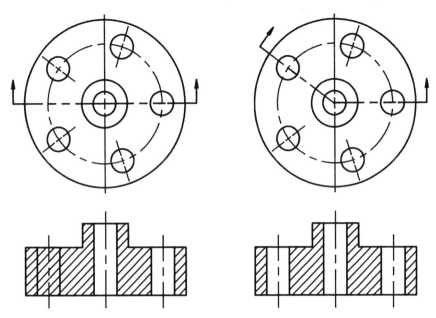

Fig. 12-21. For symmetrical objects with an odd number of holes, rotate the cutting plane to show the holes at their distance from the center. Left. A true projection looks confusing. Right. Proper aligned section.

section view shows two holes at their proper distance from the center. The actual projection, may be misleading. See Fig. 12-21.

Sectioning Assemblies. An assembly view shows connected parts. When sectioning assemblies, rotate the hatch pattern to a different angle on each piece, Fig. 12-22. Shafts, bolts, pins, rivets, nuts, or balls bearings in an assembly are not sectioned when the cutting plane passes through passes through them lengthwise. However, they are sectioned when the cutting plane passes through them across their axis.

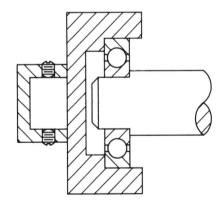

Fig. 12-22. Each part in a sectioned assembly has a hatch pattern at a different angle. Shafts, screws, and ball bearings are not sectioned along their length.

PICTORIAL DRAWINGS

Pictorial drawings look like three-dimensional views of an object. There are two methods to draw pictorial drawings–oblique and isometric.

Oblique Drawing

An *oblique drawing* shows the front of an object in true size and shape. The depth, however, is represented by lines extending back at an angle between 30 and 60 degrees. See Fig. 12-23. When these lines are drawn full length, the drawing is a *cavalier oblique drawing*. When these lines are drawn half length, the drawing is a *cabinet oblique drawing*.

Circular shapes, holes, and curved edges in the front view of an oblique drawing are shown as circles and arcs. However, in the side view they are shown as ellipses, partial ellipses, or curves. When determining which side is to be used as the front face of an oblique object, choose the side with the most contour. This will prevent you from having to draw ellipses and curves in the side view. Also, for long objects, place the object so that the longest dimension is horizontal on the drawing and not shown as depth.

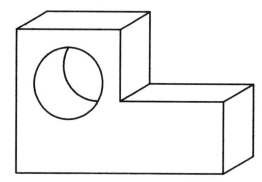

Fig. 12-23. Cavalier oblique drawing. The front is shown in true size and shape. Depth is shown with lines extending back at a 30 degree angle.

Isometric Drawing

Isometric drawings use three views to show the front, top, and side of an object. Vertical edges of the object are drawn vertical. Horizontal edges are drawn at a 30 degree angle from horizontal in each direction. Edges in an isometric drawing are drawn full size. Holes and other circular shapes are represented with ellipses.

To draw an isometric drawing, first set up a special grid. Set both the grid and snap with an X to Y ratio of 1.732 to 1. You might set snap at a .1732 to .1 ratio for better precision. Now, grid points are positioned at the proper angle of the three isometric axes. The isometric grid will help you draw the horizontal lines at the proper angle. See Fig. 12-24.

Next, draw three base construction lines to represent the front edge of the object. One line is vertical, the other two are drawn at 30 degree angles from the horizontal plane. Then, draw an isometric box with construction lines to outline the largest dimensions of the object. Finally, draw the front and side edges with full-length vertical lines and depth lines at a 30 degree angle.

Circular shapes and holes are shown with isometric circles. Isometric circles look much like ellipses, but are not true ellipses. To draw an ellipse, first draw an isometric square the same size as the circle. Draw construction lines from the corners of the isometric squares to the midpoints of the square as shown in Fig. 12-25. Then construct arcs with the centers placed as shown and edges meeting the midpoints of the sides of the isometric square. (Hint: It may be helpful to draw cicles with the Center and Intersect Attach modes and then break out the unneeded portion.)

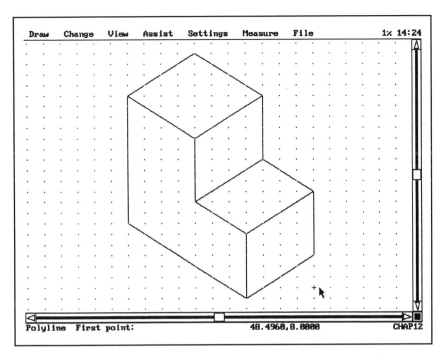

Polyline   First point: 48.4960,8.0000   CHAP12

Fig. 12-24. With the grid at a X to Y ratio of 1.732 to 1, you can easily draw isometric drawings.

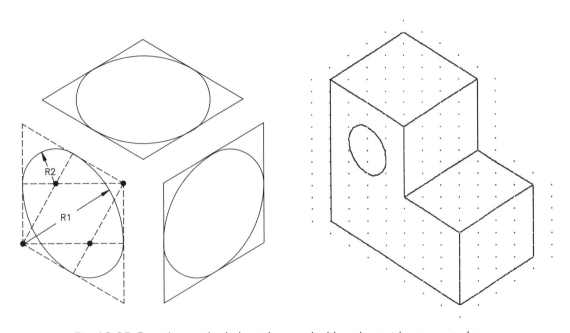

Fig. 12-25. Draw isometric circles using arcs inside an isometric square as shown.

CHARTS

Charts show the relationship of recorded data in a way that is more easily understood. Engineers use charts to record measurements of flow, vibration, movement, etc. Hospitals use charts to track the temperature, pulse, and blood pressure of patients. Businesses use charts to show sales, production, and profit over time.

Line Chart

A *line chart* shows the measurement of one or more variables at certain points of a third incremented value. Lines chart show trends or changes, usually measured over time. For example, a line chart could show points scored and points allowed in basketball games during the season, Fig. 12-26. The incremented value is games. The two variables are offensive points (our team) and defensive points (them). The trend may show that the team is scoring more, but giving up even more points. Line charts are often used to show weather changes, sales trends, and population changes.

The *key,* given at some place near the chart, indicates what data the charted lines represent. For example, the key in Fig. 12-26 shows that the dotted line represents points allowed, and the solid line represents points scored. Keys are used in almost all charts. There should be a drastic difference between the types of patterns used for charts.

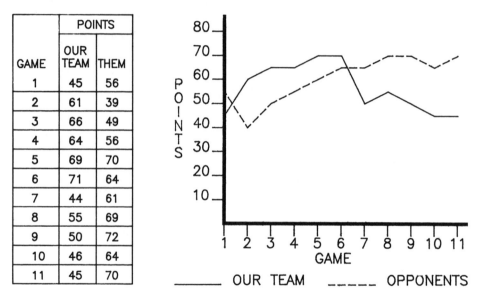

Fig. 12-26. Left. Data in numerical form is hard to understand. Right. When drawn as a line chart, you can see that the team's offense sputtered late in the season. The key at the bottom of the chart shows which linetype represents each set of data.

Bar Chart

A *bar chart* uses a rectangle, or bar, to show data measured against another value. Bar charts can be used like line charts to show changing measurements. Fig. 12-27 shows a bar chart for the offensive points data given in Fig. 12-26. Bar charts are the most familiar because they are easiest to understand. They are commonly found in the daily newspaper.

Stacked Bar Chart

A *stacked bar chart* shows two or more sets of data measured against a third value. When used to measure changing values, you could use a stacked bar chart to measure total points per game while still showing individual team points, Fig. 12-28. You can also use stacked bar

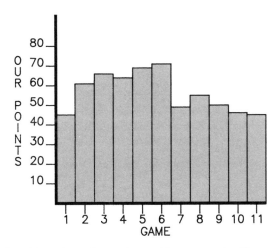

Fig. 12-27. A bar chart shows data with a rectangle. They are easy to understand.

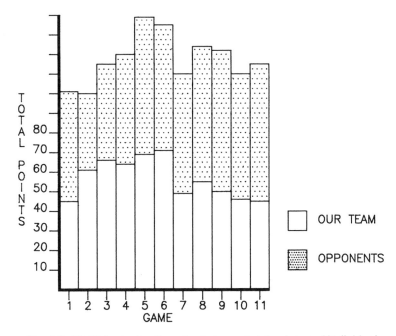

Fig. 12-28. This stacked bar chart shows total points and individual team points.

charts to show the fixed value of several variables. Each bar may be colored or patterned to distinguish it from the others.

Pie Chart

A *pie chart* shows percentages of a whole. A full circle represents 100 percent, or the whole amount. Sectors, or pieces of the circle, represent parts of the whole. Pie charts are often used to show market percentages of a business, Fig. 12-29. Each sector is usually given its own color or pattern.

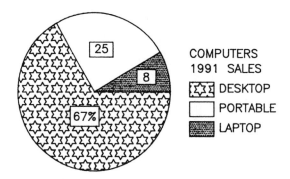

COMPUTERS
1991 SALES

▨ DESKTOP
☐ PORTABLE
▦ LAPTOP

Fig. 12-29. A pie chart shows percentages of a whole. This particular chart shows the breakdown of computer types sold by one manufacturer.

Pictorial Charts

Pictorial charts are similar to bar charts, except that they use pictures or symbols instead of bars. The chart in Fig. 12-30 shows the type of furniture sold during the year by an office supply store. Pictorial charts you see in newspapers or magazines are often very artistic and colorful. They are much more pleasing to view than standard line and bar charts.

1991 Furniture Sales
(in thousands)

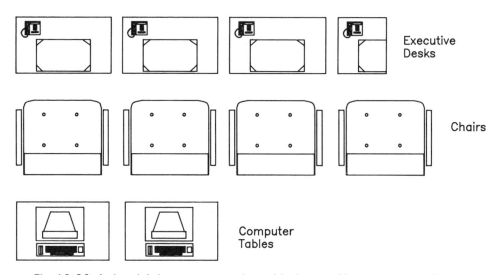

Executive Desks

Chairs

Computer Tables

Fig. 12-30. A pictorial chart represents data with pictures. Here you can see that the company sold mostly chairs.

Organization Chart

Organization charts show hierarchy, or an ordered arrangement. They typically show the level of persons in an organization, or company, Fig. 12-31. With the company president or CEO near the top, each level charts shows the manager or supervisor for a specific group of employees.

Flowchart

A *flowchart* shows the path or sequence of operations. They are often used to show the series of operations it takes to manufacture or construct a product. Flowcharts are also used in computer programming to show steps of the program. The organization chart in Fig. 12-31 is much like a flowchart because it shows the flow of authority within the company.

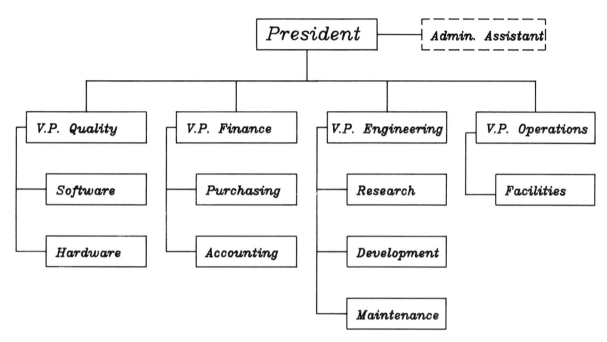

Fig. 12-31. An organizational chart shows the chain of command of an organization.

SUMMARY

Advanced geometric construction allows you to combine lines, arcs, and circles accurately. The **Bearing** command and polar coordinates are frequently used when combining these objects. AutoSketch Version 3.0 provides a Perpendicular Attach mode. This allows you to place lines and polylines at a 90 degree angle to other objects.

Curves are created by picking a start point, control points, and an endpoint. AutoSketch uses a mathematical formula to form the curve based on the control points. A maximum of 100 control points can be used. The closer the control points are placed, the closer the curve will resemble the frame.

Section views are used to show the interior features of an object. Section views are generally used to describe a product that has a complex interior. There are several types of section views including full sections, half sections, offset sections, broken out sections, revolved sections, removed sections, and aligned sections. A section view consists of several elements–a cutting-plane line, hatch pattern, and section view label. The linetype, spacing, and angle of the hatch pattern indicates the material of which the object is made. AutoSketch Version 3.0 offers a variety of hatch patterns. You must create your own hatch patterns when using Version 2.0.

Pictorial drawings look like the real object. There are two methods for creating pictorial drawings–oblique and isometric. An oblique drawing shows the front of an object in true size and shape. The depth is represented by lines extending back at a 30 to 60 degree angle. An isometric drawing uses three views to show the top, front, and side of an object. Vertical edges of the object are drawn vertical. Horizontal edges are drawn at a 30 degree angle.

Charts are used to show the relationship of recorded data in graphic form. A variety of charts are used including the line chart, bar chart, pie chart, pictorial chart, organizational chart, and flowchart.

NEW TERMS

Parallel lines, perpendicular lines, regular polygon, curve frame, drawing segments, section view, cutting plane, cutting-plane line, hatch pattern, full section, half section, offset section, broken-out section, revolved section, removed section, thin section, aligned section, conventional break, oblique drawing, cabinet oblique drawing, cavalier oblique drawing, isometric drawing, charts, line chart, bar chart, stacked bar chart, pie chart, pictorial chart, organization chart, flowchart.

REVIEW QUESTIONS

Write your answers on a separate sheet of paper. Do not write in this book.
1. The _____ command and _____ coordinates are very important to geometric construction with CAD.
2. _____ lines are equal distance from each other along their length.
3. Regular polygons have equal sides and different internal angles. True or false?
4. What construction line must you draw before you can draw a circle that touches two points?
5. AutoSketch does not provide a command that lets you draw an arc using a center point. True or false?
6. The segments that connect the control points you pick to draw a curve make up the _____.
7. You can **Stretch** a curve without the frame displayed. True or false?
8. The location of a section view's cutting plane is shown in one view as a(n) _____.
9. List five types of section views and give an example of each.
10. Where should you place section views in relation to the direction that the cutting-plane line arrows point?
11. In a(n) _____ section, the cutting plane cuts away one-quarter of the object.
12. In a(n) _____ section, the cutting plane is stepped at one or more places to show or avoid a certain detail.
13. A(n) _____ pictorial drawing shows the front of an object in true size and shape.
14. When depth lines are drawn at half length, the drawing is called a(n) _____ oblique drawing.
15. The X to Y ratio for an isometric grid is _____ to _____.
16. In an isometric drawing, circular shapes and holes are shown with _____ which look much like _____.
17. _____ show the relationship of recorded data in a way that is more easily understood.

18. The _____, given at some place near the chart, indicates what data a charted line or bar represents.
19. A(n)_____ chart uses a rectangle to show data measured against another value.
20. A(n) _____ shows the path or sequence of operations.

ACTIVITIES

Here is a mixture of drawing activities to develop your skills with developing geometric constructions, section views, and charts. Save your AutoSketch drawings on your file disk, not on the program disk. Clear the previous drawing from screen and memory using **New** before completing each activity.

1. Draw a 3 inch line at some angle. Next, draw a parallel line 1 inch away from the existing line. Finally, draw a perpendicular line 3 inches long, and 1 inch away from the parallel lines. See the illustration.

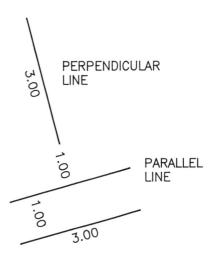

2. Draw a 3 inch line at some angle. Next, draw a second 3 inch line, touching one endpoint, at a 30 degree angle to the existing line. Finally, draw a 3 inch bisecting line. See the illustration.

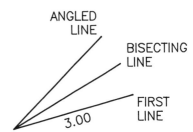

3. Draw these regular polygons: hexagon (six sides), octagon (eight sides), and equilateral triangle (three sides). Make each side 3 inches long.

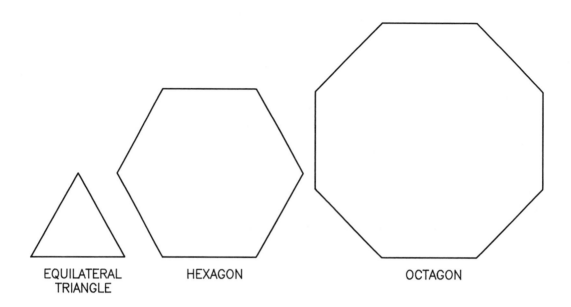

EQUILATERAL
TRIANGLE

HEXAGON

OCTAGON

4. Draw these views, but make one view a full section.

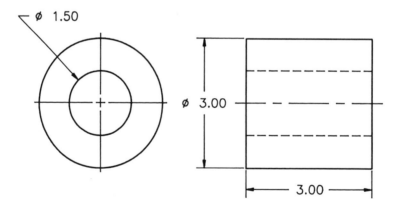

Ø 1.50

Ø 3.00

3.00

5. Draw these views, but make one view a half section.

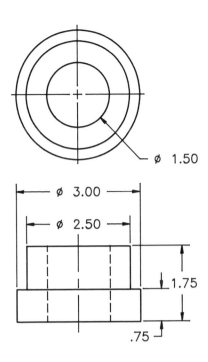

6-10. For the objects in Activities 6 through 10 of Chapter 11, make an appropriate section view drawing.

11-15. For the multiview drawings given in Activites 1-5 of Chapter 11, create both oblique and isometric drawings.

16. Draw a line chart that plots the average price of gas per gallon over the past 5 years.

1986 1.00

1987 1.10

1988 1.25

1989 1.01

1990 1.30

17. Draw a bar chart using the same data given in Activity 16.

18. Draw a pie chart to show the population distribution in the following four regions of the country. Label your drawing with text.

Northeast = 30%

North Central = 25%

South = 11%

West = 34%

19. Draw a pie chart showing the estimated percentages of areas in which you spent money last month. Examples would be food, entertainment, and school supplies.

20. Draw a pictorial chart showing the number of classes in each of these areas of school: English (8), Math (6), Science (4), History (5), Vocational (9). Use appropriate pictures for each area.

21. Create an organizational chart from the following description:

Mr. Johnson is the President of the WYE Company. This company is organized into three divisions. Each division is headed by a Vice President. The first division–the Administrative Division–consists of a person in charge of finance, a person in charge of the warehouse, and a person in charge of accounting. The second division–the Sales Division–consists of the Vice President and four salespeople. The Production Division includes a purchasing agent, a hardware specialist, and a software specialist.

22. Draw the following PERT flowchart.

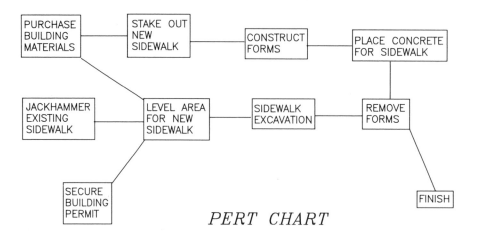

PERT CHART

23. Draw the following production flowchart.

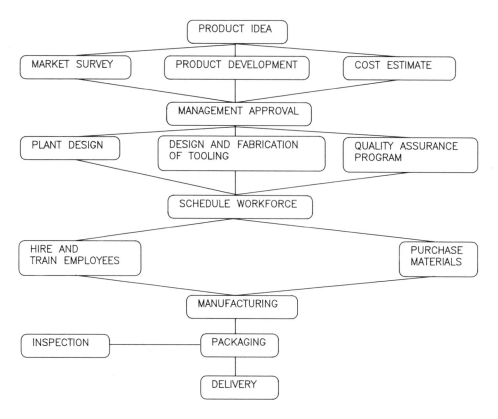

Chapter 13

ADDING DIMENSIONS

After studying this chapter, you will be able to:
- Define the difference between size and location dimensions.
- Identify the lines, symbols, and other elements used when placing dimensions.
- Comply with recommended dimensioning standards.
- Select the arrowhead type and units of measurement for placing dimensions.
- Place horizontal, vertical, and aligned linear dimensions.
- Place angular dimensions.
- Place diameter and radius dimensions.
- Follow the general guidelines for dimensioning common shapes.

Two important aspects of product design are shape and size description. The chapters up to this point have discussed adding objects to outline shapes. *Dimensions* are added to show size and location. The dimension may consist of numerals, lines, symbols, and notes, Fig. 13-1. Each drafting field (mechanical, architectural, civil) dimensions drawings differently. For example, dimensioning for mechanical applications follows the American National Standards Institute ANSI Y14.5M–1982 document, *Dimensioning and Tolerancing*. However, the basic techniques common to all fields are discussed here.

CAD systems, such as AutoSketch, have made dimensioning a much quicker process. In traditional drafting, dimension lines are drawn by hand and measurements are made using a scale. With AutoSketch, you only have to pick where the dimension begins and ends, and where to place it. AutoSketch adds the needed lines, arrows, and inserts the measurement.

SIZE AND LOCATION DIMENSIONS

Generally, dimensions describe either the size or location of features, Fig. 13-2. The term *feature* refers to any distinct part of a product. Features on a manufactured product might

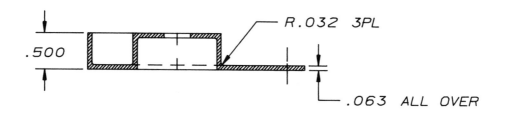

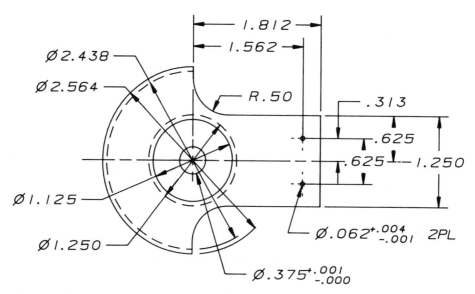

Fig. 13-1. Dimensions consist of numerals, lines, symbols, and notes to show size and location.

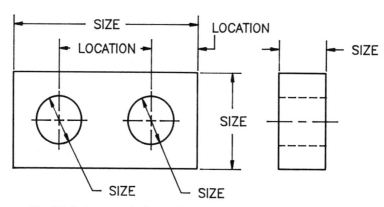

Fig. 13-2. In general, dimensions describe either size or location.

include a surface, edge, hole, or slot. Features on a architectural drawing can include walls, windows, doors, appliances, and cabinets. Even a complex product can be described by the size of its many simpler parts.

Size dimensions give the width, length, height, diameter, or radius of a feature. For example, size dimensions might show the thickness of a piece of metal or the width of a window. There can be many size dimensions on a drawing. Each one describes the measurements of a specific part of the product.

Location dimensions give the position of a feature or shape. The position is measured from an edge, center, surface, or another feature. For example, a location dimension might locate the center of a hole from a finished surface or the center of another hole. An architectural example is measuring the center of a window from an exterior wall.

ELEMENTS IN DIMENSIONING

A variety of lines, symbols, and notes are used when dimensioning a technical drawing. Fig. 13-3 shows the most common elements on a mechanical drawing. You should be familiar with the following terms.

Extension Lines
Extension lines, also known as witness lines, mark the beginning and end of a dimension. The lines generally begin .06 inch away from the shape being dimensioned. This distance is called the *extension line offset.* Extension lines extend .12 inch beyond the dimension line. Extension lines are not used when the dimension is located within a shape.

Dimension Lines
Dimension lines show the direction and extent of a dimension. The line is straight for a linear dimension and curved for an angular dimension. The dimension line is typically

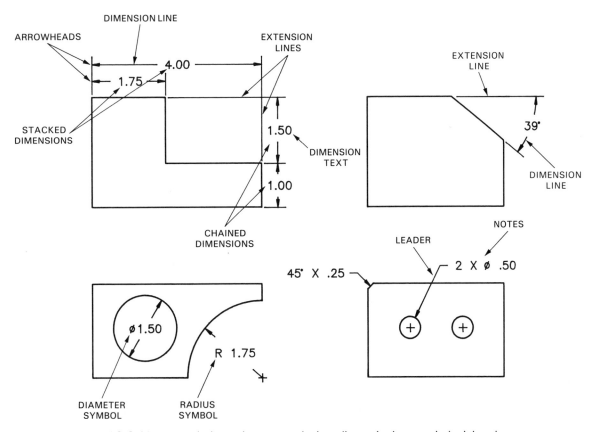

Fig. 13-3. Lines, symbols, and notes used when dimensioning a technical drawing.

broken near the middle for placement of dimension text. However, in architectural and structural drawings, the dimension text is often placed on top of the line. Refer to Fig. 13-4.

A dimension line should be at least .375 to 1 inch (10 to 25 mm) away from the view. This depends on the space available and complexity of the drawing. Stacked dimension lines should be spaced at least .375 to .5 inch (10 to 13 mm) apart. Where there is limited space, the dimension line and dimension text are placed outside the extension lines.

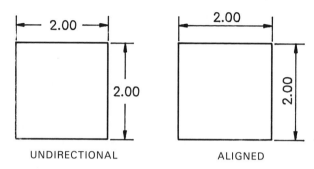

Fig. 13-4. Unidirectional dimensions are placed horizontally with a break in the dimension line for text. Aligned dimensions are placed parallel with the dimension lines and the text reads from the bottom or right.

Arrowheads

In mechanical drafting, dimension lines end with *arrowheads*. In architectural drafting, dimension lines may end with arrows, tick marks, or dots. AutoSketch Version 2.0 automatically adds open arrows. Version 3.0 offers five types. Select the **Settings** menu and **Arrow** command to open the **Dimension Arrow Type** dialogue box, Fig. 13-5. If you create your own arrowheads, the recommended size is .18 inch (4.5 mm) long and one-half as wide.

Dimension Text

Dimension text is the numerical value of the measurement plus any needed symbols or notes. Most CAD systems and AutoSketch calculate the distance picked and insert the measurement automatically. AutoSketch draws dimension text using the current height and font set for regular text. The dimension text height should be .125 to .18 inch. Use larger text if the drawing is to be reduced in size later. Titles and subtitles should be .18 to .25 inch high so that they stand out. See Chapter 9 for setting text features.

Units of measurement. The standard units of measurement on mechanical drawings are decimal inches and metric units given in millimeters. A zero always precedes metric dimensions for measurements less than 1, such as 0.03. A zero does not precede inch measurements less than 1, such as .03. Fractional dimensions may appear to indicate standard stock sizes, such as 1/2″ cold-rolled steel. When all dimensions represent inches or millimeters, a general note should appear on the drawing: UNLESS OTHERWISE SPECIFIED, ALL DIMENSIONS ARE IN INCHES (or MILLIMETERS). Architectural drawings are dimensioned in fractional inches, or feet and inches written as 12′-0″.

Unidirectional and aligned systems. Unidirectional and aligned systems refer to how dimension text is placed in relation to the dimension line, Fig. 13-4. *Unidirectional dimensions* are placed horizontally within a break in the dimension line. In this manner, any

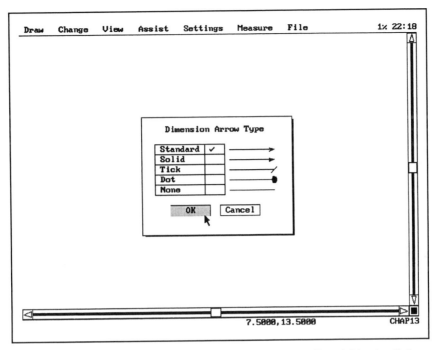

Fig. 13-5. Four types of arrows are available with AutoSketch Version 3.0.

dimension can be read from the bottom of the drawing. The manufacturing industry follows the unidirectional system for most mechanical drawings. *Aligned dimensions* are placed parallel to the dimension lines. They read from the bottom or right side of the drawing. Dimension text can be placed above or within a break in the dimension line. Architectural and structural drawings commonly follow the aligned system of dimensioning.

Unidirectional and aligned dimensions should not both be used on the same drawing. Also, with aligned dimensions, full and broken dimension lines should not both be used on the same drawing. The current ANSI standard specifies that dimensions and notes read from the bottom of the drawing.

Dual dimensioning. *Dual dimensioning* contains both conventional (inch/feet) and metric measurements. See Fig. 13-6. The placement of the two dimensions varies. In the United States, the customary measurement appears above the metric. In Europe, the metric measurement appears above the customary. Some CAD systems place the measurements side by side separated by a slash or brackets.

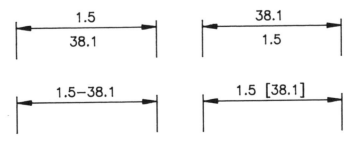

Fig. 13-6. Dual dimension contains both conventional and metric measurements.

Leader

A *leader* is a thin line leading from a note or dimension to the place on the drawing where it applies. Refer to Fig. 13-3. Leaders allow you to place dimensions away from the view. In this manner, the dimension does not interfere with the view. A leader consists of a short (.125 inch) horizontal line and a second line that extends at a 15 to 75 degree (but usually 45 or 60 degree) angle to the place where it applies. The leader stops with an arrowhead, or dot when the leader note applies to a surface.

Leaders placed close together should be parallel. However, leaders should not be placed parallel to extension or dimension lines. A leader which points to a circle or arc should be aligned with the circle or arc's center. Dimensioning circles and arcs with leaders is discussed later in the chapter.

Notes and Symbols

Notes and symbols appear frequently on technical drawings. Notes may be general or specific. *General notes* apply to the entire drawing. For example, a general note might read: HEAT TREAT AND TEMPER RC 44-48. General notes appear in the lower-left or upper-left corner of the drawing area, or next to the title block. *Specific notes* refer to specific features on a drawing. They are attached to the feature described or dimensioned by a leader

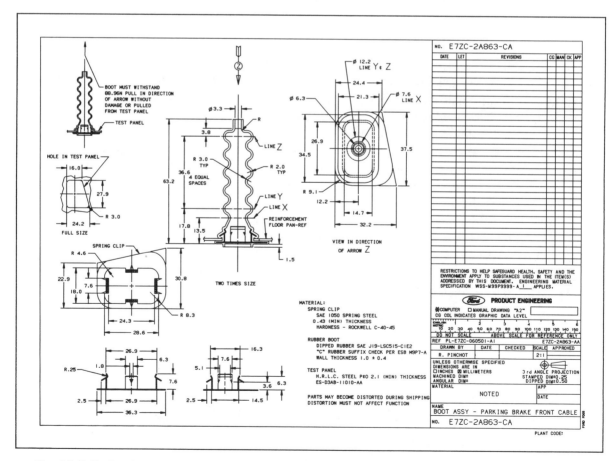

Fig. 13-7. Notice that the general notes appear at the bottom-right corner of the drawing. Then, look at the specific notes, each pointing to features with a leader. (Ford Motor)

line. See Fig. 13-7. Notes are always placed horizontally, even if dimension text follows the aligned system.

Symbols are used to denote certain standards. Some of the more common symbols that appear are shown in Fig. 13-8. In addition, there is a specialized segment of dimensioning called geometric dimensioning and tolerancing. It involves many other symbols that describe the form and position of features on a product.

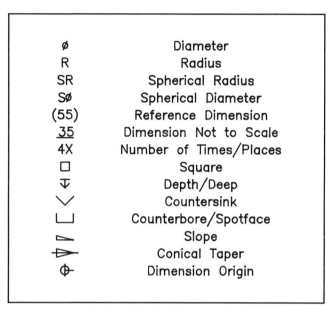

Fig. 13-8. Common symbols found on mechanical drawings.

DIMENSIONING WITH AUTOSKETCH

AutoSketch does not support all of the dimensioning standards just discussed. For example, all AutoSketch-placed dimensions follow the aligned system with the dimension text placed above the dimension line. AutoSketch does not support dual dimensioning. If your drawing requires strict adherence to dimension standards, you may have to place some dimensions manually.

Setting Units of Measurement
AutoSketch provides a means to set the units of measurement display. Pick the **Settings** menu and **Units** command. AutoSketch displays the **Units Display Format** dialogue box, Fig. 13-9. Pick either *Decimal* or *Architectural* format. Use Decimal format for any measurement that can be measured in whole units and parts divisible by 10 (tenths, hundredths, thousandths, etc.). You can use decimal format for inches, millimeters, miles, meters, and most other measurements. Use Architectural format for dimensions you want placed in feet and inches (12′-4″).

After you pick the format, pick to what precision you want dimensions displayed. Mechanical precision is usually 3 digits behind the decimal point (0.000). Architectural drawings are usually dimensioned to the nearest 1/8 or 1/16 inch. You can also enter a

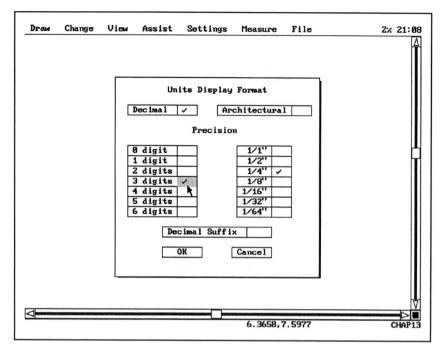

Fig. 13-9. In the Units Display Format dialogue box you pick the format for dimension text.

decimal suffix, such as "mm" or "inch" in the *Decimal suffix* box. The suffix is not added with the Architectural format, or when dimensioning angles.

ADDING LINEAR DIMENSIONS

Linear dimensions measure straight distances. Linear dimensions that measure size might show the height, width, or length of a product. Those that measure location might show the position of the center of a hole measured from a finished edge. The dimension can be placed vertically, horizontally, or parallel (aligned) to an object at an angle.

The general method for linear dimensioning is to pick a dimensioning command from the **Measure** menu, Fig. 13-10. Next, pick the two points to measure. Then pick the position of the dimension line.

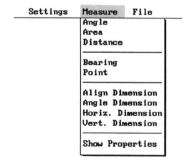

Fig. 13-10. Dimensioning commands are found in the Measure menu.

Placing Horizontal Dimensions

Horizontal dimensions measure a horizontal linear distance. To place a horizontal dimension, Fig. 13-11, pick the **Measure** menu and **Horiz. Dimension** command. The first two prompts that appear are:

Horizontal Dimension Points to dimension:

Horizontal Dimension To point:

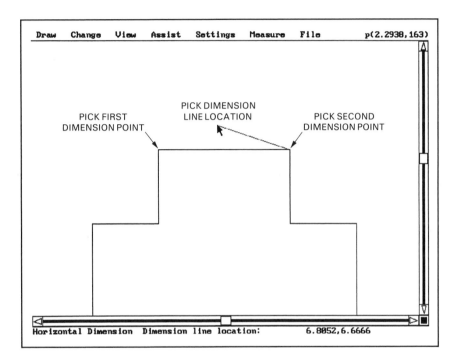

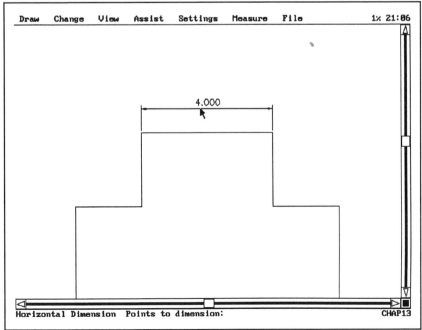

Fig. 13-11. To place a horizontal dimension, pick two dimension points and the location of the dimension line.

Pick two points that mark the extents of the dimension. Use Attach modes or Snap to place these points precisely. The next prompt that appears is:

Horizontal dimension   Dimension line location:

AutoSketch needs to know how far away to place the dimension. Pick a location that follows the recommendations given earlier in the chapter. Once you pick the dimension line location, AutoSketch draws in the extension lines, dimension lines, arrows, and places the measurement.

Placing Vertical Dimensions

Vertical dimensions measure vertical linear distance. To place a vertical dimension, pick the **Measure** menu and **Vert. Dimension** command. The first two prompts that appear are:

Vertical Dimension   Points to dimension:

Vertical Dimension   To point:

Pick two points that mark the extents of the dimension. Pick the points from the bottom up, so that the dimension will read from the right, Fig. 13-12. If you pick the points from the top down, the dimension will read from the left, Fig. 13-13. This is incorrect. Use Attach modes or Snap to locate these two points precisely. The next prompt that appears is:

Vertical Dimension   Dimension line location:

AutoSketch needs to know how far away to place the dimension. Pick a location that follows the recommendations given earlier in the chapter. Make sure the line is far enough out so that the measurement text does not overlap the object. Once you pick the dimension line location, AutoSketch draws in the extension lines, dimension lines, arrows, and places the measurement.

Placing Aligned Dimensions

Aligned dimensions measure the true length of a surface drawn at an angle. The dimension line is parallel to the angled surface. To place an aligned dimension, Fig. 13-14, pick the **Measure** menu and **Align Dimension** command. The first two prompts that appear are:

Aligned Dimension   Points to dimension:

Aligned Dimension   To point:

Pick two points that mark the extents of the dimension. Use Attach modes or Snap to locate these two points precisely. The next prompt that appears is:

Aligned Dimension   Dimension line location:

AutoSketch needs to know how far away to place the dimension. Pick a location that follows the recommendations given earlier in the chapter. Once you pick the dimension line location, AutoSketch draws in the extension lines, dimension lines, arrows, and places the measurement at the proper angle.

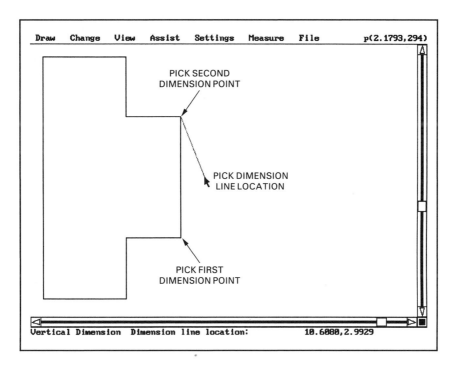

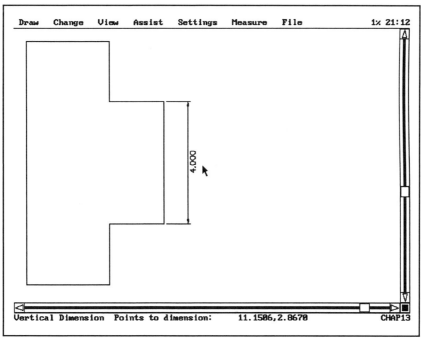

Fig. 13-12. To place a vertical dimension, pick two dimension points (bottom to top) and the location of the dimension line.

Chained and Stacked Dimensions

There are two basic methods to place linear dimensions that measure multiple features–chained and stacked. The combination you choose depends on the intended accuracy of the drawing and the drafting field.

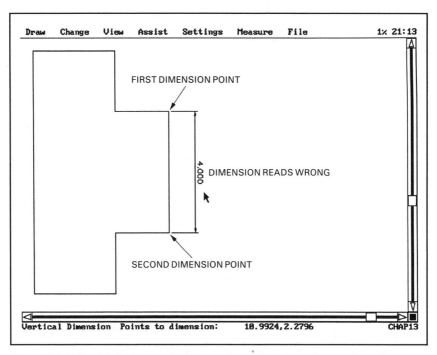

FIRST DIMENSION POINT

4.000   DIMENSION READS WRONG

SECOND DIMENSION POINT

Vertical Dimension   Points to dimension: 10.9924,2.2796   CHAP13

Fig. 13-13. Avoid picking vertical dimension points from the top down because the text then reads from the left.

Chained dimensions, or point-to-point dimensions, continue a linear dimension from the second extension line of the previous dimension, Fig. 13-3. This breaks one long dimension into shorter segments that add up to the total distance. Chained dimensions are common in architectural drafting. They can also be found in mechanical designs requiring less precision. Chained dimensions are less accurate since each dimension depends on others in the chain.

Stacked dimensions, also called datum dimensions, continue linear dimensions from a common edge or surface, Fig. 13-3. Stacked dimensions are often found when very precise location and sizes are required. Precision is gained by measuring all size and locations from a single point or surface, called the datum. Dimension lines of stacked dimensions are spaced .375 to .5 inch apart.

Both chained and stacked dimensions are typically found on most drawings. Chained dimensions show size and location between features. A stacked dimension shows overall length. One dimension is left blank because it can be found by subtracting given dimensions from the overall dimension.

ANGULAR DIMENSIONING

Angular dimensions measure the angle formed by nonparallel surfaces, Fig. 13-15. Past practices suggested that angles be measured in degrees, minutes, and seconds. However, more industries now use decimal degrees, such as 45.67 degrees. AutoSketch dimensions angles to the precision you set in the **Units Display Format** dialogue box. In addition, AutoSketch adds the degree symbol behind an angular dimension.

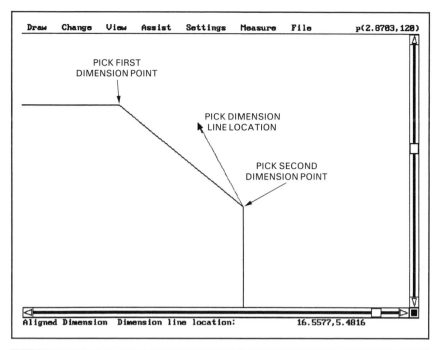

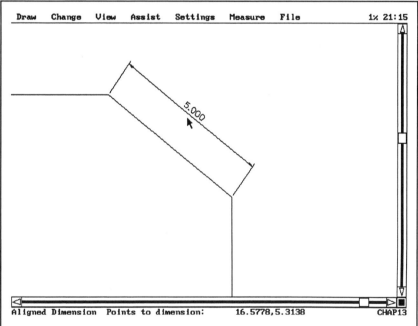

Fig. 13-14. To place an aligned dimension, pick two dimension points and the location of the dimension line.

To place an angular dimension with AutoSketch, pick the **Measure** menu and **Angle Dimension** command. The first two prompts that appear are:

Angular Dimension Select first line:

Angular Dimension Select second line:

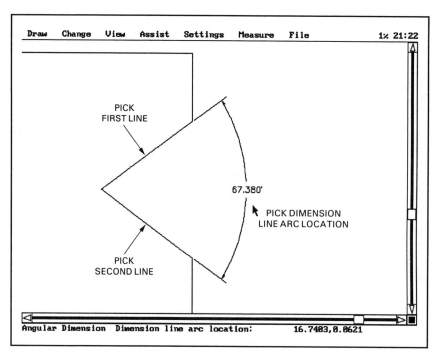

Fig. 13-15. To place an angular dimension, pick the two lines forming the angle and the location of the dimension line.

Pick two lines that form the angle you want to dimension. The next prompt that appears is the following:

Angular Dimension   Dimension line arc location:

AutoSketch needs to know how far away to place the dimension from the lines. Pick a location that follows the recommendations given earlier in the chapter. If you pick the location beyond the lines, AutoSketch adds extension lines. If you attempt to dimension lines which form too small of an angle, the dialogue box shown in Fig. 13-16A appears. AutoSketch then allows you to place the text where it fits. See Fig. 13-16B. The precision of angular dimensions is set by using the *Decimal format* box of the **Units Display Format** dialogue box.

ASSOCIATIVITY

AutoSketch dimensions are *associative,* meaning that they are associated with the points you pick to place the dimension. The result is that when you edit AutoSketch dimensions, they adapt as you perform the editing function.

You must include the dimension points in your selection set for associative dimensioning to work properly. *Dimension points* are the points you pick to measure the dimension. The *selection set* simply means the objects you select to edit. In some instances, the selection set must include the points you pick for the location of the dimension line and dimension text.

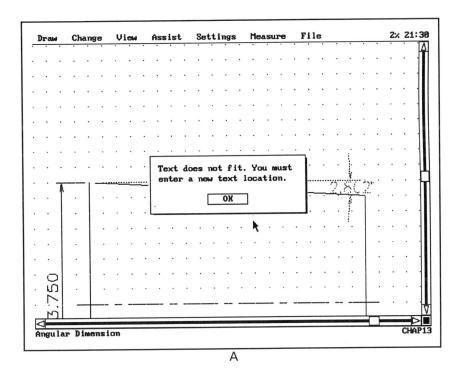

A

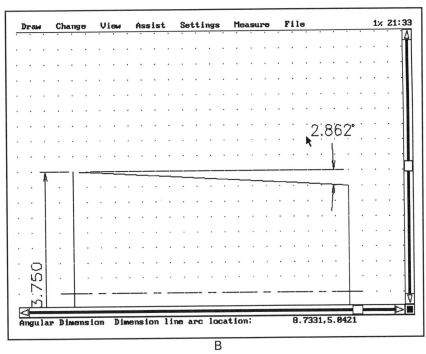

B

Fig. 13-16. If the dimension text won't fit between the two lines, AutoSketch
lets you place it elsewhere.

Associative Linear Dimensions

A linear dimension is a single object, You can stretch it and its dimension text toward or away from the dimension points. If you stretch an existing dimension point, the entire dimension is remeasured and redrawn, depending on the type of dimension (horizontal, vertical, or aligned).

Fig. 13-17 shows a triangle dimensioned with horizontal, vertical, and aligned dimensions. The top corner was stretched to a new location. Notice that the affected dimensions changed according to the new location. The vertical dimension still measures vertical distance. The aligned dimension remains aligned. The horizontal dimension was unchanged because no point associated with that dimension was moved.

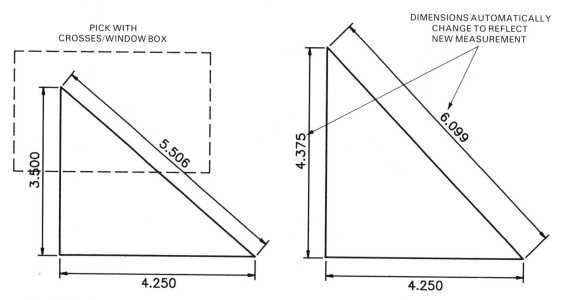

Fig. 13-17. Because AutoSketch dimensions are associative, the dimension will stretch with your drawing if you include a dimension point in the Crosses/window box.

The **Scale** command has a similar effect on dimensions. Include the dimensions within a Crosses/window box of the object to be scaled. The dimension will change according to the scale factor.

Rotating objects with horizontal and vertical dimensions has a peculiar effect. See the before and after effects of the rectangle dimensioned in Fig. 13-18. If you rotate a horizontal dimension 90 or 270 degrees, its dimension text changes to 0 units because what used to be a horizontal dimension is now a vertical dimension. In the same manner, if you rotate a vertical dimension 90 or 270 degrees, its dimension text changes to be 0 because what used to be vertical is now horizontal. If you plan to rotate objects with linear dimensions, use aligned dimensions instead. Then, dimension lines and text remains unchanged as you rotate those objects using any rotation angle.

Associative Angular Dimensions

Angular dimensions are not totally associative. For example, if you rotate one of the lines picked to measure the angle, the angle will not change accordingly. However, if you stretch the same line and one of the dimension points, the dimension will stretch accordingly, Fig. 13-19. Other commands that affect angular dimensions are **Ring Array, Mirror, Rotate, Scale,** and **Stretch.**

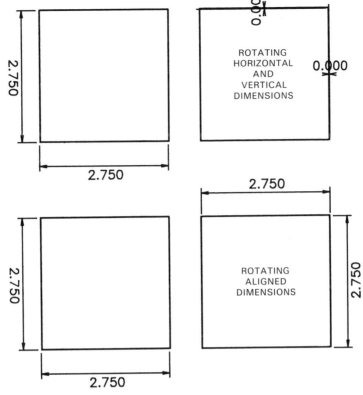

Fig. 13-18. If you plan to rotate dimensioned rectangular objects, dimension the objects with aligned dimensions.

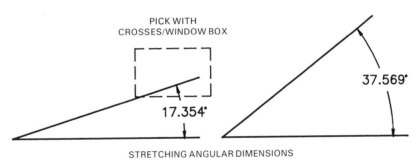

STRETCHING ANGULAR DIMENSIONS

Fig. 13-19. An angular dimension will stretch if you include one dimension point in the Crosses/window box.

Angular dimension text always remain horizontal. For example, if you rotate two lines which were dimensioned, select them with a Crosses/window box. Include the dimension in the selection set. When you rotate the two lines, the dimension also rotates, but the text remains horizontal, Fig. 13-20. If you stretch a dimensioned line so that the angular measurement will not fit in the modified space, the dimension is then moved outside, Fig. 13-21.

DIAMETER DIMENSIONING

Diameter dimensions indicate the size of circles, cylinders, holes, and other circular shapes. Diameter dimensioning can be done with or without a leader. Refer to Fig. 13-3.

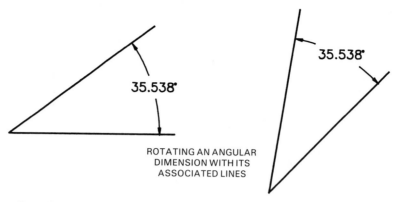

ROTATING AN ANGULAR
DIMENSION WITH ITS
ASSOCIATED LINES

Fig. 13-20. When angular dimensions are rotated, the dimension text remains horizontal.

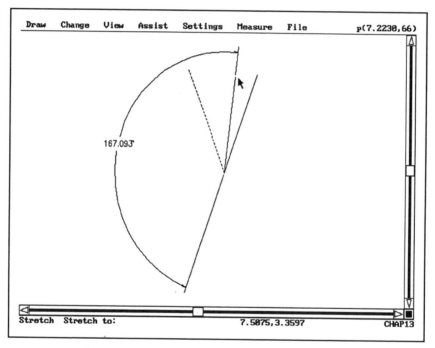

Fig. 13-21. If you stretch an angular measurement too close for the dimension to fit, AutoSketch places the dimension outside the lines being dimensioned.

Without a leader, the measurement is placed within the circle. This is done on larger circles. With a leader, the diameter is placed outside and the leader points toward the circle's center but just touches the circle. Leaders are used for smaller circles where the measurement would not fit within the circles. Leaders are also used when the measurement would clutter the view.

The diameter symbol (ϕ) precedes diameter measurements. This symbol replaces the DIA. formerly located behind diameter dimensions.

AutoSketch does not have a specific command to dimension circular shapes. To place a dimension inside a circle, use an aligned dimension and dimension using the attach mode

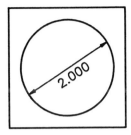

Fig. 13-22. To dimension the
diameter of a circular feature,
use an aligned dimension.

Quadrant. Then pick opposite sides of the circle. The dimension will indicate the true diameter, Fig. 13-22. To place a leader, follow the directions given later in this chapter.

RADIUS DIMENSIONING

Radius dimensions specify the size of arcs and other partial circles. Like diameter dimensions, the radius dimensions measurement can be placed inside the curve. However, most radius dimensioning is done with a leader pointing to the circular shape. Refer to Fig. 13-3. The letter "R" is used to indicate radius and precedes all radius dimensions.

AutoSketch does not have a specific command to dimension arcs. To dimension large arcs where the dimension is placed inside the circle, use an aligned dimension and dimension using the attach points Center and Midpoint, Fig. 13-23. To place a leader, follow the directions in the next section.

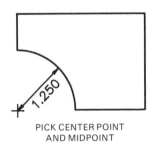

PICK CENTER POINT
AND MIDPOINT

Fig. 13-23. To dimension large arcs, use an aligned dimension
and the Attach modes Center and Midpoint.

LEADERS

Leaders are used to point out dimensions and notes. AutoSketch does not have a specific command to place leaders on the drawing. You will have to draw an arrow and the proper lines as mentioned earlier in the text. It is best to draw just the arrow and one line first. Then, copy the leader by the arrow vertex and place it where needed. After placing the leader, rotate it to the proper angle. Finally, add the .125 inch horizontal tail to the leader and place the text. See Fig. 13-24.

Arrowheads usually look better solid. You can make a solid arrowhead using the **Fill Region** command. Set the Grid and Snap spacing to .09. Draw an arrowhead .18 inch long

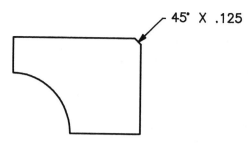

Fig. 13-24. Placing a leader used to dimension a chamfer.

and .09 inch wide. To create a leader, connect a line to the tip and extend it outward about 2 inches. You can always pick the leader to move by using the Attach mode Endpoint and picking the leader line closer to the arrow.

GENERAL RULES FOR DIMENSIONING

There are common rules drafters should follow when placing dimensions:

- Place dimensions on views that show the true shape of the feature being measured.
- Avoid crossing dimension lines. If an extension line must cross a dimension line, most drafters break the extension line around the dimension line. This is not possible with AutoSketch-placed dimensions since you cannot use the **Break** command on dimensions.
- Avoid dimensioning to hidden lines. Dimension features in the view where they appear as object lines.
- The same dimension should not be repeated on different views, unless required to understand the drawing.
- Smaller dimensions are placed nearest the view, while larger, or overall dimensions, are farthest from the view. See the section on stacked dimensions.
- The person reading the drawing should be able to determine all sizes and shapes, without having to use a ruler. (In fact, some CAD plots are not to scale.)
- Locate dimensions together, rather than scattering them about the drawing. This practice makes the dimensions easier to read.
- On manufactured parts, dimensions should be given from finished surfaces and center lines. On architectural drawings, dimensions should be given from the outside of exterior walls and the centers of interior walls.

TYPICAL DIMENSIONING PRACTICES

Items to be dimensioned can be broken down into geometric shapes. Here are some typical dimension practices for common geometric shapes. Consult a comprehensive drafting text for additional dimensioning practices.

Rectangular shapes. Dimension both the width and height of rectangular shapes. In a two-view drawing, place the dimension between the two views unless the object is large. Extension lines are extended from the most descriptive view. Square shapes may be dimensioned using the square symbol. See Fig. 13-25 for examples.

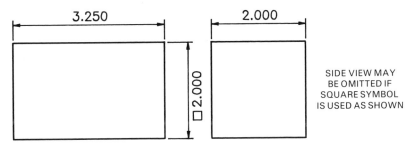

Fig. 13-25. Dimensioning rectangular shapes.

Cylindrical shapes. Dimension cylindrical shapes in the view where the part appears rectangular. This includes both the diameter and length. For simple cylindrical shapes, the circular view may be omitted. See Fig. 13-26.

Conical shapes. Conical shapes are dimensioned by the end diameters and length. You can also give the base dimension, taper angle, and length. See Fig. 13-27.

Dimensioning holes. Internal cylinders, or holes, are dimensioned with a diameter dimension in the view where the feature is circular. Holes may be drilled or reamed. They can also

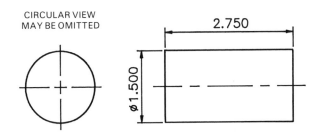

Fig. 13-26. Dimensioning cylindrical shapes.

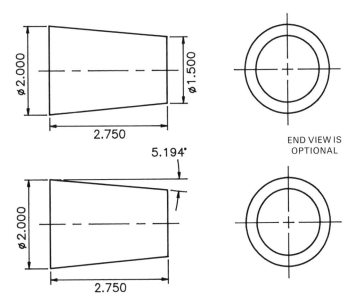

Fig. 13-27. Dimensioning conical shapes.

be counterbored to a specific depth, countersunk, or spotfaced. When holes are counterbored or countersunk, dimensions should indicate this with a local note or symbol. See Fig. 13-28. Where it is not clear that a hole goes through the part, the word "THRU" should follow the dimension.

Slotted holes. Slots provide room for adjustment when fastening parts. They can be milled in solid metal or punched into sheet metal. There are two general methods for dimensioning slotted holes. When punched into sheet metal, the center of the slot is usually located. When milled in thicker stock, the centers of the ending arcs are generally located. See Fig. 13-29.

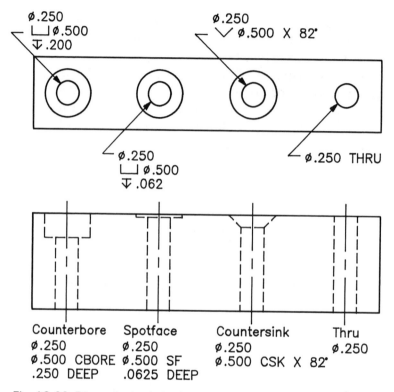

Fig. 13-28. Dimensioning holes for manufactured products. Note how symbols can be used to represent various drilling and machining operations.

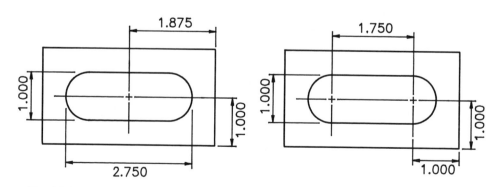

Fig. 13-29. Dimensioning slotted holes. Dimension the size and slot center for punched slots, and the size and both radius centers for milled slots.

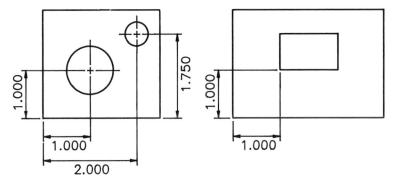

Fig. 13-30. Locate holes by their centers and rectangular features by their corner.

Locating holes and rectangular features. Holes and round parts are always located by their centers, not by the edges. Rectangular features are located by one corner, Fig. 13-30. When in a circular pattern, the holes may be dimensioned using rectangular or polar coordinate dimensioning methods, Fig. 13-31.

Fillets and rounds. Fillets and rounds are dimension by their radius. They can be dimensioned individually, as repetitive features, and/or with a general note, such as: UNLESS OTHERWISE SPECIFIED, ALL FILLETS AND ROUNDS R.0625.

Angles. Two methods for dimensioning angles are coordinate and angular dimensions. Coordinate dimensioning uses horizontal and vertical linear commands. These dimensions mark the edges of the angle. The angular dimensioning method gives a linear dimension to one corner and the angle in degrees. See Fig. 13-32.

Chamfers. Chamfers can be dimensioned with a leader when they are 45 degrees. Refer to Fig. 13-24. Chamfers that are not 45 degrees are dimensioned with two linear measurements, or a linear and angular dimension. See Fig. 13-32.

Repetitive features. Multiple holes or fillets of the same radius can be dimensioned on one hole or arc. A note giving the number of times the feature is found is added to the dimension. Specify the number of features, then an "X", followed by the size. Refer to Fig. 13-31.

ALTERNATE DIMENSIONING PRACTICES

A current trend in manufacturing is to use computers to control machining and drilling operations. This has affected some dimensioning practices. Computers commonly move in precise increments measured from a specific place. Therefore, most dimensions are measured from a common point, called a *datum.* Datum dimensioning methods do not necessarily require dimension lines. With *coordinate dimensioning,* dimension text is aligned with the extension lines. The distances of features are given from the datum. Holes are identified with a size symbol, usually a letter. The sizes are usually shown in a table beside or below the drawing. See Fig. 13-33.

Tabular dimensioning is another technique using the principles of rectangular coordinate dimensioning. Measurements are taken from the X, Y, and Z axes and recorded in a table, Fig. 13-34. They are not dimensioned directly on the drawing. Hole diameters or other feature sizes are also given in the table. This method is particularly useful where there are a large number of features to locate.

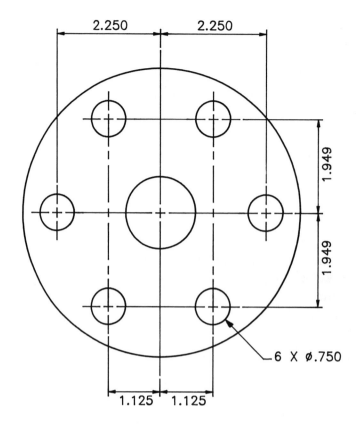

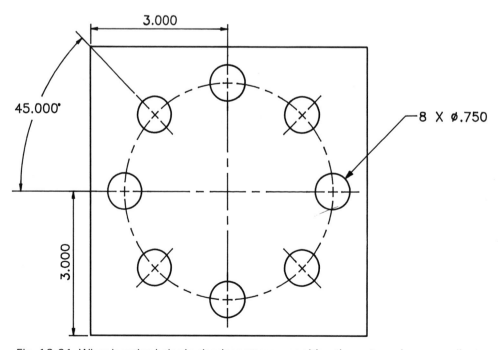

Fig. 13-31. When locating holes in circular pattern, use either the rectangular or coordinate method. Note how the number of holes is indicated with an ''X.''

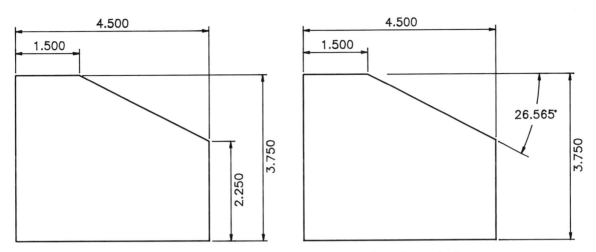

Fig. 13-32. Dimensioning angles by linear and angular methods.

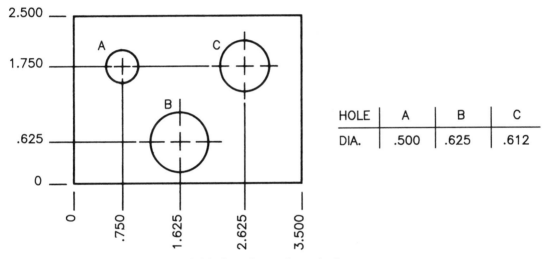

HOLE	A	B	C
DIA.	.500	.625	.612

Fig. 13-33. Coordinate dimensioning system.

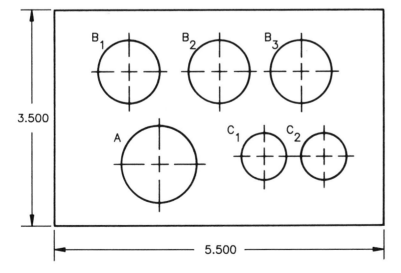

HOLE	SIZE	X	Y	Z
A	⌀.750	2.225	.575	THRU
B_1	⌀.500	1.110	3.010	THRU
B_2	⌀.375	3.235	3.030	THRU
B_3	⌀.425	4.025	2.750	THRU
C_1	⌀.125	3.750	1.000	THRU
C_2	⌀.100	4.700	1.000	THRU

Fig. 13-34. Feature size and location are shown in a table with the tabular dimensioning system.

SUMMARY

Dimensions are important aspects of most technical drawings. Dimensions, consisting of numerals, lines, symbols, and notes, provide information about the size and shape of a product. AutoSketch makes the process of applying dimensions to a drawing an easy task.

Dimensions generally describe the size or location of product features. Size dimensions give the width, length, height, diameter, or radius of a feature. Location dimensions give the position of a feature.

Several elements are used when dimensioning a drawing. The most common elements include extension lines, dimension lines, arrowheads, dimension text, leaders, and notes or symbols. When these elements are combined correctly, they provide exact information about how a product is constructed.

AutoSketch provides a means of applying horizontal, vertical, and aligned linear dimensions. The units of measurement can be displayed in either decimal or architectural format, depending on your application. In addition, AutoSketch Version 3.0 provides five different types of arrowheads to meet your needs.

Angular dimensions can also be applied using AutoSketch. This can be used to dimension two nonparallel surfaces. If an area in which you wish to insert a dimension is too small, AutoSketch allows you to move it to a new position.

AutoSketch dimensions are associative, meaning that the dimensions are associated with the points you pick when placing them. When editing drawings with dimensions, you must include the dimensions in your selection set. When the object you are editing is modified, the dimensions will also be changed to reflect the new measurement.

Dimensioning practices vary from industry to industry. However, the basic dimensioning standards are very similar. When dimensioning standards are followed, it allows for consistency and readability from one industry to another.

NEW TERMS

Dimensions, feature, size dimensions, location dimensions, extension line, dimension line, arrowhead, **Arrow** command, dimension text, unidirectional dimensions, aligned dimensions, dual dimensioning, leader, general notes, specific notes, **Units** command, Decimal format, Architectural format, decimal suffix, linear dimensions, horizontal dimension, **Horiz. Dimension** command, vertical dimension, **Vert. Dimension** command, **Align Dimension** command, chained dimensions, stacked dimensions, angular dimensions, **Angle Dimension** command, associativity, dimension points, selection set, diameter dimension, radius dimension, coordinate dimensioning, tabular dimensioning.

REVIEW QUESTIONS

Write your answers on a separate sheet of paper. Do not write in this book.
1. Dimensions show _____ and _____.
2. How does AutoSketch make dimensioning an easier process?
3. _____ dimensions give the width, length, height, diameter, or radius of a feature.
4. _____ lines mark the beginning and end of a dimension.
5. List the elements of a typical horizontal dimension.

6. Dimension text is the numerical value of the _____ plus any needed symbols or _____.
7. Explain the difference between unidirectional and aligned systems of dimensioning.
8. Give examples of when leaders are used.
9. Explain the difference between general and specific notes.
10. Where do you set the unit of measurement that determines how dimension text is displayed?
11. What AutoSketch commands allow you to place linear dimensions?
12. To place a linear dimension, how many points must you pick?
13. To stretch an angular dimension, you must include all the dimension points in the selection set. True or false?
14. Radius dimensions should be used to dimension holes and cylindrical parts. True or false?
15. What two methods might you choose to dimension circles and arcs with AutoSketch?
16. The same dimension can be repeated on different views if required to understand the drawing. True or false?
17. Dimension cylindrical shapes in the view where the part appears _____ .
18. Two methods to dimension angles are _____ and _____ methods.
19. With _____ dimensioning, measurements are taken from the X, Y, and Z axes and recorded in a table. Measurements are not shown directly on the drawing.

ACTIVITIES

Here is a mixture of drawing activities to develop your skills with dimensioning. Save your AutoSketch drawings on your file disk, not on the program disk. Clear the previous drawing from screen and memory using **New** before completing each activity.

Develop each drawing. Determine the drawing area required, and set limits or select a prototype developed in the activities of Chapter 10. Add the proper dimensions, following accepted dimensioning practices, except where AutoSketch specifically does not follow these practices. For example, open arrows and the aligned dimensioning system are allowed. Place different linetypes on different layers. Also use the colors recommended in this text for the linetypes. Place dimensions on a separate layer. Save the drawing as C13A?, replacing the question mark with the activity number.

1-5. Develop each drawing. Add the proper dimensions, following accepted dimensioning practices.

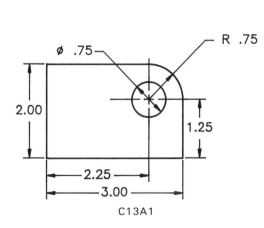

C13A1

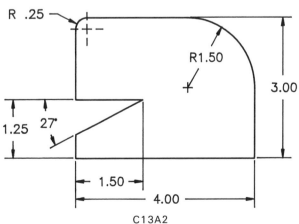

C13A2

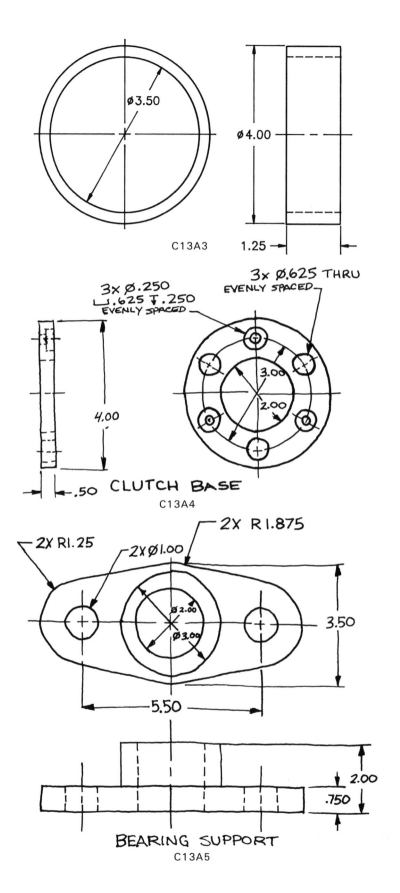

ø3.50

ø4.00

C13A3   1.25

3x ø.250
⌴.625 ⊤.250
EVENLY SPACED

3x ø.625 THRU
EVENLY SPACED

3.00

2.00

.50   CLUTCH BASE
C13A4

2X R1.25

2X ø1.00

2X R1.875

ø2.00

ø3.00

3.50

5.50

2.00

.750

BEARING SUPPORT
C13A5

6-10. Develop each drawing. Use the .25 grid spacing for size reference. Add the proper dimensions, following accepted dimensioning practices.

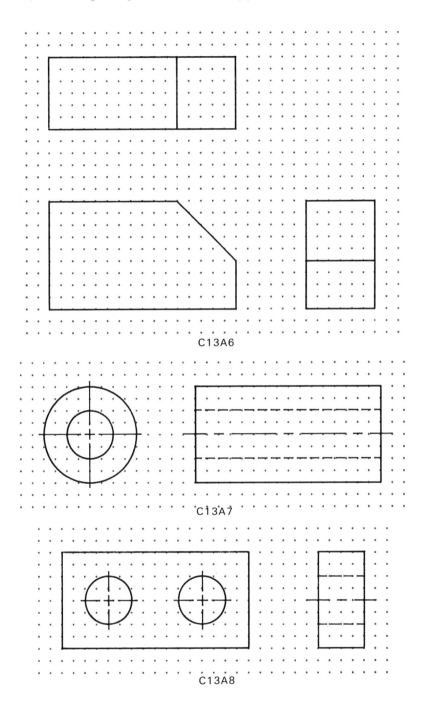

C13A6

C13A7

C13A8

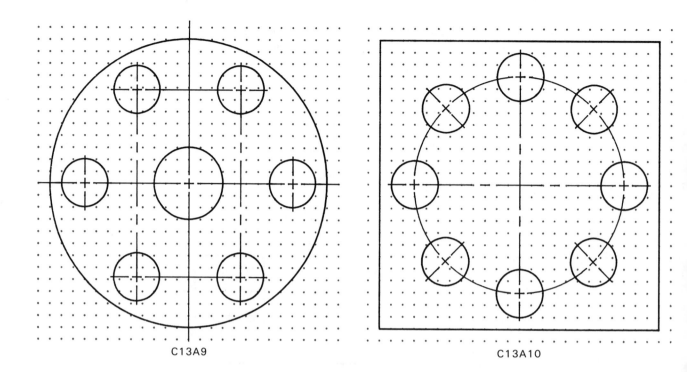

C13A9

C13A10

11-25. Place dimensions on 10 of the following 15 drawings completed in activities found in previous chapters: C7A17, C7A18, C7A19, C7A20, C7A21, C8A2, C8A3, C8A4, C8A5, C10A11, C10A12, C11A6, C11A7, C11A8, C11A9. Follow accepted dimensioning practices, except where AutoSketch does not follow these practices.

Chapter 14

PLOTTING AND PRINTING DRAWINGS

After studying this chapter, you will be able to:
- List the steps to plot or print a drawing.
- Set plot and print specifications to adjust how the drawing will appear on paper.
- Plot drawings to disk files.
- Recognize various plotting media.
- Select the proper plotter pen for the type of plot.
- Troubleshoot and correct plotting and printing problems.
- Identify tips to make plotting and printing quicker and easier.

Plotting is the process of making a hardcopy print of a drawing by sending the drawing data to a printer or plotter. You can make a plot at any time while working on a drawing.

Two types of plots are typically made. *Check plots* are low-resolution prints made with a dot matrix or laser printer. These are created for a quick check on the design progress. *Final plots* are high-quality prints made with a pen plotter or other high-quality output device. They are used for copying and distributing the design. AutoSketch also allows you to plot the drawing to a file on disk. The file can later be plotted outside of AutoSketch, or imported into a desktop publishing program.

The four plotting commands are found in the **File** menu. If you configure AutoSketch with a plotter, the commands are **Pen Info, Plot Area, Plot Name,** and **Plot,** Fig. 14-1A. If you configure AutoSketch with a printer, the commands are **Pen Info, Print Area, Print Name,** and **Print,** Fig 14-1B. All of these commands are grayed out if a plotter or printer was not chosen when AutoSketch was installed and configured.

Make sure that the plotter or printer is connected and set up properly before trying any plot. There are special set-up steps for certain types of hardcopy devices. These procedures are covered thoroughly in the *Installing AutoSketch* guide, *AutoSketch User Guide* (Version 2.0), and the plotter's user manual.

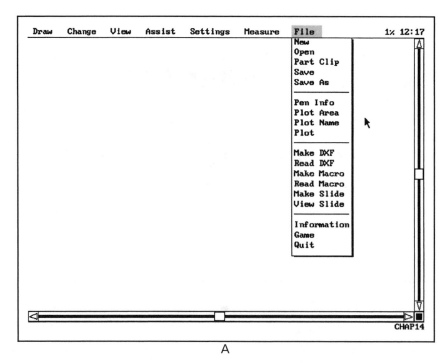

A

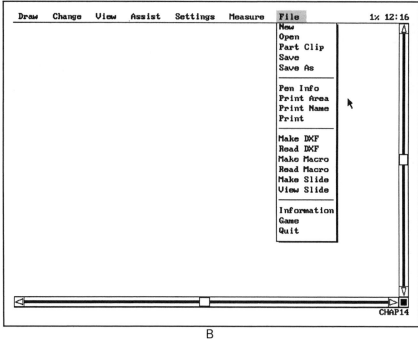

B

Fig. 14-1. Plotting commands are found in the File menu.

MAKING A QUICK FIRST PLOT

AutoSketch Version 3.0 allows you to plot the drawing on screen without first making any settings to the **Pen Info, Plot Area,** or **Plot Name** commands. Simply select the **Plot** command. Your drawing will be output to the full extent of the paper size. This procedure assumes that you set up your hardcopy device properly, and that you did not change any plot settings before plotting the drawing.

PLOTTING PROCEDURE

In most cases, however, you want more control of how your drawing is plotted. You should then follow these plotting steps rather than using the "quick first plot" method.

Setting the *plot specifications* is the most important and time-consuming part of the plotting procedure. The final appearance of the drawing depends on how you set these options. Do not expect to get the correct plot the first time. You may waste a few sheets of paper until you learn how plot specifications affect the final output. The following general procedure can be used to plot a drawing.

1. Use the **Pen Info** command to set which pen number plots what color objects on screen. (This step is not required for single-pen plotters or printers.)
2. Define the paper size and plot area using the **Plot Area** command.
3. Enter a plot file name using the **Plot Name** command only if you will be plotting to a file rather than to a hardcopy device.
4. Select the **Plot** command to start the plotting process.

PEN INFO

Pen information is needed when using a multipen plotter. The values confirm which pen is picked to plot what color objects. They also determine how fast the pen moves across the paper. Select the **File** menu and **Pen Info** command to set pen specifications. The **Pen Specifications** dialogue box then appears, Fig. 14-2.

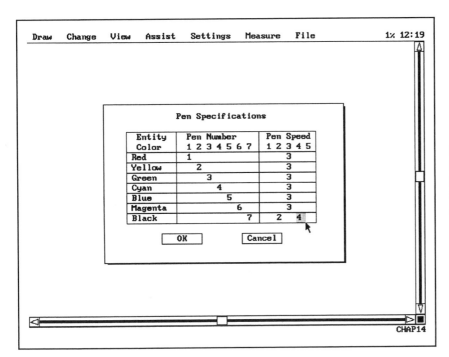

Fig. 14-2. The Pen Specifications dialogue box allows you to set the Pen Number for each color and the Pen Speed.

Setting Pen Number

The *Pen Number* value determines which pen number the plotter chooses to plot certain color objects. This setting is used only for multipen plotters. It is not available when printing or using a single-pen plotter. Pick the number opposite the *Entity Color* you wish to set. The number of pens included in the **Pen Specifications** dialogue box depends on the hardcopy device that is configured with AutoSketch.

Why Use Multipen Plotters?

There are two reasons to use multipen plotters to output certain color objects:
- When creating drawings, draw objects using color to represent different line widths. Set the *Pen Number* at plot time so that the proper width pen (thin or thick) is chosen to make your drawing conform to standards.
- You might want objects plotted with the same color as they were actually drawn on screen. This is important if you are a graphic artist making a multicolor drawing.

Setting Pen Speed

Pen Speed is the speed at which the plotter draws with each pen. AutoSketch provides five settings; setting 1 is the slowest and setting 5 is the fastest. You can set a different speed for each object color. Lines become thin and light, or the pen can even skip when plotting too fast. A slower pen speed may prevent some pens from skipping and can darken lines. Generally, set the speed slower for fine-tip pens and faster for broad-tip pens. Setting pen speed is useful only if your plotter supports programmable pen speeds.

PLOT AREA

The **Plot Area** command accesses the dialogue box shown in Fig. 14-3. The number of selections may be different than shown, depending on the plotter or printer you have configured. Here you can set:
- The paper size.
- What part of the drawing is plotted.
- The scale of the drawing.
- Whether the drawing is rotated on the paper.

The dialogue box for AutoSketch Version 2.0 is laid out somewhat differently, but has the same commands. Once you set these values and pick *OK,* a Plot Box appears on screen. The *Plot Box* represents your paper size and shows the area of the drawing that will be plotted, Fig. 14-4. Plot Boxes are discussed later in the chapter.

Setting Paper Size

AutoSketch provides paper size choices for each size supported by the plotter or printer you chose during configuration. Pick the box next to the paper size you will be using. The usable area of that particular paper size appears next to *X Plot Size* and *Y Plot Size*. If desired, you can enter a special paper size up to the maximum limits of your plotter or printer. Position the pointer at the *X Plot Size* option and type in the dimensions. Press *OK* to accept the value. Follow the same procedure for the *Y Plot Size* value. If you enter a paper size that is too large, the dialogue box in Fig. 14-5 appears.

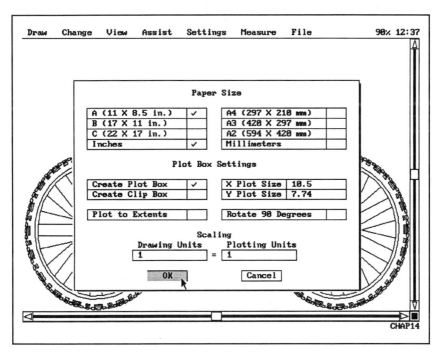

Fig. 14-3. The Plot Area command accesses this dialogue box to set the paper size, scaling, rotation, Plot Box, and Clip Box.

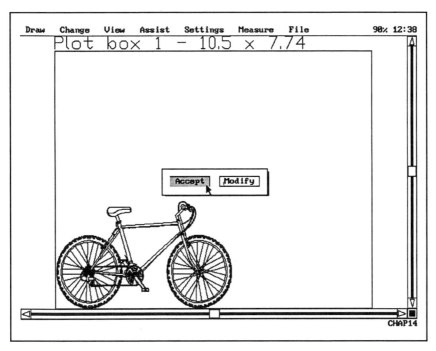

Fig. 14-4. The Plot Box shows how the drawing will fit on the paper when plotted.

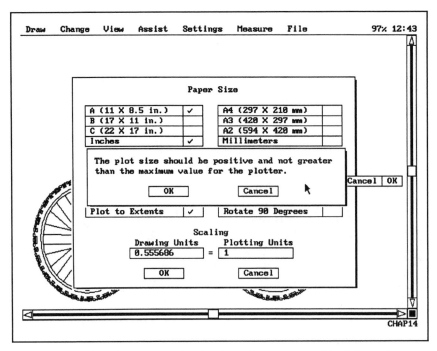

Fig. 14-5. Entering a paper size that is too large causes this dialogue box to appear.

Setting Plot Rotation

Most CAD systems plot or print a drawing so that you read it with the paper length running horizontally. This is called the *landscape format*. AutoSketch sets the *Rotate 90 Degrees* box so that this happens by default for most plotters and printers. If you want the paper length running vertically, check the *Rotate 90 Degrees* box. This is called *portrait format*. Rotating the plot affects how large you can plot the drawing. A wide drawing is best plotted with the paper length horizontal, not vertical.

Setting Plot Scale

The *plot scale* specifies the plotted drawing size as a ratio to the actual size of the drawing. This is a very powerful function. You can draw with full-size units and then when plotting or printing, you can scale the drawing so that it fits on the chosen paper size. Fig. 14-3 shows that 1 drawing unit will equal 1 plotted unit (full scale).

Plotting to Extents. AutoSketch Version 3.0 has a special scaling option, called *Plot to Extents*. When you pick this option, AutoSketch automatically enters a scaling factor so the entire drawing fits as large as possible on the selected paper size. It also takes into account whether you decided to rotate the drawing. Use this option unless you need to plot or print the drawing to an exact scale.

Plotting to Extents in Version 2.0. AutoSketch Version 2.0 does not have a *Plot to Extents* option. However, you can calculate the scaling factor so that the drawing fills the paper. This method assumes that the drawing will be plotted or printed in landscape format.

1. Use the **Distance** command to measure the width of your drawing.
2. Use the **Distance** command to measure the height of your drawing.
3. Divide the longest dimension of the paper by the width of your drawing.

4. Divide the shortest dimension of the paper by the height of your drawing.
5. Enter the lower of the values in Steps 3 and 4 as *Drawing Units*.
6. Set the *Plotting Units* value to 1.

Setting Exact Scale. Chapter 10 discussed how to set limits so that you can choose an exact scale when plotting or printing. This ensures that the drawing fits on a standard-size sheet. Be sure that the *Plot to Extents* box is not checked when manually entering a scale factor.

Precaution When Scaling Drawings. A problem may arise when drawings are scaled up or down to fit a certain sheet size. The size of text and dimensions also shrink or expand. This makes the text either too small or too large to conform to standards. Several check plots may be needed to ensure that the text and dimensions are legible.

Previewing the Plot and Plot Box

AutoSketch adds a Plot Box to the current layer when you leave the **Plot Area** command's dialogue box. The *Plot Box* shows what portion of your drawing will be plotted. The Plot Box is numbered and represents the paper size on which you are plotting. This allows you to verify how the drawing will appear on paper. Fig. 14-6 shows the Plot Box that appears if you select *Plot to Extents*.

AutoSketch Version 3.0 also displays a dialogue box to *Accept* the Plot Box or *Modify* your settings. Once you accept the Plot Box, you can use the **Move** and **Scale** commands to alter the Plot Box. This allows you to plot the entire drawing or only a portion of it. AutoSketch automatically adjusts the scale if you **Scale** the Plot Box.

Using the Clip Box

You can plot only a portion of the drawing within the Plot Box using a Clip Box. The *Clip Box* allows you to retain the plot scale while focusing on one part of the drawing. When you

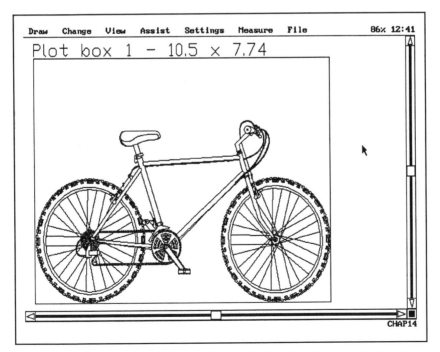

Fig. 14-6. When Plot to Extents is checked, the drawing fills the entire Plot Box.

pick the *Create Clip Box* option when setting the plot area, a default-size Clip Box appears, Fig. 14-7. It is somewhat smaller than the Plot Box and is centered within it. You can use **Move** and **Scale** commands to alter the Clip Box. See Fig. 14-8.

As a general rule, use the Plot Box to set the final scale and position of your drawing on the paper. Use the Clip Box to remove any portions of the drawing that you do not want plotted.

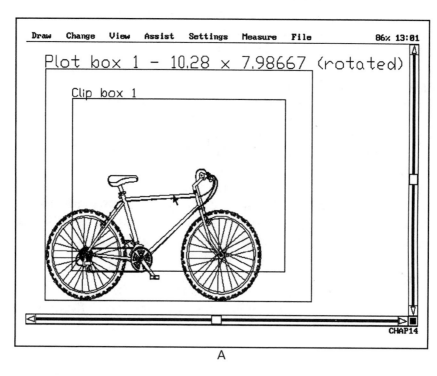

A

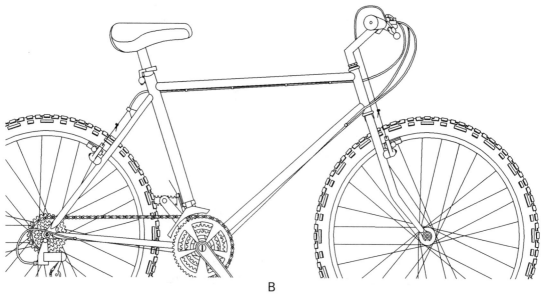

B

Fig. 14-7. A–The default Clip Box appears centered within the Plot Box.
B–Plotted drawing.

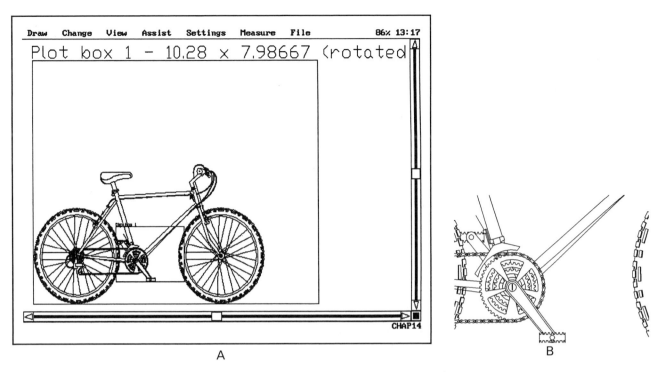

Fig. 14-8. A–Example of manipulating the Clip Box. B–Plotted drawing.

Resetting Plot Specifications

If you do not like the appearance of the Plot Box, select the **Plot Area** command again and reset the specifications. When you pick *OK* to close the dialogue box, a second Plot Box appears. Although several Plot Boxes can be created, only one can be visible at plot time. Extra Plot Boxes should be erased or placed on an invisible layer. If the Plot Box does not appear at all, check for these typical problems:

* The Plot Box is too large to fit on screen. Remedy: Use the **Last Plot Box** command from the **View** menu so that the Plot Box fills the screen. You may want to erase the box, select **Zoom Full,** and reset the plot settings to create a new Plot Box.
* The current layer is not visible. Remedy: Select the **Layer** command from the **Settings** menu and make the layer visible.

PLOTTING ON PAPER

Once you have entered the plot specifications using **Pen Info** and **Plot Area**, several steps are required to plot on paper:

1. Load the paper.
2. Install pens if you have a pen plotter.
3. Ready the plotter or printer.
4. Select the **Plot** or **Print** command.

Loading Paper

Hardcopy devices hold paper differently. Microgrip pen plotters hold the paper with pinch rollers at each end. Paper on a flatbed pen plotter is usually held with tape. Laser printers automatically take paper from a paper tray. Dot matrix printers can use either cut sheets or fan-fold sheets with a tractor feed. Load the paper according to your plotter or printer model.

Installing Pens

Pen plotters require that you prepare and insert the pens according to the manufacturer's directions. Some plotters also require that you screw the pen into an adaptor before inserting it into the plotter. When using disposable liquid ink pens, press the tip into the cartridge. Plastic-tip and fiber-tip pens simply need to be uncapped. Check that you have the proper pen and types of adaptors for your plotter model and drawing media.

Insert the pen or pen/adaptor assembly into the plotter. Pens for multipen plotters are inserted into a carousel or pen rack. Make sure the proper pen type is placed into the slot number that corresponds with the value set with the **Pen Info** command. When using single-pen plotters, insert pen number one directly into the gripper.

Readying the Plotter or Printer

Plotters and printers have local and remote (on-line) command buttons on the control panel. Make sure the device is ready to receive instructions from the computer, not the control panel. The specific buttons to press to ready the plotter or printer are identified in the owner's manual.

Starting the Plot

Begin the plotting procedure by selecting the **Plot** or **Print** command from the **File** menu. The computer will "think" for a moment and then the plot begins. Single-pen plotters that support multiple pens stop during the procedure for you to insert additional pens. When inserting a new pen, avoid touching the plot with the pen tip. Multipen plotters automatically select the proper pen. When the plot is finished, remove the paper and tightly recap all pens.

MAKING MULTIPEN PLOTS WITH A SINGLE-PEN PLOTTER

Some single-pen plotters cannot be used for multipen plots. They will not stop for you to insert a new pen to plot different colors. However, you can still make multipen plots if you follow some basic rules while creating the drawing.

1. Assign object colors to layers. For example, place green objects on layer 3. Place red objects on layer 2. Do this for all colors used in the drawing.
2. When you plot, have only one layer visible at a time. Insert the pen width or color associated with objects on that layer and plot the drawing.
3. Do not remove the paper when the first plot is finished. Instead, press the button that resets the plotter. Then, hide the visible layer and make a different layer visible. Select the pen width or color associated with objects on that layer and plot the drawing again. If your plotter has good repeatability, objects on the second plot should align properly with objects on the first plot.
4. Repeat Step 3 for each layer. When you are finished, you will have a "multipen" plot. Remember that the repeatability of your plotter determines the precision of the plot.

PLOTTING TO A FILE

AutoSketch allows you to plot a drawing to a file on disk rather than to a hardcopy device. You can then do one of two things with the plot file:

- You can send the file to a hardcopy device outside of AutoSketch. This method is helpful if your computer does not have a plotter attached, but you have access to another computer that has a plotter.
- You can import the plot file into a desktop publishing program. (See Chapter 16.)

Plot to File Procedure

A few simple steps must be followed to plot your drawing to a file. Select the **Plot Name** command from the **File** menu to name your output file. Picking **Plot Name** brings up the **Plot Filename** dialogue box. Enter the file name of the plot. Make sure you have a disk in the drive you specify. For example, Fig. 14-9 shows plotting the bicycle drawing to the A: floppy drive with the name BIKE. Pick the extended *OK* box and *OK* at the bottom of the dialogue box.

Note: The **Plot Name** command will be grayed out if you configure AutoSketch to plot drawings through the parallel or serial ports. You must reconfigure AutoSketch and select the "File" option at the Plot connection prompt.

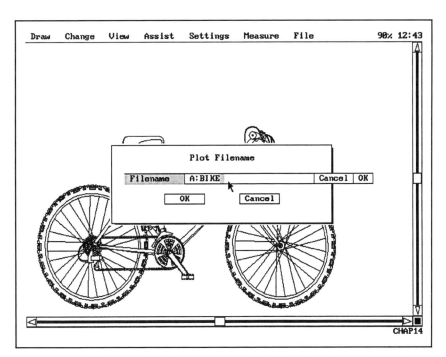

Fig. 14-9. Select the Plot Name command to plot a drawing to a disk file.
AutoSketch must be configured to plot to file.

Outputting a Plot File to a Plotter

When outputting a plot file to a plotter, you must plot to the device chosen during installation. For example, if you chose a Hewlett-Packard plotter and the "File" option, the drawing file must be copied to a Hewlett-Packard plotter outside of AutoSketch. Plotting to any other device will result in strange images, or nothing at all.

A filed drawing is plotted outside of AutoSketch by using the **COPY** command at the DOS prompt. (DOS and prompts are discussed in detail in Chapter 16.) The word FILENAME shown here refers to the name you gave the drawing at plot time.

    C〉COPY A:FILENAME.PLT PRN: /B

This command is used to send a drawing from drive A: to a printer connected to the computer's parallel port. Most hardcopy devices are connected to a different port, called the *serial port*. Most computers have at least two serial ports. You must first use the **MODE** command to set up the communication between computer and serial port to use the serial port. This procedure is covered in the *Installing AutoSketch* guide (Version 3.0) or the *AutoSketch Reference Manual*. Then, enter one of the following commands:

    C〉COPY A:FILENAME.PLT COM1: /B

    C〉COPY A:FILENAME.PLT COM2: /B

The command that you enter depends on which serial port (COM1: or COM2:) the plotter is connected to. Once you enter the **COPY** command, the plotter should begin outputting the drawing. If problems arise, consult the AutoSketch documentation.

DRAWING MEDIA

Drawing media are the materials that you plot on. Drawing media includes paper, vellum, and film. Most are cut sheets, except for dot matrix paper which is often fan-folded for tractor-feed printers. Some devices, such as laser printers, may require special media.

Paper refers to a variety of wood- and rag-base media. *Bond paper* is a low-cost, opaque, white paper similar to duplicating paper. *Rag bond* is a cotton-fiber mediumthat is more durable than bond paper. *Gloss paper* is clay-coated and provides high-contrast plots. It is often used when bright multiple-color effects are used for graphics and charts. *Translucent paper* is a semi-transparent medium, similar to tracing paper. It is a low-cost substitute for vellum.

Vellum is a rag-base paper. It is treated with resin to make it transparent, strong, and durable. This media shows ghost marks if you fold or bend it. Most types of pens work on vellum.

Film is a polyester-base transparent media. It is used for high-quality plots. The film may be coated on one or both sides to accept pen ink. A matte finish is a nonglossy coating that accepts liquid ink pens quite well. Clear film is used for overhead transparencies. It has a water-base coating for use with felt- and plastic-tip pens. The combination produces crisp, bright colors.

PLOTTER PENS

Several types of plotter pens are available. They include liquid ink (refillable and disposable), fiber-tip, plastic-tip, roller ball, and pressurized ballpoint pens.

Liquid ink pens are high-quality pens in which a liquid ink flows through a narrow metal tip. They are commonly used for final engineering and architectural plots. Refillable liquid ink pens require a great deal of handling and maintenance. Disposable liquid ink pens do not require as much handling, yet still provide good-quality plots. Stainless steel, jewel, tungsten carbide, or ceramic tips may be used for liquid ink pens. They vary in durability and line quality.

Fiber-tip and *plastic-tip pens* have a tip with medium hardness. They are excellent for graphics and charts where an area is to be filled with a solid color. There is a wide selection of bright colors and bold or fine lines. These types of pens are not suitable for final plots because the tip widens with use. Plastic tips wear less, but should still be used with caution.

Fiber-tip and plastic-tip pens are usually available for use with two types of inks. One is designed for use on paper. The other is designed for use on clear film. If film ink is used on paper, it may bleed into the paper.

Roller ball and *pressurized ballpoint pens* are used less frequently in industry. Roller ball pens plot well on clear overhead film. They produce darker and more consistent lines than fiber-tip pens, but are not available in as many colors. Pressurized ballpoint pens can operate at extremely high speeds and complete many plots during a day. However, the line quality is generally not as good as other pen types.

MAINTENANCE

Proper maintenance of drawing media and pens is important. Store drawing media flat, not vertical or rolled up. It should not be exposed to excessive humidity. Cap the pens after each use. Store them in an airtight plastic container with a damp sponge to keep them in good working condition.

TROUBLESHOOTING PLOTTER PROBLEMS

No matter how carefully you select pens for the drawing media, troubles will arise. These may be caused by worn-out pens, unfit plot speeds, improper pen pressure, or environmental problems. The chart in Fig. 14-10 provides causes and solutions for common pen plotting problems.

PLOTTING TIPS

Plotting can be a time-consuming process. Plots may take a couple minutes for a check plot or over an hour for a final plot of a complex drawing. Take these helpful hints into account as you prepare to plot your drawings.
- Use preprinted borders and title blocks, when possible, to save time.
- Make reduced scale plots to avoid plotting drawings on large media. This not only saves time, but also pen ink and paper.
- Reproduce multiple prints. It is not feasible to produce multiple sets of prints with a plotter.
- Plot at the highest speed. Use the pen that will plot the fastest, yet still provide the necessary line quality.
- Establish a plotting center, plotting times, or a plotting service in your school or business. A plotter running all the time can disturb drafters and consume valuable computer time.

Problem	Cause	Solution
Pen does not write	Pen is clogged because: 1. Ink is dry at tip 2. Pen is out of ink	1. Clean pen, and restart 2. Refill or replace pen
Pen writes by hand, but not on plotter	Pen height set wrong	Adjust pen height
Pen writes on plotter initially, then quits	1. Worn-out pen 2. Pen-down force too high 3. Bad start-up technique 4. Pen/media mismatch 5. Pen ran out of ink 6. Dirty or contaminated surface	1. Replace pen* 2. Reduce pen-down force 3. Change to correct technique 4. Change pen or change media 5. Refill or replace pen 6. Clean surface *If this happens often, or too soon: change media
Pen writes on plotter, but lines skip	1. Dirty pen 2. Plotting too fast 3. Ink/media mismatch	1. Clean or replace pen 2. Decrease plotting speed 3. Change ink or change media
Line width decreases from start to middle of line	Plotting too fast	Decrease plotting speed
Line width varies	Poor quality media	Change media
Lines feather	1. Ink/media mismatch 2. Plotting too slow	1. Change media or change ink 2. Increase plotting speed
Ink beads on surface	Ink/media mismatch	Change media or change ink
Lines too wide	Worn out pen	Replace pen
Lines not dark enough	1. Wrong type pen 2. Plotting too fast 3. Wrong type ink 4. Pen down force too high	1. Use v-groove pen on film \\ 2. Decrease plotting speed 3. Change ink 4. Reduce pen down force
Line darkness varies	Ink/media mismatch	Change media or change ink
Ink smudges on surface	1. Wrong type ink 2. Ink not given enough time to dry 3. Area is too humid	1. Change ink 2. Change program to allow for longer drying time 3. Reduce humidity
Pen leaks	1. Bad start-up technique 2. Dirty pen	1. Change to correct technique 2. Clean or replace pen

Fig. 14-10. Causes and solutions to common plotting problems. (Koh-I-Noor Rapidograph)

- Eliminate unnecessary plots. Never plot a drawing just to see it on paper unless there is a need for a check or approval.
- Use single pen widths and colors. Plotting multiple line widths and colors require that the plotter exchange pens.
- Reduce costs by using the lowest acceptable quality supplies.
- Use solid linetypes when possible. Hidden and center lines take much more time to plot.
- Hold down the [Ctrl] key while pressing C to abort the plotting process if the plot is incorrect. This will save valuable drawing time.

SUMMARY

Plotting is the process of making a hardcopy print of a drawing. You can send the drawing data to a printer, plotter, or file to be plotted outside of AutoSketch or sent to a desktop publishing program. The first step in plotting a drawing is setting plot specifications–pen number, pen speed, paper size, scale, and rotation. A Plot Box appears on screen to show the area of the drawing that will be plotted after you enter these values. The Plot Box can be edited using the **Move** and **Scale** commands. Once the Plot box is sized and positioned, the **Plot** or **Print** command sends the data to the output device or file.

NEW TERMS

Plotting, check plot, final plot, **Plot** command, **Pen Info** command, **Plot Area** command, **Plot Name** command, *Pen Number* value, *Pen Speed* value, Plot Box, Clip Box, *X Plot Size* value, *Y Plot Size* value, *Rotate 90 Degrees* box, landscape format, portrait format, plot scale, *Plot to Extents* box, drawing media, liquid ink pen, fiber-tip pen, plastic-tip pen, roller ball pen, pressurized ballpoint pen.

REVIEW QUESTIONS

Write your answers on a separate sheet of paper. Do not write in this book.
1. Low-resolution prints that are made using a dot matrix or laser printer are called _____.
2. High-quality prints that are made using a pen plotter or other high-resolution output device for copying and sharing the design are called _____.
3. List the four plot-related commands found in the **File** menu.
4. The _____ value determines which pen AutoSketch selects to plot certain color objects.
5. The _____ value is the speed at which the plotter draws with each pen.
6. List the options that appear when you select the **Plot Area** command.
7. How many paper sizes are offered when you select the **Plot Area** command?
8. What is the plot scale if you set the *Drawing Units* to 4 and the *Plotting Units* to 1?
9. What plot scale would you use for a mechanical drawing with the following limits on A-size paper? Give the *Drawing Units* value. Assume that the *Plotting Units* value is 1.
   Left Limit = 0
   Right Limit = 40.5
   Top Limit = 30
   Bottom Limit = 0
10. When two Plot Boxes appear on screen, the largest visible Plot Box is the one used by the **Plot** command. True or false?
11. List the editing commands you can use to change the Plot Box?
12. What option must be selected when installing or reconfiguring AutoSketch so that you can plot drawings to a disk file?
13. Name the three general categories of drawing media.
14. The highest quality plotter pen is the _____.
15. List three plotting tips.

ACTIVITIES

1. Select a drawing from a previous chapter that will fit full scale on a paper size that your plotter supports. Plot the drawing using 1 for Drawing Units and 1 for Plotting Units. Time how long it takes to plot the drawing.
2. Plot the drawing in Activity 1 at half scale. How much less time was required to plot the drawing?
3. If you have access to both a dot matrix printer and a pen plotter or laser printer, make a check plot and a final plot. Use the *Plot to Extents* scaling option if you are using Version 3.0. Compare the time required to plot each.
4. If you have a multipen plotter, plot a multicolor drawing using a different pen for each color. The drawing should fill the entire paper.
5. If you have a pen plotter and it supports multiple pen speeds, make one plot of a drawing at the slowest pen speed. Make another at the highest pen speed. Time both plots. Compare the times and line quality.
6. Select a drawing from a previous chapter to plot. Edit the Plot Box four times so that you plot the entire drawing in four corners of the same sheet of paper.
7. Plot a drawing from a previous chapter using the landscape format. Plot the drawing so that it fills the entire paper. Rotate the drawing to a portrait format and plot the drawing again. What was the difference in size of the plotted drawing? Why?
8. Select a drawing from a previous chapter that will fit full scale on a paper size that your plotter supports. Use a Clip Box so that only the left half of the drawing is plotted.
9. Plot the title block from one of your prototype drawings. Then, recall a drawing from a previous chapter. Plot the drawing without its title block on the sheet preplotted with the title block. Make sure the drawing fits properly on the sheet.
10. Plot drawings that you created in previous chapters. Experiment with different settings, as well as various pen types and drawing media. Note which combination of settings creates the most readable plot.

Chapter 15

CREATING AND USING PARTS

After studying this chapter, you will be able to:
- Identify the advantages of inserting drawings as parts.
- Describe how to use AutoSketch parts as symbols.
- List advantages of inserting parts over drawing symbols manually.
- Follow the procedure for drawing a part to be used as a symbol.
- Identify the steps taken to add a part to a drawing.
- Explain how editing functions affect parts.

One advantage of a CAD program is that once an item is drawn, you should never have to draw it again. Instead, the item can simply be copied. However, what if you need the same shape in several drawings? The **Copy** command cannot copy items from drawing to drawing. What do you do? The answer is that AutoSketch allows you to insert any existing drawing into your current drawing. This is done using the **Part** command, located in the **Draw** menu. Shapes that will be needed in several drawings should be created first as separate drawings. You can then insert them when needed to save time and effort. You can also use the **Part** command to merge whole drawings together.

USING PARTS AS SYMBOLS

A *symbol* is a collection of objects that represents a standard component, assembly, or feature. See Fig. 15-1. Symbols are used in charts, drawings, diagrams, and schematics. For example, architectural drawings contain symbols that represent doors, windows, appliances, trees, and lights. Mechanical drawings contain symbols for nuts, bolts, and washers. Electrical drawings contain symbols for resistors, diodes, and transistors. In addition, there are symbols that you use to dimension drawings.

In traditional drafting, symbols are drawn by hand. A plastic template may be used as a guide in some cases. Unfortunately, this method is time consuming and the quality can vary.

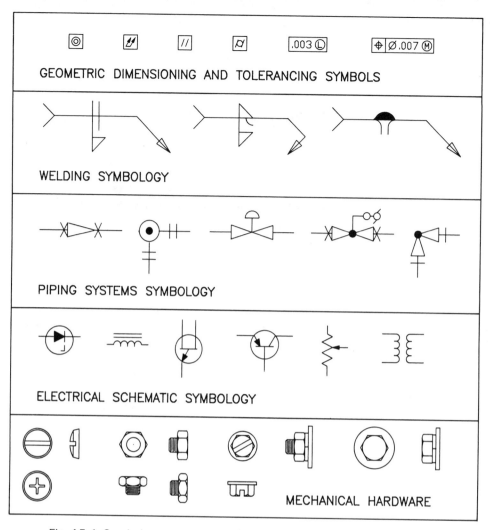

Fig. 15-1. Symbols represent a standard component, assembly, or feature.
(CAD Technology Corp.)

Also, there may not be a template made for the unique symbols that you or your company needs.

Symbols are used in AutoSketch by drawing and saving the symbol as a *part*. The symbol can then be inserted into other drawings as a part. You can create and store an entire library of parts for future use. Each one can be recalled and inserted as many times as needed. The basic steps used to create and insert a part are:

1. Draw the part full scale.
2. Use the **Group** command to group the part.
3. Select a part base using the **Part Base** command.
4. Save the part drawing using a descriptive name.
5. Insert the part in any drawing using the **Part** command.

DRAWING AND SAVING PARTS

Certain steps should be followed when creating parts. If you work for a company, how you draw the part may be a joint decision among product engineers, design engineers, and other drafters. Certain part types and sizes that will be used in more than one drawing must be accurate. The steps listed here apply whether you are drawing for yourself or when drafting for a company.

Draw the Part

Determine the objects that make up the part shape before drawing the part. There are both standard and custom shapes. Standard part shapes are typically set by a *standards organization*. The American Welding Society, for example, governs the size and shape of standard welding symbols, Fig. 15-2. Custom part shapes are those you might create for one drawing. You might be drawing an office layout, for example. You could make parts to represent several styles of desks. Keep custom parts simple when drawing them. Remember, a part only represents an item, Fig. 15-3. You do not have to fully describe the actual item.

Once you've decided how to draw the part, it is best to create it as a separate drawing. This is necessary for AutoSketch Version 2.0. However, with the **Part Clip** command of Version

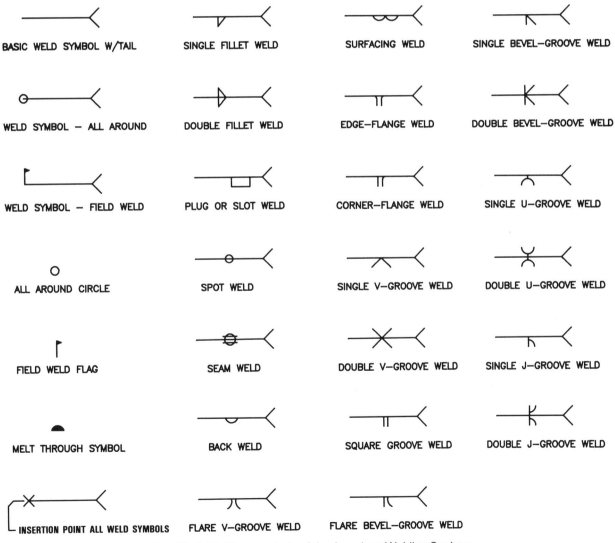

Fig. 15-2. Welding symbols of the American Welding Society.

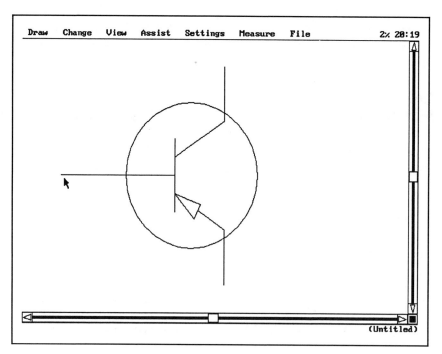

(Untitled)

Fig. 15-3. This symbol represents a type of transistor.

3.0 you can save objects out of an existing drawing as a separate drawing. For example, after drawing part of a house plan you notice that you keep drawing the same window symbol over and over. Group one of your window symbols and then save it using **Part Clip**. Now, you can insert it as a part whenever needed.

Make sure that you accurately draw parts to *full scale*. They can be rescaled or rotated as needed after being inserted into another drawing.

Group the Part

Group the objects after you draw the part. When you insert the part into another drawing, the part acts like a single object. This step is very important. If you are using the **Part Clip** command to save objects out of an existing drawing, make sure to also group those objects first. When you have completed selecting objects in the group, chose another command to complete the group.

Choose a Part Insertion Base Point

When you insert a part, the pointer drags the part on screen by pulling its *part insertion base point*. This point is important because every part connects to objects around it in a certain way. A door symbol, for example, connects to a wall by its hinge point. Other parts might connect by their center or edge. Pick the part insertion base point where the symbol typically connects to features around it.

The part insertion base point is picked by selecting the **Settings** menu and **Part Base** command. The **Part Insertion Base Point** dialogue box then appears, Fig. 15-4. The default for the part insertion base point is the origin of the drawing (X = 0, Y = 0). However, the best base point is some position on the part itself. The method used to pick the part insertion base point is different for AutoSketch Versions 2.0 and 3.0.

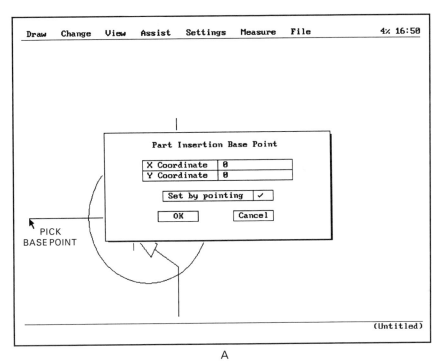

A

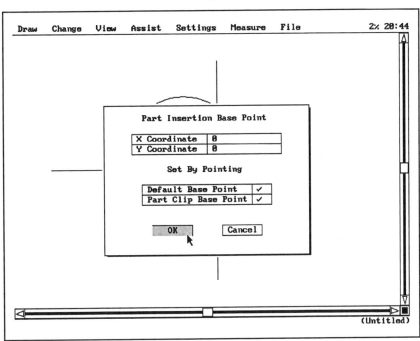

B

Fig. 15-4. A–The Part Insertion Base Point dialogue box for Version 2.0.
B–The Part Insertion Base Point for Version 3.0.

Version 2.0. When *Set by Pointing* is checked, Fig. 15-4A, and you pick *OK* to close the dialogue box, AutoSketch prompts you to pick a "Part insertion base:" for the drawing. If *Set by Pointing* is not checked, the current *X Coordinate* and *Y Coordinate* values are used for the part insertion base point.

Version 3.0. The **Part Insertion Base Point** dialogue box for Version 3.0 also includes *X Coordinate* and *Y Coordinate* values. However, there are two options to set the part insertion base point by pointing, Fig. 15-4B.

- When neither *Default Base Point* or *Part Clip Base Point* are checked, AutoSketch uses the current *X Coordinate* and *Y Coordinate* values for the default base point. The values are also used when you use the **Part Clip** command.
- When checked, *Default Base Point* allows you to pick the default base point for the drawing. Once you pick *OK* to close the dialogue box, AutoSketch prompts you to pick a "Part insertion base:".
- When checked, *Part Clip Base Point* allows you to pick the part insertion base point at the time you use the **Part Clip** command. AutoSketch prompts you with "Part Clip Part insertion base:".

Both *Default Base Point* and *Part Clip Base Point* can be checked at the same time.

Save the Part

Save the part to disk when you have finished it. Make sure that you have selected another command after grouping the objects, and before saving it as a part. Select the **Save** or **Save As** command if the entire drawing is a part. Use the **Part Clip** command of Version 3.0 to save just a few objects from a larger drawing. Make sure the drawing name or part clip filename you enter identifies the part. For example, the transistor part in Fig. 15-3 might be saved as TRANS102. Naming it TRANS might not be a good idea since there may be more than one transistor symbol. The additional number is more descriptive.

Parts are often saved to a special disk, or into a special disk directory. This place is called a *parts library* or *symbols library*. When saving a part to a floppy disk, remember to type the disk drive letter (A: or B:) in front of the part name. Fig. 15-5A shows how to use the **Save As** command to save the transistor symbol to floppy disk drive A:. When saving parts to a hard disk, create separate directories whose names reflect the type of parts stored. Fig. 15-5B shows how to use the **Part Clip** command to save the transistor symbol to the ELECTRIC directory of the hard disk drive (drive C:). A directory for architectural symbols might be named ARCH. Directories are discussed in Chapter 16.

INSERTING A PART IN A DRAWING

A part is inserted in a drawing by picking the **Draw** menu and **Part** command. The **Select Part File** dialogue box then appears. Here you chose the part you want to insert. This dialogue box is somewhat different for AutoSketch Versions 2.0 and 3.0, Fig. 15-6. Version 3.0 shows the parts stored on disk as icons, rather than names.

The box opposite *Directory* should show the drive and directory in which parts are stored. For example, one part created earlier in this chapter was stored on the A: drive. Fig. 15-6A shows retrieving the part from the A: drive. Notice that only one part is stored on that disk–the one created as an example in this chapter. Fig. 15-6B shows picking the part icon from the ELECTRIC directory of the hard disk drive (drive C:).

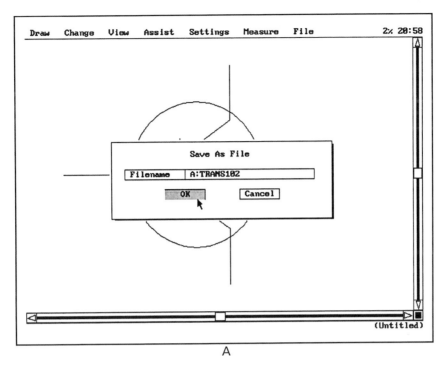

A

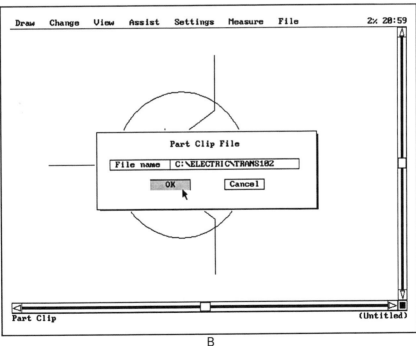

B

Fig. 15-5. A–Saving the part drawing, as TRANS102 on to the A: drive.
B–Using the Part Clip and saving the symbol to the ELECTRIC directory
on the C: drive.

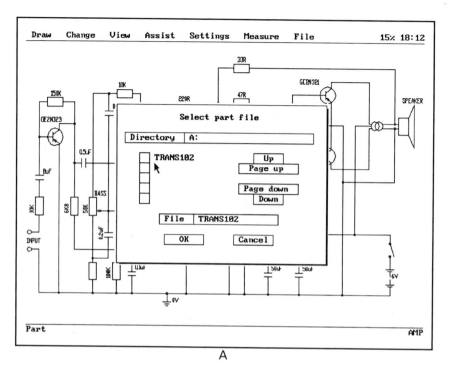

A

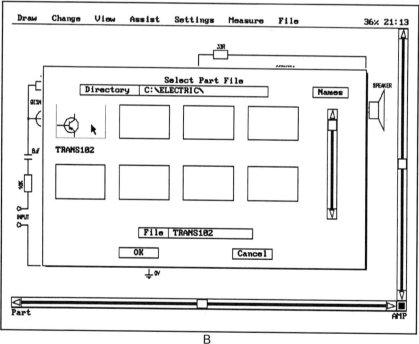

B

Fig. 15-6. A–The Version 2.0 Select part file dialogue box appears, from which you select the part to insert. B–The Version 3.0 Select Part File dialogue box shows the parts as icons. Note the drive and directory from which the part is being retrieved.

Once you pick the part to insert, its name appears in the *File* box. When you pick *OK,* the part appears on screen attached to the pointer, Fig. 15-7.

You can visually "drag" the part into place. The part is attached to the pointer by the part insertion base point. Pick the final position of the part when you are satisfied with the part's location. Use Attach modes when placing parts with the pointer. This ensures that the part connects precisely to other objects. In some cases you might enter coordinate values to locate the part.

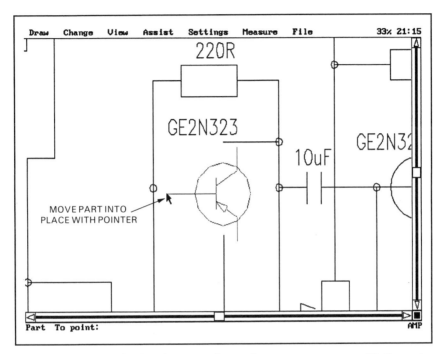

Fig. 15-7. After selecting the part to insert, it appears on screen with the part insertion base point attached to the pointer.

EDITING PARTS

A change may be required after you insert the part. You can edit parts just as you would lines, circles, and arcs. However, a part is treated like a single object if you grouped it before saving it. When you pick a grouped part to edit, all objects that make up the part are affected. Thus, you can **Move, Copy, Rotate,** or **Scale** the entire part. However, to edit individual objects of the part, you must first ungroup it. If the changes needed in the part are permanent, go back to the original part drawing and change it.

SYMBOL LIBRARY MANAGEMENT

Keeping track of parts can be a major task. Parts may constantly be added if other drafters, engineers, and designers are creating them. A printed *part library handbook* should be created to keep track of the parts. It contains all parts and information relating to the part. This might include a diagram or sketch, dimensions, the part name/number, entire part name, part insertion base point, color, and layer. Organize the handbook by the products the parts represent. For example, to find the part for a PNP transistor, refer to the handbook section on transistors.

SUMMARY

Parts are individual AutoSketch drawings that are inserted into other drawings. Parts are most often used as symbols to represent a standard component or assembly. A symbol is created by drawing it full size, group it, and select a part insertion base point. When you insert the part, the pointer drags the part on screen by pulling the part insertion base point. You can edit the inserted part just like any group. However, to edit the objects that make up the part, you must first ungroup the part.

NEW TERMS

Symbol, part, standards organization, part insertion base point, **Part base** command, parts library, symbols library, **Part** command.

REVIEW QUESTIONS

Write your answers on a separate sheet of paper. Do not write in this book.
1. Explain the difference between copying objects in the same drawing and copying objects between several drawings.
2. A _____ is a collection of objects that represents a standard component, assembly, or feature.
3. Explain the difference between drawing symbols by hand and using AutoSketch.
4. Standard part shapes (symbols) are typically set by _____.
5. Parts should be drawn _____, and then sized once they are inserted.
6. How does grouping a symbol before saving it affect it once inserted into another drawing?
7. When you insert a part, the pointer drags the part on screen by pulling its _____.
8. What location is best for a part insertion base point?
9. Using _____ when placing parts with the pointer assures that the part connects precisely to other objects.
10. To change an inserted symbol, you must either _____ it, or return to the original part drawing and change it.

ACTIVITIES

1. Draw parts for the following office furniture: desk, chair, and file cabinet. Then, create several office layouts by inserting the office furniture symbols.
2. Create a library of welding symbols using Fig. 15-2 as an example.
3. Create a library of landscape architecture parts. Draw parts for various size trees, shrubbery, and other plants you might place in a landscape. Then, create several landscape layouts by inserting the parts you created.

4. Select any two drawings created in previous chapters. Merge the two drawings by inserting one as a part into the other. Note how you can merge complete drawings.
5. Create the following site plan for the Community Center. Develop an architectural part library handbook. Be sure to include the trees, shrubbery, cars, and parking stalls. Use the **Box Array** command to create the parking stalls.

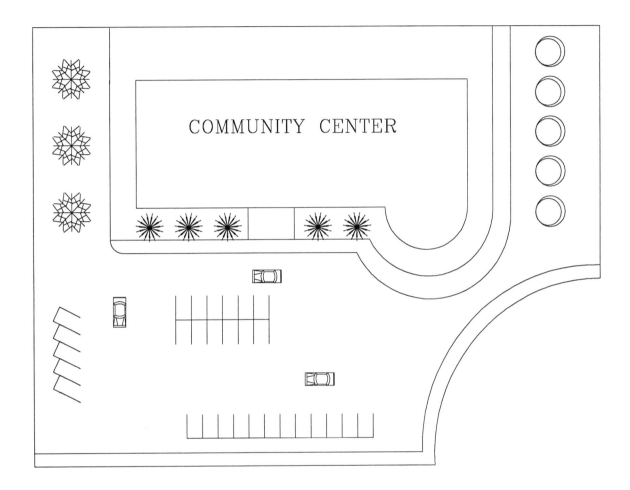

6. Create the following motor control circuit. Develop an electronics part library handbook. Be sure to include switches and terminals.

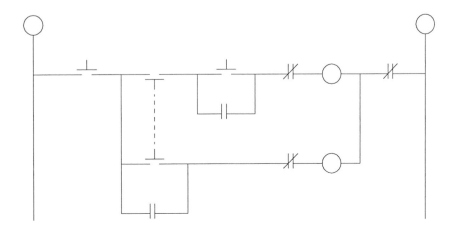

7. Create the following floor plan for this modern residence. Develop a furniture part library handbook, and add more symbols to your architectural part library handbook.

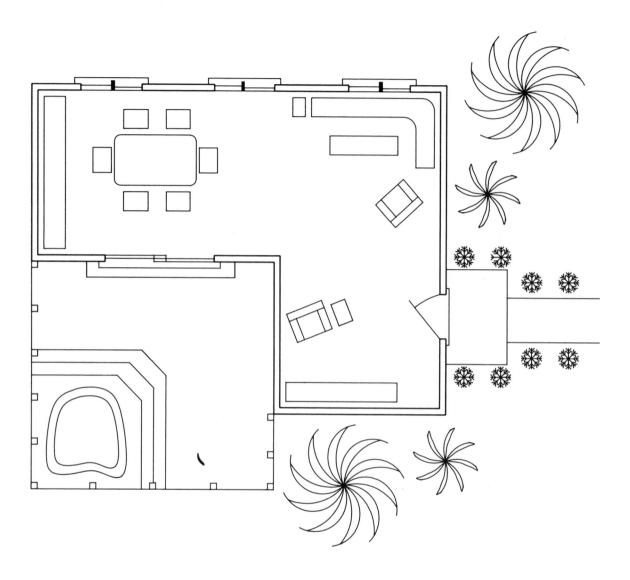

Chapter 16

MACROS, MS-DOS, AND DRAWING CONVERSIONS

After studying this chapter, you will be able to:
- Record and play a macro.
- Store a macro on disk and load a macro from disk.
- Work with MS-DOS.
- Make new directories and change directories.
- Recognize the difference between directories, file names, and file extensions.
- List the files stored on disk and in a directory.
- Copy, rename, and delete files.
- Copy the contents of entire disks.
- Export and import DXF drawings.
- Troubleshoot problems with AutoSketch.

This chapter introduces you to more specialized file operations, both inside and outside of AutoSketch. You will learn how to create and play macros, transfer drawings between AutoSketch and other CAD programs, and learn how to work with files from the operating system prompt outside of AutoSketch.

MACROS

A *macro* is a recorded series of actions you take while using AutoSketch. The macro includes commands, dialogue boxes, point locations, and objects you pick. A macro is stored in memory. It can be played back to automate repetitive tasks. The macro can also be stored to disk so that you can record the macro once and use it many times.

Recording a Macro
Select **Record Macro** from the **Assist** menu to record a macro. Then, perform the actions you want to record and select **End Macro.** While recording the macro, you can cause the

macro to pause for user input by holding down the [Ctrl] key while pressing function key [F10]. You might pause for user input to:

- Enter something at the keyboard and press [Enter].
- Pick a command.
- Pick something in a dialogue box and then pick *OK*.
- Pick an object.
- Pick the location of a point.

An example of a macro follows. This macro is used to automate the process for drawing polycircles (discussed in Chapter 12).

1. Select the **Assist** menu.
2. Select the **Record Macro** command.
3. Select the **Assist** menu.
4. Select the **Arc Mode** command.
5. Select the **Settings** menu.
6. Select the **Polyline** command.
7. Position the cursor in the *Polyline Width* box.
8. Press [Ctrl] + [F10] to allow for user input.
9. Press the [Enter] key.
10. Pick the *OK* button.
11. Select the **Draw** menu.
12. Select the **Polyline** command.
13. Press [Ctrl] + [F10] to allow for user input.
14. Pick the first point of the polycircle.
15. Enter P(.7071,45) and press the [Enter] key.
16. Enter P(.7071,315) and press the [Enter] key.
17. Enter P(.7071,225) and press the [Enter] key.
18. Enter P(.7071,135) and press the [Enter] key.
19. Select the **Assist** menu.
20. Select the **End Macro** command.

Playing a Macro

The **Play Macro** command is available only if you have recorded a macro, or have loaded a macro from disk. The **Play Macro** command is accessed through the **Assist** menu. When you select this command, the macro performs all the recorded actions. A macro with a pause for user input stops for the user to do one of the five things mentioned earlier. Pressing [Enter] causes the macro to resume when you are entering text. Picking *OK* when in a dialogue box causes the macro to resume. Otherwise, the macro resumes when you pick with the pointer.

Try running the macro that you just created. Make sure that **Arc Mode** is toggled off before playing the macro. When you record the macro, AutoSketch only remembers that the **Arc Mode** command is to be toggled, not whether it is on or off.

Storing a Macro on Disk

Only one macro can be in memory at any given time. If you record another macro, the current macro is dumped from memory. However, you can save a macro from memory to a disk file by selecting **Make Macro** from the **File** menu. A dialogue box appears for you to enter a macro file name that is up to eight characters.

Writing and Editing Macros with a Word Processor

You can edit macros that you stored to a disk, or write new macros, using a text editor. See Appendix C of the *AutoSketch Reference Manual* for additional information.

Loading a Macro From Disk

Select **Read Macro** from the **File** menu to load a saved macro file into memory. Any macro currently in memory is discarded. Thus, you may want to save the macro in memory before using **Read Macro**. The loaded macro is not performed immediately; you must select **Play Macro** to run the macro.

INTRODUCTION TO THE DISK OPERATING SYSTEM (DOS)

The *Microsoft Disk Operating System* (MS-DOS) is a set of computer instructions loaded into memory when the computer is turned on. This "program" handles the storage and movement of data and files between memory and the disk drives. It is the first file the computer looks for when you turn on the system.

Loading MS-DOS

The computer searches for the MS-DOS program on floppy drive A: if you have a floppy drive system, or the hard disk if you have a hard disk system. You can run AutoSketch or any other application program when MS-DOS is loaded into memory. Chapter 2 discusses how MS-DOS is loaded into the computer. Computers with floppy drives require that you insert the MS-DOS disk into the A: drive before turning on the computer. Computers with a hard disk load MS-DOS automatically upon system startup.

The System Prompt

A system prompt appears when MS-DOS has been loaded. It looks like A⟩ if your computer has a floppy drive system, or C⟩ if you have a hard disk. The *system prompt* lets you know that the computer is ready for your next command. The letter–A or C–shows which disk drive the computer looks to when you enter a command. See Fig. 16-1. Remember from

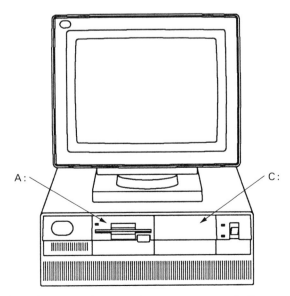

Fig. 16-1. The letter shown at the system prompt indicates which drive the computer will look to for data.

Chapter 2 that you enter the **SKETCH3** command from the system prompt to start AutoSketch.

DIRECTORIES

One function of MS-DOS allows you to divide each disk drive into smaller sections, called directories. *Directories* are used to organize files on the drive into more manageable groups. Directories are very important on hard disk systems. They are less important on floppy disk systems because floppy disks do not hold as much information. However, you can create directories on floppy disks as well.

Imagine the hard disk as a filing cabinet, Fig. 16-2. Each drawer of the filing cabinet can be compared to a directory. In each directory there are files that you store, perhaps Auto-Sketch drawings. Directories help organize files, just as filing cabinet drawers help to organize letters. The following topics show you how to change to a directory, make new directories, and remove directories.

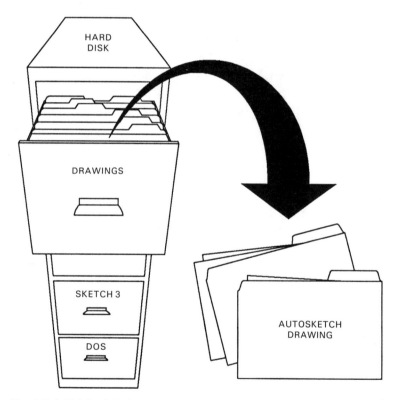

Fig. 16-2. Think of the hard disk as a filing cabinet with drawers and files.

Changing Directories

When you first start up the computer, you are not in any directory. This is referred to as being in the *root directory*. Compare this to standing in front of a file cabinet with all of the drawers closed. Entering a directory is like pulling open a drawer. The command to enter is:

C⟩**CD\DIRECTORY**

CD means "Change Directory." A space follows the CD. The backslash (\) always precedes a DIRECTORY name. Refer to Chapter 2 where starting AutoSketch on a hard disk system was discussed. Notice that hard disk users type in CD \ SKETCH for Version 2.0 before entering the SKETCH command to start AutoSketch. This is because the files needed to run AutoSketch are stored in a directory called SKETCH.

Making Directories

MS-DOS allows you to make new directories, or drawers, in which to store files. You might want to make a new directory to store your AutoSketch drawings. Make a new directory by first exiting any directory you might be in by entering:

C>**CD **

The backslash without a directory name means to exit any directory (close all file drawers). Then, enter the following command:

C>**MD DIRECTORY**

DIRECTORY is the name of the new directory you wish to create. You can think of the MD command as "Make Directory." The directory might be named DRAWINGS in which you can then store your drawings.

C>**MD DRAWINGS**

The directory name can be from 1 to 8 characters, using letters, numbers, or symbols. However, you *cannot* use the following characters: " / \ [ ] : 〈 〉 + = ; , : .

Remember that you can move between directories with the CD command. For example, to move between directories on the hard disk, enter:

C>**CD\SKETCH3**

C>**CD\DRAWINGS**

C>**CD**

The first entry changed the current directory to the SKETCH3 directory. The second entry changed the current directory to the DRAWINGS directory. The last entry removed you from all directories and placed you at the root directory. Notice that a backslash precedes a directory name in all cases.

Removing Directories

Remove a directory by first deleting all files in that directory. You can delete the files individually, or delete them all at once using a wildcard character. (Wildcard characters are discussed later in this chapter.) Exit that directory using CD \. Then, enter the RD command and the directory name. You can think of RD as "Remove Directory". Suppose you have copied all of your AutoSketch drawings from the DRAWINGS directory to a floppy disk, and have erased them from the hard disk. The DRAWINGS directory is now removed by entering the following command:

C>**RD DRAWINGS**

Notice that you do not need to precede the directory name with a backslash when removing the directory.

FILE NAMES AND EXTENSIONS

You have been working with file names throughout this text. When saving a new drawing, you entered a file name of up to eight characters. When opening a drawing, you picked the drawing from a list of files stored on disk. However, this was done entirely within Auto-Sketch. AutoSketch shows you only part of the file name as it is stored on disk. Now we need to look at how MS-DOS thinks of file names.

A *file name,* by MS-DOS definition, includes up to eight characters and up to a three-character extension separated by a period. See Fig. 16-3. When saving a drawing, AutoSketch automatically adds the extension to the file name. AutoSketch also adds .DXF and .SLD file extensions when you export drawings and work with slides. However, when you copy, delete, or rename files *outside of AutoSketch,* you must enter the file name plus the period and extension. Otherwise, you receive the message, "File not found."

Fig. 16-3. A file name includes up to eight characters, with an extension up to three characters.

AutoSketch drawings are saved with an .SKD file extension. A slide made in AutoSketch or AutoCAD has an .SLD extension. A drawing converted to the Drawing eXchange Format has a .DXF extension. An AutoCAD drawing has a .DWG extension. The Disk Operating System also reserves the following extensions:

.ASM	.AUX
.BAK	.BAS
.BAT	.COM
.CON	.EXE
.NUL	.PRN
.SYS	

Do not erase or otherwise alter files with these extensions. They are usually important to the operation of the computer. Deleting these files might cause serious problems. In addition to these extensions, AutoSketch reserves the following file extensions:

.DXF	.SKD
.SLD	.OVL
.SHX	.MCR
.CFG	.MID

When copying or renaming drawing files, be sure to include the extension. If you do not include the extension, AutoSketch or AutoCAD will not recognize the file as being a drawing.

PATHS

A *path* represents the location of a file within a directory and disk drive. You may need to enter paths to tell AutoSketch where to store or look for files. The path is the combination of drive, directory, and a file name. Refer to Fig. 16-4 for an example. Note that the hard disk drive name is C:, and the two removable disk (floppy or microdisk) drives have A: and B: names. The hard disk also has the directories DRAWINGS, SKETCH3, and DOS. The path for these "drawers" is the disk drive name and the directory name. Remember that a directory name is preceded by a backslash.

Now, to find some AutoSketch drawings! They are found by entering the drive name, directory (if any), and the file name plus extension. Notice that when there are no directories, the path is simply the drive name plus file name. However, in the hard disk, the path includes the drive name, directory, and file name, plus the .SKD extension that identifies an Auto-Sketch drawing.

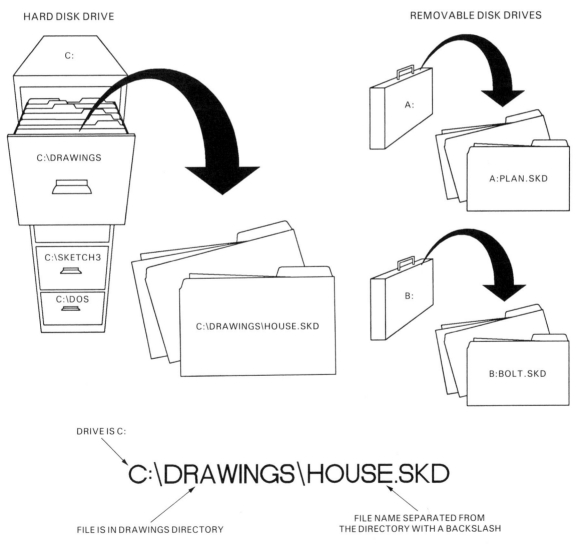

HARD DISK DRIVE

REMOVABLE DISK DRIVES

C:

C:\DRAWINGS

C:\SKETCH3

C:\DOS

C:\DRAWINGS\HOUSE.SKD

A:

A:PLAN.SKD

B:

B:BOLT.SKD

DRIVE IS C:

C:\DRAWINGS\HOUSE.SKD

FILE IS IN DRAWINGS DIRECTORY

FILE NAME SEPARATED FROM
THE DIRECTORY WITH A BACKSLASH

Fig. 16-4. The path is the combination of drive, directory, and a file name.

Suppose you wanted to delete the AutoSketch drawing HOUSE stored in the DRAWINGS directory of the hard disk drive. You would have to enter the following to delete that file:

C)DEL C:\DRAWINGS\HOUSE.SKD

MS-DOS commands that are used to delete, copy, and rename files are covered later in this chapter.

ENTERING DIRECTORIES AND PATHS WITHIN AUTOSKETCH

When you select the **Open** command to load an AutoSketch drawing, a dialogue box appears, Fig. 16-5. Drawings are loaded from the disk drive and directory indicated in the *Directory* box. If you are using AutoSketch on a hard disk, the *Directory* box will probably appear as shown in Fig. 16-5. Notice that AutoSketch is looking for drawings in the C: drive (hard disk) and SKETCH3 directory. However, suppose you have been storing files in the DRAWINGS directory. Pick the ⟨..⟩ entry to exit the current directory. You probably will not see any drawings listed, Fig. 16-6, but you will see several directories. Any entry within greater than (⟩) and less than (⟨) symbols is a directory. Pick the entry ⟨DRAWINGS⟩ to make that directory current. Now, you should see a list of your files.

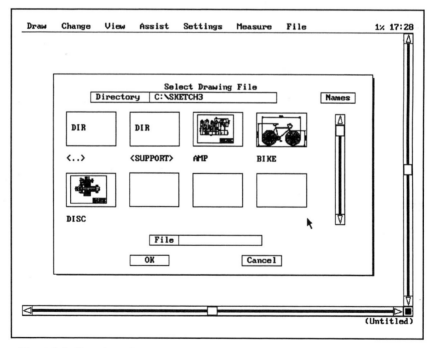

Fig. 16-5. Opening a file in AutoSketch may require that you change the drive and directory shown in the Directory box.

Suppose you want to retrieve drawings stored on a floppy disk or microdisk. Get drawings from a different disk drive by moving the pointer to highlight the *Directory* box, Fig. 16-7. Type in the new drive letter (A or B) followed by a colon and pick the extended *OK* box. The drawings stored on that drive then appear in the file list.

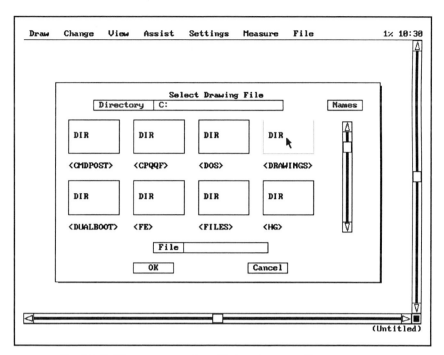

Fig. 16-6. The names enclosed in brackets are directory names.

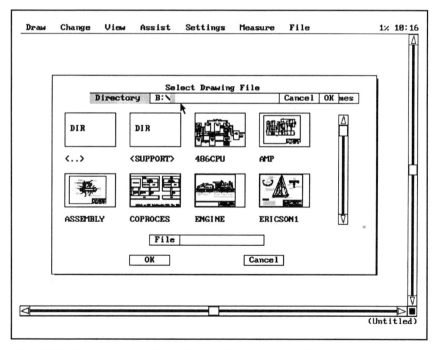

Fig. 16-7. Drawings stored on a floppy disk are retrieved by entering the floppy
drive letter (and colon) in the Directory box.

Now suppose you want to save drawings on another disk drive. In this case, you want to save the drawing on screen as PLAN on the A: drive (floppy disk). Simply select the **Save As** command from the **File** menu, and enter A:PLAN next to the *File name*. The drive name, A:, indicates where the file should be placed. If you want to save a drawing as BRACKET on the hard disk in the DRAWINGS directory, simply enter C:\DRAWINGS\BRACKET. Note how a backslash is used to separate the directory from the file name. Do not add the .SKD extension since AutoSketch does this for you.

MS-DOS COMMANDS

MS-DOS includes commands that allow you to copy disks, list files stored on disk, and delete files, in addition to managing files in your computer. You should know some basic MS-DOS commands to make your work with the computer more enjoyable and productive.

Changing the Active Drive
The *active drive* is where the computer looks for files when you enter a MS-DOS command. You always know the active drive by the letter that appears at the system prompt. The first and second floppy disk drives are generally known as A: and B: drives. The hard disk is known as C: drive. Many computers with hard disks do not have a B: drive.

Change the active drive of the computer by typing its name (its letter followed by a colon). The prompt will change to indicate the active drive.

C⟩**A:**

A⟩**C:**

C⟩

Notice how the prompt changes to reflect the active drive. The first entry changed the system prompt to the A: drive. The second entry changed it back to the C: drive.

Prompt
Most computers only show the active drive at the system prompt. However, you can enter a command so that the system prompt shows the active drive *and* the directory:

C⟩**PROMPT PG**

C:\⟩

Now, the prompt shows the drive and directory. The prompt C:\⟩ without a directory name means that you are in the root directory. However, suppose you enter the SKETCH3 directory as follows:

C⟩**CD\SKETCH3**

C:\SKETCH3⟩

Notice how the prompt now shows that you have moved into the SKETCH3 directory. This MS-DOS command is a helpful sign to tell where you are working.

Listing Files

When you wish to copy or rename files, you should first display a list of files stored on the drive. The DIR (DIRectory) command lists the files stored in the current disk drive and directory. The DIR command also shows size of the file (in bytes, or characters) and the date and time the files were last created or edited.

Type DIR at the system prompt and press [Enter] to list the files. A list appears as shown in Fig. 16-8.

B:\>**DIR**

```
B:\>DIR

Volume in drive B has no label
Volume Serial Number is 110C-17E1
Directory of  B:\

UNITY    CH5    270984 11-16-89  11:13a
UNITY    LG4    264602 11-16-89   4:48p
L5-MML   LG       1663 11-06-89  12:06p
L5-POST  LG       7898 10-11-89   2:06p
L4-SOFT  LG       7442 11-12-89   6:19p
UNITY    LG5    271211 11-16-89   5:27p
OK-POST  LG       7898 10-11-89   2:06p
OK-SOFT  LG       7442 11-12-89   6:19p
OK-MML   LG       2522 11-16-89   5:26p
ENGINE   SKD     55073 04-06-89  10:25a
ERICSON1 SKD     30630 04-06-89  10:33a
FLOORPLN SKD    104680 04-06-89  10:42a
ORDER    SKD    116442 04-06-89  10:45a
PULSE    SKD     43283 04-06-89  10:54a
PUMP     DXF    109387 11-22-89   1:00p
        15 File(s)     153088 bytes free

B:\>
```

Fig. 16-8. The MS-DOS command DIR
displays a list of files stored on disk.

There are two other variations of the DIR command. The command, DIR/P, tells the computer to pause when a full screen of files is displayed. See Fig. 16-9A. Press any key to see the next full screen of files.

C:\>**DIR/P**

The DIR/W command shows a wide, or windowed, version of the file list, Fig. 16-9B. This command omits the date and size of files so that more files can fit on screen.

C:\>**DIR/W**

The DIR command also displays the "total bytes free" at the bottom of the list. The number of bytes held by commonly used disks is shown in Fig. 16-10. A typical AutoSketch

```
 .                      <DIR>      10-12-89   12:40p
 ..                     <DIR>      10-12-89   12:40p
SKETCH   EXE       112688 04-03-89   7:18p
FLOPPY   BAT          233 02-27-89   9:14p
DS8514   EXE        43920 02-27-89   9:17p
DSMCGA   EXE        18144 02-27-89   9:15p
ROMANS   SHX         4926 02-27-89   9:16p
ROMANC   SHX         6901 02-27-89   9:16p
SCRIPTC  SHX         7699 02-27-89   9:17p
ITALICC  SHX         7483 02-27-89   9:16p
SYMAP    SHX         6103 02-27-89   9:17p
SYMATH   SHX         6035 02-27-89   9:17p
SYMUSIC  SHX         6910 02-27-89   9:17p
MONOTXT  SHX         2828 02-27-89   9:16p
SKETCH5  MID          226 04-04-89   9:42a
SKETCH   OVL       270272 04-03-89   7:18p
SKETCH4  MID          223 04-04-89   9:37a
ENGINE   SKD        55073 04-06-89  10:25a
ERICSON1 SKD        30630 04-06-89  10:33a
FLOORPLN SKD       104680 04-06-89  10:42a
ORDER    SKD       116442 04-06-89  10:45a
PULSE    SKD        43283 04-06-89  10:54a
README   DOC         7125 04-04-89  10:35a
Press any key to continue . . .
                         A
```

```
 .                  ..               SKETCH   EXE    FLOPPY   BAT    DS8514   EXE
DSMCGA   EXE    ROMANS   SHX    ROMANC   SHX    SCRIPTC  SHX    ITALICC  SHX
SYMAP    SHX    SYMATH   SHX    SYMUSIC  SHX    MONOTXT  SHX    SKETCH5  MID
SKETCH   OVL    SKETCH4  MID    ENGINE   SKD    ERICSON1 SKD    FLOORPLN SKD
ORDER    SKD    PULSE    SKD    README   DOC    SKETCH3  MID    SKETCH   CFG
BOLD     SHX
        26 File(s)    42844160 bytes free
                         B
```

Fig. 16-9. The DIR/P and DIR/W versions of the DIR command display pages and windows of files.

Size/Type	Density	Capacity
5.25 Floppy	Double	360 Kilobytes
5.25 Floppy	High	1.2 Megabytes
3.5 Microdisk	Double	720 Kilobytes
3.5 Microdisk	High	1.44 Megabytes
Hard Disk	xxx	20 to 650 Megabytes

Fig. 16-10. Data storage capacity of typical removable disks and hard disk drives.

drawing contains from 20,000 to 100,000 bytes of information. Avoid crowding a disk with data; never save files to the point that a disk is full. Always leave about 50,000 bytes of free space. This is the reason for using the DIR command to list files and free space. When possible, remove old and unneeded files, especially backup files (files with a .BAK extension).

You can list files stored on another disk drive without first making it current by simply entering the path name. Suppose you are working in the A: drive, but want to list files stored on the hard disk in the SKETCH3 directory. Enter the following:

A>**DIR C:\SKETCH3**

Formatting New Disks

Floppy disks and microdisks must be formatted before you can store files on them. *Formatting* prepares the surface of new disks into a format readable by the computer. This is done from the MS-DOS system prompt before starting AutoSketch. The FORMAT command was discussed in Chapter 3. Remember that formatting is designed to prepare a new disk. Formatting a disk with files erases any data stored on the disk. Make sure you perform a DIR command on a disk to make sure it does not contain needed files before formatting it.

Copying Files

The COPY command allows files to be copied from one disk to another, and from one directory to another. It also allows you to change the file name as you copy it. When copying files to a floppy or microdisk, it must already be formatted. See Chapter 3 for instructions on formatting disks.

The simplest COPY command might be entered to copy an AutoSketch drawing from the A: drive to the B: drive as follows:

C:\>**COPY A:NETWORK.SKD B:**

This command copies the AutoSketch drawing, NETWORK, from the A: to the B: drive.

A file name can be changed when copying a file from one drive to another. If you want the drawing placed under a different name on the B: drive, enter:

C:\>**COPY A:NETWORK.SKD B:OLDNET.SKD**

In this example, the NETWORK drawing on the A: drive is copied to the B: drive and given the name, OLDNET.

Another command might copy a file from the A: drive into a directory on the hard disk. Here is one example.

C:\>**COPY A:MYDRAW.SKD C:\SKETCH3\ASSIGN1.SKD**

This command copies the AutoSketch drawing, MYDRAW, from the A: drive to the C: drive, and places the drawing in the SKETCH3 directory under the name ASSIGN1. This is probably the most complex copy command you would ever enter.

Another command might copy a drawing between hard disk directories.

C:\>**COPY C:\SKETCH3\HOUSE.SKD C:\DRAWINGS**

This command copies the AutoSketch drawing, HOUSE, from the SKETCH3 directory of the C: drive into the DRAWINGS directory of the C: drive.

Renaming Files

Renaming files may be desired to change the name of a drawing without creating a copy. When necessary, you can rename a file by entering REN, the old name, and the new name.

C:\>**REN A:OLDNAME.SKD NEWNAME.SKD**

Do not include the drive name and directory for the new name. MS-DOS automatically places it in the same drive and directory. Now look at this more complex renaming task.

C:\\>REN C:\\DRAWINGS\\HOUSE.SKD NEWHOUSE.SKD

In this case, the AutoSketch drawing, HOUSE, in the DRAWINGS directory was renamed NEWHOUSE and placed in the same directory. Notice that you do not place the C:\\DRAWINGS\\ path preceding the new name. MS-DOS does not need it.

Deleting Files

The DEL (DELete) command is used to remove files from disk. Use this command with care. It is difficult, and often impossible, to restore an erased file. If you accidentally erase a file, stop and get help. There are utility programs that allow you to retrieve deleted files. However, you must not save anything else on the disk before using the utility program.

Enter DEL and the file name plus extension to delete a file.

A:\\>DEL MYDRAW.SKD

This command removes the drawing MYDRAW from the A: drive. Remember that you must enter the drive name (and directory, if any) to delete files stored somewhere other than the current drive and directory. If you want to delete the file, ENGINE, from the SKETCH3 directory of the C: drive when you are currently in the A: drive, enter the following:

A:\\>DEL C:\\SKETCH3\\ENGINE.SKD

Using Wildcard Characters

MS-DOS allows you to use wildcard characters. *Wildcard characters* represent a single character, or any number of characters. They are best used when copying and deleting files. One wildcard character, the asterisk, may represent any number of characters. For example:

C:\\>COPY A:*.SKD B:

The previous command copies all files on the A: drive with an .SKD extension to the B: drive. Another example:

C:\\>COPY A:DR*.SKD B:

This command copies all files on the A: drive that begin with DR and have an .SKD extension from the A: drive to the B: drive. You can use the DEL command to delete, rather than copy, the drawings.

Another wildcard character is the question mark. It represents a single character. For example:

C:\\>DEL A:HOUSE?PL.SKD

This command deletes only those drawings on the A: drive that begin with HOUSE, end with PL, and have an .SKD extension. Since the question mark represents only a single character, drawings named HOUSE1PL.SKD and HOUSE2PL.SKD would be deleted, but one named HOUSEPLA.SKD would not be deleted.

Copying Entire Disks

MS-DOS allows you to copy an entire floppy disk or microdisk at one time with the DISKCOPY command. This command is useful to make a back-up copy of the disk on which you store AutoSketch drawings. If you have two floppy disk drives, or two microdisk drives, place the MS-DOS disk in drive A: and enter:

A:\\>**DISKCOPY A: B:**

A prompt will ask you to insert the *source disk* in the A: drive and the *target disk* in the B: drive. Remove the MS-DOS disk. Place your working disk in the A: drive, place the backup disk in the B: drive, and press the [Enter] key. The target disk does not need to be formatted; it will automatically be formatted.

Note! You cannot use the DISKCOPY command if the A: and B: drives are different sizes or densities. Also, the DISKCOPY command will copy over everything stored on your target disk. Make sure the target, or backup, disk is new or does not contain needed files.

If you have a hard disk and two floppy or microdisk drives, enter the **DISKCOPY A: B:** at the C> prompt. Follow the same procedure. However, you do not need to insert and remove the MS-DOS disk because the DISKCOPY program is stored on your hard disk.

If you have only one floppy or microdisk drive, use the following command:

C:\\>**DISKCOPY A: A:**

The computer first copies the contents of one disk into memory. You then insert the target disk and the data is copied from memory to the backup disk. The computer will prompt you to exchange disks one or more times.

EXPORTING AND IMPORTING DXF DRAWINGS

A current trend is to exchange drawings between CAD programs and graphics drawing programs. Unfortunately, most graphics programs store drawings differently. Therefore, you must use conversion software to transfer drawings. Several standard formats for drawing exchange have been developed. AutoSketch can export and import drawings using the *Drawing eXchange Format (DXF)* developed by Autodesk, Inc. The DXF format has become the most commonly used drawing conversion for microcomputer-based CAD programs. You can convert AutoSketch drawings into DXF format and import them into AutoCAD, another CAD program, or desktop publishing software. This feature offers several advantages:

- If you upgrade to a higher-level program, you can use drawings created in AutoSketch.
- The easy-to-use nature of AutoSketch allows you to first "sketch" your ideas. Then, you can convert them and use the advanced functions of AutoCAD or another CAD program to prepare complex working drawings.
- You can prepare illustrations, convert them to DXF format, and then import them into a desktop publishing program.
- You can send the drawing data via DXF format to a computer-aided manufacturing (CAM) system.

There is no need to create DXF files unless you have access to AutoCAD or a program that can read them. Versions of AutoSketch previous to 2.0 could only export a DXF file. You can import and export DXF files with AutoSketch Version 2.0 and Version 3.0.

Converting AutoSketch Drawings to DXF Format

When converting a file to DXF format, first have the drawing on screen. Then, pick the **File** menu and **Make DXF** command. Enter the file name in the **Make DXF File** (or **Write DXF File** in Version 2.0) dialogue box, Fig. 16-11. You can accept the default file name by pressing the [Enter] key; AutoSketch uses the drawing name as the DXF file name. This new file does not overwrite the drawing file. Instead, AutoSketch automatically adds a three-character file extension to the end of the file name.

If you want to name the DXF file, move your pointer to highlight the *Filename* box. Enter the new name and press the [Enter] key or pick *OK*. You can use up to eight characters to name the file; do not use an extension. AutoSketch automatically saves the DXF file to disk with a .DXF file extension.

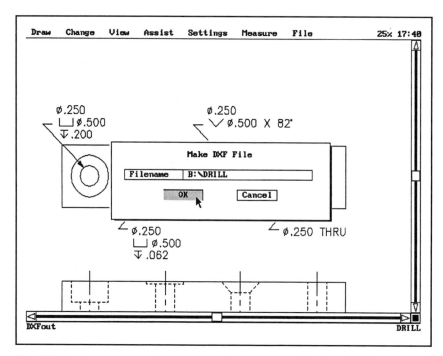

Fig. 16-11. Dialogue box that appears after you select the Make DXF command.

Importing DXF Drawings into AutoSketch

When importing a DXF file into AutoSketch, first clear the screen of any drawing using the **New** command. Then, pick the **File** menu and **Read DXF** command. The **Select DXF File** dialogue box appears listing all DXF files stored on the current disk drive. If no file names appear, enter the drive and/or directory where the files are stored in the *Directory* box. Pick the drawing you wish to convert and then *OK*. The drawing will appear on screen after a few moments. You can then use the **Save** command to save the drawing as an AutoSketch drawing file.

Control Settings (Version 3.0). Version 3.0 offers two control settings for importing AutoCAD DXF drawings.

• *Explode Large Blocks* causes AutoCAD blocks (groups) containing more than 1000 objects to be exploded (ungrouped) as they are brought into AutoSketch. If this setting is not checked, AutoCAD blocks that exceed this limit are discarded. Blocks containing less than 1000 objects are brought into AutoSketch as groups.

- *Import Visible Attributes* causes text associated with AutoCAD blocks to be imported as normal text in AutoSketch. If this setting is not checked, the attribute text associated with AutoCAD blocks is discarded.

Restrictions. There are restrictions on what objects will convert between AutoSketch and AutoCAD. Refer to the proper appendix of the *AutoSketch Reference Manual* or *Auto-Sketch User Guide* (Version 2.0) for a complete list of these restrictions. Objects in the DXF file which have no AutoSketch equivalent are ignored.

OTHER DRAWING CONVERSIONS

There are two other formats that are commonly used –HPGL (Hewlett-Packard Graphics Language) and EPS (Encapsulated PostScript). These formats are generally used to prepare AutoSketch drawings for import into desktop publishing programs and similar graphics programs.

HPGL

HPGL is an acronym for Hewlett-Packard Graphics Language. *HPGL* code is a "language" that a Hewlett-Packard plotter can understand. However, the HPGL format has other uses. Companies have found that the HPGL format is a good way to send technical illustrations to desktop publishing software. Plot the drawing to a disk file instead of plotting on paper. This is not a drawing file. Rather, the *disk file* contains the same code as if the drawing were sent to a plotter. The desktop publishing program reads the HPGL file and inserts the drawing on screen.

HPGL files are created by selecting a Hewlett-Packard plotter (use model 7475) and "File" for the plot connection when installing AutoSketch. See Fig. 16-12 for the prompts that appear during installation. If needed, you can reconfigure AutoSketch for a Hewlett-Packard plotter using the methods included in *Installing AutoSketch* or the *AutoSketch User Guide* (Version 2.0). When you plot the drawing, the HPGL file will be saved to disk with a .PLT extension.

Encapsulated PostScript

PostScript is a page description language developed by Adobe Systems, Inc. A PostScript file describes how graphics should be created and can be read by a PostScript printer. When configuring AutoSketch, you can select PostScript for the output and print directly to a PostScript printer. You can also print PostScript output to a disk file.

PostScript files are created by first choosing "PostScript Laser Printer" and "File" for the plot connection when configuring AutoSketch. See Fig. 16-13 for the prompts that appear during installation. When you plot the drawing, the plot file has the same name as the drawing file with a .PLT extension. When using Version 3.0, the file that is created is *Encapsulated PostScript (EPS)*. This format can be imported directly into a desktop publishing program. You may need to rename the file to have an .EPS extension.

Version 2.0 Conversion. A PostScript file that you plot to disk cannot be inserted directly into other graphics programs with AutoSketch Version 2.0. It must be edited to become Encapsulated PostScript. This involves adding one extra line and editing two lines in the plot file. These changes are made using a word processor that works in the ASCII text mode.

Select plotter or printer:

1.   No printer/plotter
2.   Autodesk Device Interface Plotter
3.   Autodesk Device Interface Printer
4.   Epson/IBM Graphics Printer
5.   Hewlett-Packard LaserJet
6.   Hewlett-Packard PaintJet
7.   Hewlett-Packard Plotter
8.   Houston Instrument Plotter
9.   IBM Proprinter
10. Okidata Printer
11. PostScript Laser Printer
12. TI 800 Omni Printer

Plotter or printer selection: 7
Select plotter model:

1.   7220
2.   7470
3.   7475
4.   7550
5.   7580
6.   7585
7.   7586

Model selection: 1 to 7 <1>: 3
Plot connection:

1.   Serial port (XON/XOFF)
2.   Serial port (Hardware handshake)
3.   Parallel port or system printer
4.   File

Connection selection: 4

Fig. 16-12. These prompts appear during installation when you select HPGL to plot to disk files.

Select plotter or printer:

1.   No printer/plotter
2.   Autodesk Device Interface Plotter
3.   Autodesk Device Interface Printer
4.   Epson/IBM Graphics Printer
5.   Hewlett-Packard LaserJet
6.   Hewlett-Packard PaintJet
7.   Hewlett-Packard Plotter
8.   Houston Instrument Plotter
9.   IBM Proprinter
10. Okidata Printer
11. PostScript Laser Printer
12. TI 800 Omni Printer

Plotter or printer selection: 11
Plot connection:

1.   Serial port (XON/XOFF)
2.   Serial port (Hardware handshake)
3.   Parallel port or system printer
4.   File

Connection selection: 4

Fig. 16-13. These prompts appear during installation when you select PostScript to plot to disk files.

Make the changes highlighted in Fig. 16-14 to make an Encapsulated PostScript file from a PostScript file. First, rename the PostScript file you plotted, changing the original .PLT extension to .EPS. Then change the version information on the first line using an ASCII text editor. Also, move the %%Bounding Box line (next to last line) up to the second line. Add a %%EndComments line just after the last line that starts with the %% comment marker. Finally, add a %%EndProlog line under the last line that begins with a slash (/). The rest of the file remains unchanged.

MAKING AND VIEWING SLIDES

An AutoSketch *slide* is a "snap shot" of the current view of your drawing. A slide shows anything on screen, including Plot Boxes, Clip Boxes, and visible layers. The only items that

```
                                        %!PS-Adobe-2.0 EPSF-1.2
                                        %%BoundingBox: 76 293 437 582
%!PS-Adobe-1.0                          %% Creator: AutoSketch by Autodesk, Inc.
% Creator: AutoSketch by Autodesk, Inc. %% Pages: 1
% Pages: 1                              %%EndComments
/m {moveto} def                         /m {moveto} def
/l {lineto} def                         /l {lineto} def
/s {stroke} def                         /s {stroke} def
/n {newpath} def                        /n {newpath} def
20 20 translate                         %%EndProlog
0.240000 0.240000 scale                 20 20 translate
0 setlinewidth                          0.240000 0.240000 scale
n                                       0 setlinewidth
236 1139 m                              n
1736 1139 l                             236 1139 m
1736 2339 m                             1736 1139 l
 236 2339 l                             1736 2339 m
 236 1139 l                              236 2339 l
1736 1139 m                              236 1139 l
1736 2339 l                             1736 1139 m
s                                       1736 2339 l
%%BoundingBox: 76 293 437 582           s
showpage                                showpage
```

Fig. 16-14. Make the highlighted changes to convert a PostScript plot file from AutoSketch Version 2.0 to an Encapsulated PostScript plot file.

do not show are the Grid and objects on invisible layers. A slide stores the appearance of the drawing on screen, but not the actual drawing data. Thus, slides cannot be edited, plotted, zoomed, or otherwise changed in AutoSketch. However, slides display more quickly, and you can view a slide while working on another drawing.

Slides made with AutoSketch can be viewed in AutoCAD, and AutoCAD slides can be viewed in AutoSketch without any conversion process. In addition, many desktop publishing and graphics programs accept and print the slide file.

Making Slides

A slide is created by first having the view of the drawing you want captured on screen. Then, pick the **File** menu and **Make Slide** command. The **Make Slide File** dialogue box then appears. Enter the name in the *Filename* box or simply accept the default file name by pressing the [Enter] key. AutoSketch uses the drawing name for the slide file name, but adds the file extension .SLD. You do not have to enter this extension, nor will it appear when you pick a slide to view. AutoSketch simply adds the extension so it knows how to work with the drawing.

If you want to name the slide file, move your pointer to highlight the *Filename* box. Enter the new name, up to eight characters long. Press the [Enter] key or pick *OK*. AutoSketch saves the slide file to disk with a .SLD file extension.

Viewing Slides

AutoSketch and AutoCAD slides can be viewed in AutoSketch at any time, even while another drawing is on screen. Select the **View Slide** command. The **Select Slide File** dialogue box appears. Pick the slide you want to view. It then appears on screen. Select **Redraw** or pick the redraw button to remove the slide and return to the drawing.

You cannot edit slides displayed using the **View Slide** command. You must edit the original drawing and make another slide to change it. If you save the new slide under a different name, you may wish to delete the old slide file.

TROUBLESHOOTING PROBLEMS WITH AUTOSKETCH

AutoSketch is subject to periodic problems like any other software. This section covers the problems that are most likely to occur.

Disk is Full

When you select **Save, Save As,** or **Part Clip,** AutoSketch saves the drawing from memory to disk. It also saves a backup file with a .BAK file extension at the same time. When your file disk is almost full, AutoSketch may not be able to save both the drawing and its backup. In this case, you receive the error message "Error writing save file." You must insert a diskette with more free space on which to save the drawing. You might also save the drawing to the hard disk. Otherwise, you will lose your changes. Delete backup files (**DEL *.BAK**) from your drawing file disk to maximize disk space.

Memory is Full

The size of the largest drawing you can create is determined by the amount of memory installed in your computer. Each object takes up a fixed amount of memory, regardless of the object type. The memory meter in the upper-right corner shows the percentage of memory that is used by the current drawing. When that meter reaches 100 percent, and you try to add another object, a warning box appears stating "Out of Memory. Command terminated."

An immediate solution is to simplify the drawing. Try combining objects because each object takes up a fixed amount of memory. For example, replace a series of connected lines with a polyline. Long-term solutions include removing any memory-resident programs, configuring memory differently, or adding more memory to your computer. Refer to *Installing AutoSketch* for a complete explanation of memory configuration.

Another memory problem occurs when you attempt to import a large DXF drawing. You may receive the error "Memory full. Cannot add to drawing." In this case only a portion of the DXF drawing is input. In addition, the drawing may only partially be visible, or a portion of it may be visible. First, select **Zoom Full** to view the entire drawing. You then may need to erase several objects to lower the memory usage. Finally, select **Zoom Full** again.

Configuration Problems

Configuration problems are usually apparent the first time you run AutoSketch. If your mouse doesn't seem to work, the wrong mouse may have been configured, or your mouse driver may not be loaded. Sometimes, the display doesn't look quite right. Likewise, if your printer or plotter is not working correctly, check the configuration. You can do this one of two ways. At the system prompt, enter:

```
C:\SKETCH3>SKETCH /C
```

Several lines of Current Configuration information is then presented. If you are in Auto-Sketch, select **Information** from the **File** menu and similar Current Configuration information is displayed. If the configuration is incorrect, reconfigure AutoSketch using the method given in *Installing AutoSketch*. If this does not work, call the Technical Support Hotline at Autodesk, Inc. Make sure you know the exact make and model numbers of your hardware before calling.

Crashes

There are times when the computer seems to lock up or freeze. This is commonly called a *crash*. The computer appears to quit working and will not accept keyboard or mouse input. If this has happened, first look at the lights on your disk drives. Check to make sure that they are not lit. If they are lit, the computer may be looking for some data. Wait several minutes to see whether the computer has been processing some complex instruction. Some functions take a while to complete. If the computer does not respond after a few minutes, you need to take action. Do not turn the computer off right away. If you do, all changes to the drawing since you last saved it are lost.

AutoSketch provides two built-in "crash recovery" features. Sometimes the mouse is the problem. One built-in feature is to hold the [Alt] key while pressing the five keys [M] [O] [U] [S] [E]. Then, release the [Alt] key. This may reactivate the mouse. If this doesn't work, your next action should be to try another built-in feature of AutoSketch. Hold the [Alt] key while pressing the five keys [C] [R] [A] [S] [H]. Then, release the [Alt] key. If this method works, a message will ask for a file name to save the drawing.

If the built-in crash recovery features of AutoSketch don't work, you should perform a *warm boot*. It is called a warm boot because you do not shut off the computer. However, it is just like restarting the computer. If you have a hard disk, first remove any floppy disks. If you have floppy disks only, place the MS-DOS disk in drive A: before performing a warm boot. Then, press and hold down the following keys in this order: [Ctrl] [Alt] [Del].

If a warm boot does not restart the computer, see whether your system has a reset switch. Pressing the reset switch is much like performing a warm boot. It is still better than turning off the computer. If all else fails, turn off the computer. Wait for the disk drives to stop spinning, especially the hard disk. Then, turn the system back on.

SUMMARY

AutoSketch is an application program that runs when MS-DOS is loaded into computer memory. You may want to work with files outside of AutoSketch at times. In these cases, you enter MS-DOS commands at the system prompt. Typical tasks might be to create directories and store files in them, or copy, rename, and delete files.

AutoSketch can export and import drawings via the Drawing eXchange Format to communicate with other graphics software. A DXF file can be sent to another CAD program, desktop publishing, or other graphics software. AutoSketch can also create and view slides to exchange with AutoCAD or input into desktop publishing programs. A third method to use AutoSketch drawings in other software is to plot them to files. HPGL and Encapsulated PostScript files can be brought into popular desktop publishing programs.

NEW TERMS

MS-DOS, Microsoft Disk Operating System, system prompt, directories, root directory, file name, path, PROMPT command, DIR command, COPY command, REN command, DISKCOPY command, DXF, Drawing eXchange Format, **Make DXF** command, **Read DXF** command, slide, **Make Slide File** command, **View Slide** command, computer crash, warm boot, HPGL, Hewlett-Packard Graphics Language, PostScript, EPS, Encapsulated PostScript.

REVIEW QUESTIONS

Write your answers on a separate sheet of paper. Do not write in this book.
1. Transferring drawings between CAD programs requires _____ software.
2. The _____ format has become the most-used drawing conversion format for microcomputer-based CAD programs. It is built into AutoSketch.
3. List the steps required to convert a file to DXF format.
4. List the steps required to import a DXF file into AutoSketch.
5. A slide can be edited. True or false?
6. MS-DOS is an application program similar to AutoSketch. True or false?
7. The _____ appears after MS-DOS loads, showing that the computer is ready to accept commands.
8. Directories are logical divisions of the hard disk, in which you store files. True or false?
9. The file extension .SKD indicates the file is a(n) _____.
10. List the series of commands to do the following. Assume that you are currently in the C: drive.
    a. Change to the A: drive.
    b. Change to the C: drive.
    c. Change to the root directory.
    d. List files stored in the root directory.
    e. Make a new directory called NAME.
    f. Change to the NAME directory.
11. Given the path C:)\DRAWINGS\HOUSE.SKD, on what drive and in what directory is the AutoSketch drawing, HOUSE, located?
12. What does the following MS-DOS command do?
    COPY A:HOUSE.SKD C:\DRAWINGS
13. What does the following MS-DOS command do?
    COPY C:\SKETCH*.SKD A:*.OLD
14. What special steps should be taken when configuring AutoSketch to plot HPGL and PostScript files to disk?
15. What changes must you make to change an AutoSketch Version 2.0 PostScript plotted file to an Encapsulated PostScript?
16. Only one macro can be in memory at a time. True or false?
17. While recording the macro, you can cause the macro to pause for user input by pressing what key sequence?
18. After a macro pauses for user input in a dialogue box, what item must you pick for the macro to resume?

19. What command must you select to tell AutoSketch that you are finished recording a macro?
20. To load a saved macro file from disk into memory, what command must you select?

ACTIVITIES

1. Select a drawing from a previous activity to export to DXF format. Export the drawing, and then import it. Record any differences between the imported drawing and the original drawing.
2. Open a drawing from a previous activity. Zoom in on one section of the drawing and make a slide. Pan to another section of the drawing, and then view the slide you made. Select **Redraw** to remove the slide from the screen.
3. Use the DISKCOPY command to make a back-up copy of one of your drawing activities disks. Place the backup disk in the A: drive and change to that drive. The system prompt should show A⟩. Then, make a directory called DRAWINGS on the floppy disk.
4. Use the backup disk from Activity 3 to copy three drawings from the root directory into the new DRAWINGS directory. Use the MS-DOS command DIR to verify that the drawings were copied to the DRAWINGS directory.
5. Reconfigure AutoSketch by entering the command SKETCH /R at the system prompt. Select the proper choices for pointing device and display. When selecting a plotter, choose a Hewlett-Packard 7475 plotter and the File connection option. Then, plot a drawing from a previous chapter to file. If you have a desktop publishing program, or another program that imports HPGL files, try inserting the drawing.
6. Reconfigure AutoSketch by entering the command SKETCH /R at the system prompt. Select the proper choices for pointing device and display. When selecting a plotter, choose a PostScript plotter and File connection option. Next, plot a drawing from a previous chapter to file. Finally, edit the PostScript file using an ASCII text editor so that it is an Encapsulated PostScript file. If you have a desktop publishing program, or another program that imports EPS files, try inserting the drawing.
7. Create a macro that draws a .5-inch box at any location you might pick.
8. Create a macro that draws a 1-inch diameter circle at any location you might pick.
9. Create a macro that changes the property of a text object to ROMANS font, .18 height, and *Center* justification. The macro should allow you to pick any text object. After changing the text object, the macro should reset the text features to ROMANC font, .3 height, and *Left* justification.
10. One drawback to patterns is that if you rotate them, the pattern boundary rotates, but the pattern angle itself remains the same. Create a macro that allows you to measure a bearing, and then change the pattern angle to that bearing. The macro should assume that Attach modes are on and that the *Pattern* option of the **Property** command (**Settings** menu) is checked. This macro is useful if you need to rotate parts in a drawing, and then change the patterns accordingly.

APPENDIX A Function Key Reference

Press . . .	To Use . . .	Press . . .	To Use . . .	Press . . .	To Use . . .
F1	Undo	Alt + F1	Line	Ctrl + F1	Arc Mode
F2	Redo	Alt + F2	Polyline	Ctrl + F2	Box Array
F3	Erase	Alt + F3	Arc	Ctrl + F3	Mirror
F4	Break	Alt + F4	Circle	Ctrl + F4	Ring Array
F5	Move	Alt + F5	Ortho	Ctrl + F5	Rotate
F6	Copy	Alt + F6	Grid	Ctrl + F6	Scale
F7	Stretch	Alt + F7	Snap	Ctrl + F7	Box
F8	Pan	Alt + F8	Attach	Ctrl + F8	Ellipse
F9	Last View	Alt + F9	Group	Ctrl + F9	Pattern Fill
F10	Zoom Box	Alt + F10	Ungroup	Ctrl + F10	User Input (Macro)

APPENDIX B AutoSketch Command Summary
(Versions 3.0 and 2.0)

* denotes new command in Version 3.0
+ denotes command is available in Version 2.0 only

Draw Menu

Arc	Draw an arc by picking the start point, point on the arc, and endpoint.
Box	Draw a rectangle by picking its opposite corners.
Circle	Draw a circle by picking the center point and a point on the circle.
Curve	Draw a curve by picking points of a frame that controls the curve.
*Ellipse	Draw an ellipse by one of three methods–center and axes, axis and rotation, or foci.
Line	Draw a line between two endpoints.
Part	Insert an existing AutoSketch drawing into the current drawing.
*Pattern Fill	Draw a series of connected lines and/or arc segments that form a closed polygon and fill the interior with a solid color or pattern.
+Fill Region	Draw a series of connected lines that form a closed polygon and fill the interior with a solid color.
Point	Draw a point at the location given.
*Polyline	Draw an object that consists of connected line and/or arc segments which can have thickness.
+Polygon	Draw an object that consists of connected line segments.
*Quick Text	Add single lines of text to the drawing.
*Text Editor	Text editing utility to place multiple lines of text.
+Text	Add text to the drawing.

Change Menu

Undo	Reverses the outcome of the previous drawing or editing operations.
Redo	Reverses the effect of the last Undo.
Group	Group a set of objects together so they act as one object for editing.
Ungroup	Explode a group into its component objects.
Box Array	Make multiple copies of selected objects in a rectangular pattern.
Break	Remove a portion from an object, or trim off one end of an object.
Chamfer	Chamfers two nonparallel lines by trimming them a certain distance and connecting their endpoints.
Copy	Copy one or more objects in a drawing.

Erase	Erase single objects, or those within or crossing a picked box.
Fillet	Connect two objects with a smoothly fitted arc of a specified radius.
Mirror	Reflect existing objects about a mirror line.
Move	Move one or more objects from one location on the drawing to another.
Property	Change the color, layer, linetype, pattern, text, polyline width, or dimensions units of an object to the current settings.
Ring Array	Make multiple copies of selected objects in a circular pattern.
Rotate	Rotate existing objects about a pivot point by dragging or entering a rotation angle.
Scale	Shrink or enlarge one or several objects in a drawing.
Stretch	Stretch the shape of one or several objects.
* Text Editor	Text editing utility to edit text.

View Menu

Last View	Toggle between the current view of the drawing and the previous view.
Last Plot Box	Fill the screen with the extents of the last plot box created in your drawing session.
Zoom X	Enlarge or reduce the view of the drawing by a given magnification factor.
Zoom Box	Pick a box around the portion of the drawing to display.
Zoom Limits	Redraw the screen showing the entire drawing area set with the **Limits** command.
Zoom Full	Redraw the screen so that only the area of the drawing containing objects fills the screen.
Pan	Shift across the current view of the drawing without changing the magnification factor.
Redraw	Redraw the screen to clean up the drawing after using editing functions.

Assist Menu

* Arc Mode	Toggle between drawing line segments and arc segments when using the **Polyline** and **Pattern Fill** commands.
Attach	When toggled on, any picked location snaps to a precise position on an existing object.
Coords	Display absolute coordinate position of the pointer on the prompt line.
* Fill	Determines whether the interiors of pattern fills and polylines are displayed.
Frame	When toggled on, displays the curve frames that control the position of curves in your drawing.
Grid	When toggled on, displays a rectangular pattern of dots for reference.
Ortho	When toggled on, allows you to draw and edit objects only in horizontal and vertical directions.
Snap	When toggled on, the cursor moves only in precise increments.
* View Icons	Determines whether text fonts, patterns, and drawings are displayed by their names or by icons.
* Record Macro	Begin recording a series of commands and picks the user makes, called a "macro."
* End Macro	Stop recording the series of user actions started with the **Record Macro** command.
* Play Macro	Play back the series of steps the user made between selecting Record Macro and End Macro.
* User Input	Allow for user input while recording a macro.

Settings Menu

* Arrow	Set the type of terminating symbol for dimension lines–open arrow, closed arrow, tick, dot, or no symbol at all.
Attach	Set the location(s) to which a picked point may snap on existing objects when Attach mode is on.
Box Array	Define the number of copies in each direction and distance between objects for a **Box Array**.
Chamfer	Set the distance the **Chamfer** command will trim back each line to place the chamfer.
Color	Set the current color with which all new entities will be drawn.
Curve	Set how precisely AutoSketch draws each segment of a curve.
Fillet	Set the radius of the arc placed with the **Fillet** command.
Grid	Set the horizontal and vertical spacing of the visible reference **Grid**.
Layer	Set the current layer and make any of the ten available layers visible or invisible.
Limits	Set the lower-left and upper-right corners that bound the usable drawing area.
Line Type	Set the current linetype with which all new entities will be drawn.
Part Base	Set a reference point used when the drawing is inserted into another drawing.
* Pattern	Set the pattern used to fill the interior of polylines and pattern fills.
Pick	Set the distance AutoSketch will look when you pick entities to edit or to Attach.
* Polyline	Set the width and interior fill used for all subsequent polylines.
Property	Set the combination of properties affected by the **Change Property** command.
Ring Array	Define the center point, number of items, and angle between items in a **Ring Array**.
Snap	Set the horizontal and vertical spacing of the snap grid.
Text	Set the font, height, baseline angle, width factor, obliquing angle, and justification for new text.
Units	Select between decimal and architectural formats as the way AutoSketch displays drawing units for dimensions.

Measure Menu

Angle	Measure an angle formed by three picked points, a base point and two direction points.
Area	Calculate and display the area and perimeter of a region bordered by picked points.

Distance	Measure and display the distance between two points picked on the drawing.
Bearing	Pick two points to determine one the second point's bearing angle from the first.
Point	Display the current coordinates of the screen pointer.
Align Dimension	Draw a linear dimension aligned between two points.
Angle Dimension	Dimension the angle between two nonparallel lines.
Horiz. Dimension	Draw a linear dimension measuring the horizontal distance between two points.
Vert. Dimension	Draw a linear dimension measuring the vertical distance between two points.
Show Properties	Display the object type, color, layer, linetype, units, precision, and font of an object in the drawing.

File Menu

New	Clear the current drawing from the screen to begin a new drawing.
Open	Select and load an existing drawing from disk into memory for further editing.
*Part Clip	Save a portion of the current drawing as a separate AutoSketch drawing.
Save	Save the current drawing to disk under the same name.
Save As	Save the current drawing to disk under a new name.
Pen Info	For multipen plotters, select a pen number and pen speed for each standard screen color.
Plot/Print Area	Select the paper size, scale factor, and rotation angle of the plot or print.
Plot/Print Name	Enter a plot output file name. Offered if "Plot to file" was chosen during configuration. installation.
Plot/Print	Send the current drawing to the configured plotter or printer.
Make DXF	Make a Drawing eXchange Format (DXF) file of the current drawing.
Read DXF	Read into AutoSketch a Drawing eXchange Format (DXF) file made with another CAD program.
*Make Macro	Store the recorded macro currently in memory to disk. This must be done to save the macro before another macro is recorded.
*Read Macro	Load into memory a macro stored on disk so that it can be played.
Make Slide	Produce an AutoCAD slide file of the current drawing.
View Slide	Display a slide file produced with AutoCAD or AutoSketch.
Information	Display the AutoSketch version and serial numbers, and current configuration.
Game	A "four-in-a-row" game.
Quit	Quit AutoSketch and return to operating system prompt.

APPENDIX C   AutoSketch Fonts

FONT: Italic Complex
FONT FILENAME: ItalicC

FONT: Script Complex
FONT FILENAME: ScriptC

FONT: Standard
FONT FILENAME: Standard

FONT: Monotext
FONT FILENAME: Monotxt

FONT: Roman Simplex
FONT FILENAME: RomanS

A	a	1	[
B	b	2	]
C	c	3	{
D	d	4	}
E	e	5	\
F	f	6	|
G	g	7	;
H	h	8	:
I	i	9	'
J	j	0	"
K	k	‘	,
L	l	~	.
M	m	!	<
N	n	@	>
O	o	#	/
P	p	$	?
Q	q	%	
R	r	^	
S	s	&	
T	t	*	
U	u	(	
V	v	)	
W	w	—	
X	x	_	
Y	y	=	
Z	z	+	

FONT: Roman Complex
FONT FILENAME: RomanC

A	a	1	[
B	b	2	]
C	c	3	{
D	d	4	}
E	e	5	\
F	f	6	|
G	g	7	;
H	h	8	:
I	i	9	'
J	j	0	"
K	k	‘	,
L	l	~	.
M	m	!	<
N	n	@	>
O	o	#	/
P	p	$	?
Q	q	%	
R	r	^	
S	s	&	
T	t	*	
U	u	(	
V	v	)	
W	w	—	
X	x	_	
Y	y	=	
Z	z	+	

FONT: Music Symbols
FONT FILENAME: Symusic

A	·	a	·	1	1	[	[
B	◡	b	◡	2	2	]	]
C	◠	c	◠	3	3	{	{
D	○	d	○	4	4	}	}
E	○	e	○	5	5	\	\
F	●	f	●	6	6	|	|
G	♯	g	♯	7	7	;	;
H	♮	h	♮	8	8	:	:
I	♭	i	♭	9	9	'	'
J	—	j	—	0	0	"	"
K	-	k	-	‘	‘	,	,
L	×	l	𝄽	~	~	.	.
M	𝄞	m	𝄞	!	!	<	<
N	𝄞	n	𝄞	@	@	>	>
O	𝄢	o	𝄢	#	#	/	/
P	𝄡	p	𝄡	$	$	?	?
Q	·	q	☉	%	%		
R	›	r	☿	^	^		
S	---	s	♀	&	&		
T	⌐	t	⊕	*	*		
U	^	u	♂	(	(		
V	≡	v	♃	)	)		
W	▽	w	♄	—	—		
X		x	♅	_	_		
Y		y	♆	=	=		
Z		z	♇	+	+		

FONT: Math Symbols
FONT FILENAME: Symath

A	ℵ	a	←	1	1	[	[
B	′	b	↓	2	2	]	]
C	|	c	∂	3	3	{	{
D	‖	d	∇	4	4	}	}
E	±	e	√	5	5	\	\
F	∓	f	∫	6	6	|	|
G	×	g	∮	7	7	;	;
H	·	h	∞	8	8	:	:
I	÷	i	§	9	9	'	'
J	=	j	†	0	0	"	"
K	≠	k	‡	‘	‘	,	,
L	≡	l	∃	~	~	.	.
M	<	m	∏	!	!	<	<
N	>	n	∑	@	@	>	>
O	≤	o	(	#	#	/	/
P	≥	p	)	$	$	?	?
Q	∝	q	[	%	%		
R	~	r	]	^	^		
S	√	s	{	&	&		
T	⊂	t	}	*	*		
U	∪	u	⎰	(	(		
V	⊃	v	⎱	)	)		
W	∩	w	√	—	—		
X	∈	x	∫	_	_		
Y	→	y	≈	=	=		
Z	↑	z	≅	+	+		

FONT: Map Symbols
FONT FILENAME: Symap

A	○	a	✵	1	1	[	[
B	□	b	⚓	2	2	]	]
C	△	c	♧	3	3	{	{
D	◇	d	♡	4	4	}	}
E	☆	e	✺	5	5	\	\
F	+	f	·	6	6	|	|
G	×	g	•	7	7	;	;
H	*	h	∘	8	8	:	:
I	●	i	○	9	9	'	'
J	■	j	○	0	0	"	"
K	▲	k	◯	‘	‘	,	,
L	◀	l	◯	~	~	.	.
M	▼	m	◯	!	!	<	<
N	▶	n	◯	@	@	>	>
O	★	o	♡	#	#	/	/
P	⚑	p	♡	$	$	?	?
Q	⚓	q	‖	%	%		
R	✝	r	⊥	^	^		
S	⚒	s	∠	&	&		
T	⩓	t	∴	*	*		
U	⚘	u	♠	(	(		
V	⛵	v	♡	)	)		
W	✧	w	◇	—	—		
X	©	x	♣	_	_		
Y	✡	y	✿	=	=		
Z	🔔	z	⚜	+	+		

APPENDIX D   AutoSketch (Version 3.0) Patterns

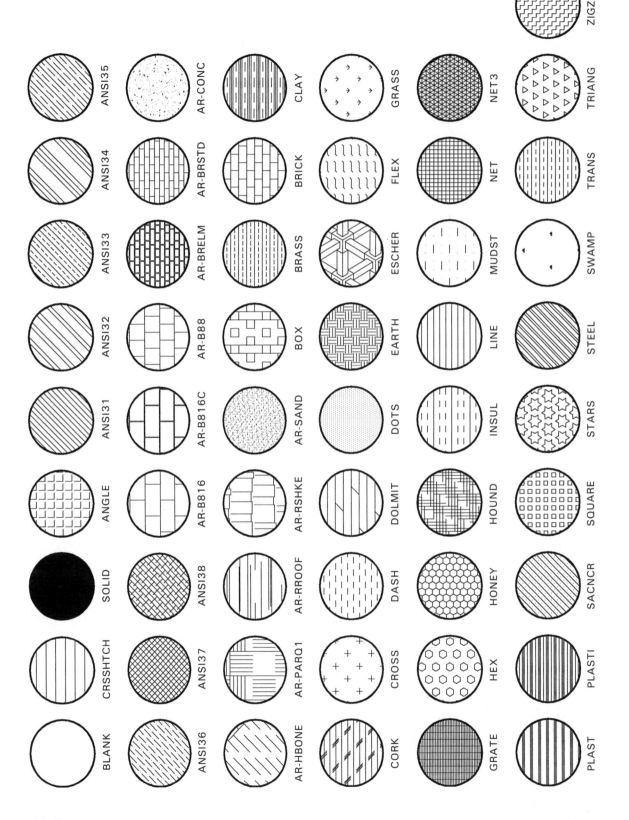

APPENDIX E AutoSketch Version 3.0 Menu Layout

Draw

Arc	A3
Box	C7
Circle	A4
Curve	
Ellipse	C8
Line	A1
Part	
Pattern Fill	C9
Point	
Polyline	A2
Quick Text	
Text Editor	

Change

Undo	F1
Redo	F2
Group	A9
Ungroup	A10
Box Array	C2
Break	F4
Chamfer	
Copy	F6
Erase	F3
Fillet	
Mirror	C3
Move	F5
Property	
Ring Array	C4
Rotate	C5
Scale	C6
Stretch	F7
Text Editor	

View

Last Plot Box	F9
Last View	F10
Zoom Box	F10
Zoom Full	
Zoom Limits	
Zoom X	
Pan	F8
Redraw	

Assist

Arc Mode	C1
Attach	A8
Coords	
Fill	
Frame	
Grid	A6
Ortho	A5
Snap	A7
View Icons	

Record Macro	
Play Macro	
User Input	C10

End Macro	
Play Macro	
User Input	C10

Settings

Arrow
Attach
Box Array
Chamfer
Color
Curve
Ellipse
Fillet
Grid
Layer
Limits
Line Type
Part Base
Pattern
Pick
Polyline
Property
Ring Array
Snap
Text
Units

Measure

Angle
Area
Distance
Bearing
Point
Align Dimension
Angle Dimension
Horiz. Dimension
Vert. Dimension
Show Properties

File

New
Open
Part Clip
Save
Save As
Pen Info
Plot Area
Plot Name
Plot
Make DXF
Read DXF
Make Macro
Read Macro
Make Slide
View Slide
Information
Game
Quit

Pen Info
Print Area
Print Name
Print

Picking a second point to the right of the first point creates a Window box. Only those objects entirely within the box are affected.

Picking a second point to the left of the first point creates a Crosses box. All objects within and crossing the box are affected.

APPENDIX F   AutoSketch Version 2.0 Menu Layout

Draw		Change		View		Assist		Settings	Measure	File
Arc	A3	Undo	F1	Last view	F9	Ortho	A5	Attach	Distance	New
Box		Redo	F2	Last plot box		Frame		Box Array	Angle	Open
Circle	A4	Erase	F3			Coords		Chamfer	Area	Save
Curve		Group	A9	Zoom X		Grid	A6	Color		Save as
Fill Region		Ungroup	A10	Zoom box	F10	Snap	A7	Curve	Point	
Line	A1			Zoom limits		Attach	A8	Fillet	Bearing	Make DXF
Part		Move	F5	Zoom full				Grid		Read DXF
Point		Copy	F6					Layer	Angle dimension	
Polygon	A2	Stretch	F7	Pan	F8			Limits	Align dimension	Pen info
Text		Property						Line type	Horiz dimension	Plot area
		Rotate		Redraw				Part base	Vert dimension	Plot name
		Scale						Pick		Plot
		Mirror						Property	Show properties	
		Break	F4					Ring Array		Information
		Chamfer						Snap		Game
		Fillet						Text		
								Units		Make slide
		Box Array								View slide
		Ring Array								
										Quit

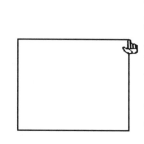

Picking a second point to the right of the first point creates a Window box. Only those objects entirely within the box are affected.

Picking a second point to the left of the first point creates a Crosses box. All objects within and crossing the box are affected.

INDEX